Motor Development: Research & Reviews

Volume 2

Jane E. Clark and James H. Humphrey, Editors
Department of Kinesiology, University of Maryland

Published by the
National Association for Sport and Physical Education
(NASPE)
an association of the
American Alliance for Health, Physical Education,
Recreation and Dance

NASPE Publications
1900 Association Drive
Reston, VA 20191-1599
(703) 476-3410
naspe@aahperd.org

International Standards Book Number (ISBN): 0-88314-743-2

Cover design by Jane Bagby
Copyediting and book production by A. Michie Shaw

Jane E. Clark, Ph.D. is Professor and Chair, Department of Kinesiology, University of Maryland, College Park. Her research interests focus on the development of movement control and coordination. Currently, she studies postural development in infants and young children.

James H. Humphrey, Ph.D. is Professor Emeritus, Department of Kinesiology, University of Maryland, College Park. He is perhaps best known for his work on the use of motor activity to promote children's learning. A prolific author, Dr. Humphrey also has written in the areas of stress, childhood, and older populations.

In memory of Allen L. Burton who inspired
us all with his exceptional insights into motor development
and unabated exuberance for *everything* and *everyone*.

CONTENTS

CONTRIBUTORS

Sam Beak has completed her doctorate at the Department of Exercise and Sport Science at Manchester Metropolitan University, UK. She is now a community sport development officer in Epsom, Surrey, UK.

Simon Bennett is a Senior Research Fellow at the Department of Optometry and Neuroscience at the University of Manchester Institute of Science and Technology, UK. His research involves the study of perception and movement systems and the neuroscientific basis of interceptive actions.

Martin E. Block is an Associate Professor in the Kinesiology Program, Curry School of Education, University of Virginia. His motor development research interests are how children perceive affordances. His pedagogy research interests focus on inclusion of children with disabilities in general physical education.

Jane E. Clark is Professor and Chair, Department of Kinesiology, University of Maryland, College Park. Her research interests focus on the development of movement control and coordination. Currently she studies postural development in infants and young children.

Keith Davids is Professor and Dean of the School of Physical Education at the University of Otago, New Zealand. He has research interests in the ecological approach to movement coordination, control and skill acquisition, particularly as related to the context of sport.

Clersida Garcia is an Associate Professor and Director of the Early Childhood Motor Development Research Laboratory and Pedagogy Laboratory in the Department of Kinesiology and Physical Education at Northern Illinois University, DeKalb. Her research interests focus on the development of the fundamental motor skills and the social aspect of the learning context.

Luis E. Garcia is an Assistant Professor and Director of the Developmental Sport Skill Research Laboratory in the Department of Kinesiology and Physical Education at Northern Illinois University, DeKalb. His research interests focus on the development of sport skill over time and its impact on children's self-esteem.

Jacqueline D. Goodway is an Assistant Professor in the School of Physical Activity and Educational Services at The Ohio State University. Her research interests focus on the promotion of motor skill development, perceived competence, and physical activity in young children who are identified as disadvantaged. The intent of this work is to develop and implement motor skill interventions in schools, communities, and families in order to facilitate the motor development and physical activity of this under-served population of children.

Michelle L. Hamilton is an assistant professor at Southwest Texas State University in San Marcos, Texas. Her research interests include the acquisition of fundamental motor skills and pedagogy.

Stephen J. Langendorfer is Associate Professor of Kinesiology at Bowling Green State University, Bowling Green, Ohio. His research interests lie in motor coordination and control from developmental and dynamic perspectives and in developmental aquatics.

Jason S. Metcalfe is a doctoral candidate and research assistant, Department of Kinesiology, University of Maryland, College Park. His current research focus is postural and perceptual development in infants.

V. Gregory Payne is Professor and Chair, Department of Human Performance, San Jose State University. His academic and research interests range from children's sport and youth fitness to aging and physical activity. He is co-author of *Human Motor Development: A Lifespan Approach*, now in its fifth edition.

Mary Ann Roberton is Professor of Kinesiology at Bowling Green State University, Bowling Green, Ohio. Her interests focus on developmental sequences and the changing constraints that affect them across the lifespan.

Mary E. Rudisill is Professor, Department of Health and Human Performance, Auburn University. Her line of research is developmental motivation and its relation to motor skill development. Currently, she is examining the influence of mastery motivational climate motor skill interventions on motor skill competence, perceptions of competence, and attitudes toward movement involvement.

Dan Southard is Professor of Kinesiology, Department of Kinesiology, Texas Christian University, Fort Worth, Texas. His primary research interest is in the area of motor pattern change from a dynamical systems perspective.

Amanda Tate is a former graduate student at the University of Houston. She is now working in a cardiac rehabilitation center in Houston, Texas.

Jerry R. Thomas is Professor and Chair of the Department of Health and Human Performance at Iowa State University. His research has focused on cognitive factors in children's motor skill performance, particularly motor expertise and motor control.

Nadia C. Valentini is a faculty member in the School of Physical Education, Universidade Federal do Rio Grande Do Sul, Porto Alegre, Brazil. Her research focus is on motor skill development. Dr. Valentini's research agenda is directed toward promoting progressive motor skill interventions for children with developmental delays.

Jin H. Yan is Assistant Professor, Department of Kinesiology, California State University at Hayward. His theoretical focus is on lifespan developmental motor control and learning. He works with individuals at all ages and with various levels of motor and cognitive capabilities.

Motor Development: Research & Reviews presents original research and reviews on contemporary issues in the field of motor development. The research in the first section focuses primarily on preschool and school-age children, whereas the second section includes two review papers that extend the focus to the later ages. These research and review articles represent our current understandings and as such should be a valuable resource for those who teach motor skills at all ages.

In the first article, Langendorfer and Roberton look at the developmental throwing profiles of children five to 13 years of age. Their findings suggest that of all possible throwing patterns a child could demonstrate when throwing "hard," only about half are ever observed. More interesting, however, is the authors' speculation that the pattern of block rotation, humerus aligned but independent and forearm lag is "phylogenetic" and the more advanced throwing patterns may be ontogenetic. The next three chapters provide further insights into the development of throwing. Southard asks what could make a throw become more advanced? His answer: changes in the mass of the child's arm and increasing velocity. This finding leads Southard to some interesting ideas about how to help develop more mature throwing patterns in both boys and girls. Hamilton and Tate raise a similar idea for teachers to consider, namely how big should the target be and how far away from the child? Rather then measure the absolute distance from the target, the authors use "body-scaled" measures, i.e., body lengths. Clersida and Luis Garcias' paper is a detailed study of 3, 469 throws of six preschool-age children observed over two years. Their findings are the first to demonstrate how variable young children are in their progression to a more mature throwing pattern.

Can teaching make a difference in the motor development of children? Goodway, Rudisill and Valentini, in two different interventions to improve catching, found positive changes. Despite relatively short instructional periods, either a direct-instruction or student-directed intervention resulted in changes in the children's catching behavior. Beak and her colleagues and Block explore the "fit" between the child and his or her environment. In the Beak study, the authors explore the fit between the child and sport equipment, in this case a tennis racquet. Ten-year-old children explored the racquet either haptically (active touch) or visually to determine which would be better for them. Their results show that when children haptically explore the racquet they select the one that would be biomechanically most efficient. The Block chapter also suggest that children know well their own capabilities. In a study in which children indicated how far they could jump (without actually jumping), Block found that three-year-old, seven-year-old, and 11-year-old children and adults estimated their ability to jump over floor mats of differing sizes rather well. These latter two studies indicate that children have a good sense of their body/environment fit.

The last two articles in this volume are reviews. Yan and his colleagues summarize and critique an extensive literature on the control of rapid arm movements. Their conclusion from this review is that children and seniors use different control mechanisms to produce fast, accurate movements when compared to healthy adults. The authors suggest several potential research questions that might be tested. The Clark and Metcalfe paper examines the use of metaphors in motor development and offers their "mountain" metaphor as a useful heuristic for understanding lifespan motor development.

Motor development has "developed" considerably as is evidence by this set of papers. With our first edited book in 1985 *Motor Development: Current Selected Research* and the four others that followed, we find in this volume incredible changes in the field. The researchers in motor development have the same fundamental questions: When, how, and why do motor skills change over the lifespan? But our knowledge continues to expand with each study. As editors, we extend our gratitude to the contributors for their patience and their willingness to share their work in this volume of *Motor Development: Research & Reviews*.

Finally, the contributors and the editors dedicate this volume to Dr. Allen Burton, Professor, University of Minnesota, who was taken from us this past September. We all enjoyed Allen's passion for our field. He was one of the cleverest and most interesting researchers in our field. His insights were always a breath of fresh air. Who could forget his study of children's books where he found that skipping and galloping were the "happy" gaits? His study of throwing "form" used by baseball players also challenged our ideas about whether a contralateral step was indeed a hallmark of all forceful throws. Allen, we will miss you.

Jane E. Clark
James H. Humphrey

DEVELOPMENTAL PROFILES IN OVERARM THROWING: SEARCHING FOR "ATTRACTORS", "STAGES", AND "CONSTRAINTS"

Stephen J. Langendorfer
Mary Ann Roberton

ABSTRACT

We studied profiles created across developmental levels of trunk, humerus, and forearm action in 1,946 trials of forceful overarm throwing generated by 39 children followed from ages 5.7 to 13 years. Of 27 theoretically possible profiles, 13 were never displayed. We speculated this non-random event ($p < .01$) reflected the action of organismic constraints. Three anatomical/biomechanical possibilities are: 1) proprioceptive discomfort associated with the close-packed glenohumeral joint position, 2) advanced arm actions emerging from angular trunk torque, and 3) differentiated trunk rotation related to the inertia of advanced arm actions. When graphed as "sample attractors" in a dynamic system, 4-6 of the 14 profiles observed were candidates as Wild's (1938) "stages." The remaining profiles illustrated the inability of the Wild stages to handle individual differences. The steady sample attractor strength of one profile (block rotation, humerus aligned but independent, and forearm lag) led us to speculate it may be phylogenetic whereas more advanced profiles may be ontogenetic.

In this study, we examined longitudinal data on forceful overarm throwing to see how the developmental levels of arm and trunk action changed relative to each other over a seven-year-period. We did this by studying the changing "profiles" formed by the conjunction of developmental levels across the movement components of trunk, humerus, and forearm action. Five measurement periods from kindergarten through seventh grade provided data describing the same children repeatedly assessed under the same environmental and task goal conditions. Our main question was whether some profiles occurred more frequently and with more stability than other profiles and whether that occurrence changed over time. We placed this information in a dynamic systems context and considered its implications for the component and total body (Wild, 1938) models of throwing developmental sequences.

Total Body or Components?

Since Wild published her 1938 cross-sectional classic on the overarm throw for force, the preponderance of applied literature in motor development has adopted her four "stages" of throwing as the definitive scheme for categorizing qualitative changes in the developing throw. In 1977 and 1978(a), Roberton presented an alternative model to that of Wild. The Roberton model has been called "the component approach" in contrast to Wild's "total body approach" (Haywood, 1993). Based both on across-trial and longitudinal analyses, the Roberton model claimed that sequential, developmental change occurs in separate body segments or joint actions rather than across the total body simultaneously. She called the qualitative changes in the components "steps" or "levels" instead of "stages" because of their apparent specificity to single skills. She argued that the term "stage" should be reserved for motor behaviors that occurred within a similar time frame across more than one motor skill (Roberton, 1978b). While we still subscribe to the Roberton perspective, in this study we shall use the term "stage" when describing the levels of Wild's whole body developmental sequence. This practice will keep our terminology consistent with the original usage of Wild, hopefully making it easier for the reader to follow our thinking.

Table 1 lists Wild's four stages of throwing; Table 2 lists Roberton's levels within components. Comparing the tables shows the key distinction between the two views: the whole body approach describes the movement of several components as characteristic of one stage. Change to a subsequent stage requires simultaneous change in most of the components. The Roberton model allows for change in one or more components without concurrent change in other components. Her model handles individual differences in throwing through the different "profiles" or combinations of developmental levels that can occur across the components because of differential rates of development within each. The Wild model has no provision for individual differences beyond the four stages.[1]

In addition to differences in the models, Roberton and Langendorfer (1980) argued that the component sequences were probabilistic rather than deterministic. That is, the sequences were characteristic of the population. The extent to which any person developed in the order predicted or showed a particular developmental level at a particular age was based on the laws of probability. Roberton, Williams, and Langendorfer (1980) developed a data-graphing technique using this probabilistic view. In addition to screening potential developmental sequences, their graphs identify the probabilities or likelihood associated with each developmental level appearing at any age on the graph. Thus, each specific age predicts the *probability* associated with the potential appearance of *every* developmental level.

Table 1
Developmental Stage Sequence for the Overarm Throw (Wild, 1938)

Stage I. Anteroposterior movements. [can be assigned to ages two to three or possibly up to four].

The reverse movement of the arm is either sideways-upward or forward-upward usually to high above the shoulder, elbow much flexed. With this reverse arm movement, the trunk extends with dorsal flexion of ankles and carries the shoulders back. The trunk then straightens, carrying the shoulders forward, and flexes forward with plantar flexion of ankles as the arm swings forward over the shoulder and down in front. Elbow extension starts early. Movements of body and arm are almost entirely in the anteroposterior plane over feet, which remain in place; the body remains facing the direction of the throw all the time; the arm is the initiating factor. There is trunk left rotation toward the end with the arm's forward reach.

Stage II. Horizontal body and arm movements. [assigned to ages three and one-half to five years]

The whole body rotates right, then left above the feet; the feet remain together in place. The arm moves either in a high oblique plane above the shoulder or in a more horizontal plane but with a forward downward follow-through. The elbow is much flexed; it may extend at once or later. The body changes its orientation and then reorientates [*sic*] to the throwing direction. The arm is the initiating factor.

Stage III. Introduction of stepping (right foot-step-forward throw). [assigned to ages five to six].

The weight is held back on the left rear foot as the spine rotates right and extends; the arm swings obliquely upward over the shoulder to a retracted position with elbow much flexed. The forward movements consist of a stepping forward with right foot, unilateral to the throwing arm, with spine left rotation, early turning of the whole body to a partial left facing and trunk forward flexion, while the arm swings forward either in an oblique-above-the-shoulder plane or in a sideways-around-the-shoulder plane, followed by a forward downward movement of follow-through. Elbow extension does not start at once. This throw has both anteroposterior and horizontal features.

Stage IV. The mature throw. [all boys six and one-half years up have it; girls have, in most cases, attained the body and foot movements, but incompletely developed forms of the arm movement].

This throw is the left-foot-step-forward throw with trunk rotation and horizontal adduction of the arm in the forward swing.

Note. Taken with minor editing from Wild (1938). Used with permission.

Table 2
Developmental Sequences for Components of the Overarm Throw for Force (Roberton & Halverson, 1984)

Trunk (pelvis-spine) action

Step 1. No trunk action or forward-backward movements. Only the arm is active in force production. Sometimes, the forward thrust of the arm pulls the trunk into a passive left rotation (assuming a right-handed throw), but no twist-up precedes that action. If trunk action occurs, it accompanies the forward thrust of the arm by flexing forward at the hips. Preparatory (trunk) extension sometimes precedes forward hip flexion.

Step 2. Upper trunk rotation or total trunk "block" rotation. The spine and pelvis both rotate away from the intended line of flight and then simultaneously begin forward rotation, acting as a unit or "block." Occasionally, only the upper spine twists away, then toward the direction of force. The pelvis, then, remains fixed, facing the line of flight, or joins the rotary movement after forward spinal rotation has begun.

Step 3. Differentiated rotation. The pelvis precedes the upper spine in initiating forward rotation. The thrower twists away from the intended line of ball flight, then begins forward rotation with the pelvis while the upper spine is still twisting away.

Humerus (upper arm) action during forward swing

Step 1. Humerus oblique. The humerus moves forward to ball release in a plane that intersections the trunk obliquely above or below the horizontal line of the shoulders. Occasionally, during the backswing, the humerus is placed at a right angle to the trunk, with the elbow pointing toward the target. It maintains this fixed position during the throw.

Step 2. Humerus aligned but independent. The humerus moves forward to ball release in a plane horizontally aligned with the shoulder, forming a right angle between humerus and trunk. By the time the shoulders (upper spine) reach front facing, the humerus (elbow) has moved independently ahead of the outline of the body (as seen from the side) via horizontal adduction at the shoulder.

Step 3. Humerus lags. The humerus moves forward to ball release horizontally aligned, but at the moment the shoulders (upper spine) reach front facing, the humerus remains within the outline of the body (as seen from the side). No horizontal adduction of the humerus occurs before front facing.

Forearm action during forward swing

Step 1. No forearm lag. The forearm and ball move steadily forward to ball release throughout the throwing action.

Step 2. Forearm lag. The forearm and ball appear to "lag," i.e., to remain

Table 2 (Continued)

stationary behind the thrower or to move downward or backward in relation to her/him. The lagging forearm reaches its farthest point back, deepest point down, or last stationary point *before* the shoulders (upper spine) reach front facing.

Step 3. Delayed forearm lag. The lagging forearm delays reaching its final point of lag until the moment of front facing.

Foot (stepping) action

Step 1. No movement. Thrower throws from whatever position feet happen to be in.

Step 2. Homolateral step. Final forward step is with the same foot as throwing hand.

Step 3. Contralateral step. Final forward step is with opposite foot from throwing hand.

Step 4. Long, contralateral step. Length of the final forward step with opposite foot is over half of the thrower's standing height.

Note. Taken with minor editing from Roberton & Halverson (1984). Used with permission.

In contrast, proponents of the whole body approach seem almost deterministic in their focus on the ages associated with certain stages. This was true of Wild (1938) who, while acknowledging individual differences in the rate of development, still ascribed a narrow age range to each of her stages (see Table 1). Thus, a specific age became a predictor of a *specific* stage. This deterministic "ages and stages" approach is still evident in some contemporary motor development textbooks.

Dynamic Systems Conceptions of Development

As implied in the preceding discussion, a developmental sequence is a description of stable coordination states ordered according to either a deterministic or probabilistic view of when they appear in developmental time. The idea of *stable coordination states forming within a probabilistic framework* fits nicely with recent dynamic systems conceptions of motor development (Clark, 1995; Goldfield, Kay, & Warren, 1993; Muchisky, Gerschkoff-Stowe, Cole, & Thelen, 1996; Roberton & Halverson, 1988). The dynamic systems perspective suggests that the various behavioral states that appear in the bodily movement of a person both within "real" time and over ontogenetic time reflect underlying movement "attractor states." These states occur with certain probabilities that change with time (age) because of "constraints" or relationships that are also changing with time.

This view sees the coordination states of human movement as a specific example of a general model of the patterns that can occur in all complex, dynamic systems (Abraham & Shaw, 1983; Gleick, 1987; Kelso, 1995).

In this model, complex systems self-organize into specific, stable states or patterns under certain boundary conditions. As the conditions change across particular critical points, the patterns transition to qualitatively new states. In the mathematics of dynamic systems, the stable states that the system can assume are called "attractors." Despite differing initial conditions, the system will eventually converge on a certain limit set, the attractor (Zanone, Kelso, & Jeka, 1993). Various attractors can exist in the "state space" of the system (Abraham & Shaw, 1983). The system can assume any of these attractive states or patterns, depending upon the boundary conditions occurring at the time. Sometimes the same boundary conditions can produce more than one stable state. Also, some states occur that are considerably less stable than others. These are known as weak attractors. More stable states are known as strong attractors.

Newell (1984, 1986) has provided a model of a "system" and its boundary conditions that is useful to motor development research. He defined the relevant system for research as one composed of the *organism*, the *task*, and the *environment*. He defined the boundary conditions or "constraints" as *relationships* within and between these three system elements. These relationships reduce the likelihood of certain behaviors and enhance the likelihood of others: "constraints can be viewed as boundaries or features that limit motion…" and "…constraints reduce the number of possible configurations of a system" (Newell, 1986, p. 347). As relationships alter across the lifespan due to changes in organism, task, or environment, the probability of stable states or attractors will shift as well. Therefore, a change in the qualitative state of a child's throw is evidence for a changed constraint (Clark, 1995). Newell's model thus focused the search for causes of development not on single, extrinsic or intrinsic forces such as "maturation" but rather on the changing relationships between mover, the task he/she is attempting, and the general environment surrounding the mover-task diad.

Proponents of the component approach (with its concomitant focus on occurrence probabilities affected by constraints) (e.g., Roberton & Halverson, 1988) accept that the developmental levels appearing in motor skill components reflect underlying "attractors" in a dynamic system. While not mathematically defined, the developmental levels themselves can be called attractors in a metaphorical sense. They are stable across trials (Roberton, 1978a; Williams, Haywood, & VanSant, 1998), are qualitatively different from each other, and are presumed to transition to other forms at times of increased intra-individual variability (Roberton, 1982). Indeed, by these criteria the developmental levels are clearly strong attractors. What has received only preliminary study (Roberton & Langendorfer, 1980), however, is whether the *profiles* formed by the combined developmental levels across several components also might be attractors.

Figure 1 illustrates one such throwing profile. The child's trunk action is level 2, his humerus action is level 2, and his forearm action is level 2 (see Table 2 for definitions). The child's profile across these components, then, is T2-H2-F2 (i.e., trunk: 2; humerus: 2; forearm: 2). (We will use this convention throughout.) An extreme interpretation of the component model would suggest that the components develop independently, making the profile in Figure 1 a random occurrence. Obviously, because the components are different parts of the same child's body, they cannot be totally independent; however, data indicate that neither are they perfectly correlated (Roberton, 1977; Roberton & Langendorfer, 1980), as implied by the whole body approach (Seefeldt & Haubenstricker, 1982).

The Roberton component model has received excellent empirical support for a number of skills (e.g., Clark & Phillips, 1985; Roberton & Halverson, 1988, Williams, Haywood, & VanSant, 1998; VanSant, 1997).

Fig. 1. Throwing profile T2-H2-F2. See Table 2 for definitions. Frame two is the point of deepest forearm lag and frame three is front facing. Tracing is from the motor development film collection, School of Human Movement, Sport, and Leisure Studies, Bowling Green State University.

Nevertheless, the persistence in the applied literature of various total-body, "stage" approaches to throwing raises the question as to whether certain throwing profiles formed across components are non-random attractors of sufficient strength that other observers have called them "stages."

The purpose of the present study, then, was to assess how developmental levels across three components of the overarm throw (humerus, forearm, and trunk actions) related to each other and how those relationships changed over time. We were particularly interested in whether the presence or absence of profiles was non-random, which we would take as evidence that constraints were acting to form attractive profiles. We also wondered if patterns across profiles would suggest the nature of those constraints. Lastly, we considered whether some profiles were strong enough attractors that they were the "stages" of traditional, whole body approaches to throwing development.

METHOD

The Data Set

In 1972, Lolas Halverson and several colleagues at the University of Wisconsin-Madison began a longitudinal study of forceful overarm throwing. They filmed more than 70 kindergarten children from two Madison, WI, middle-class neighborhoods. The children were filmed in February of 1972 and again in May. They were then re-filmed in May 1973, May 1974, and May 1979. A total of 39 children, 22 males and 17 females, were filmed on all five occasions. They averaged 5.7 years of age for their first, kindergarten filming and 13 years of age in their final, seventh grade filming. The standard deviation of their age was 0.3 years throughout the study. Numerous reports of the data collection methods and the results of these studies have been published previously (Halverson & Roberton, 1979; Halverson, Roberton, & Langendorfer, 1982; Halverson, Roberton, Safrit, & Roberts, 1977; Roberton, 1977, 1978a; Roberton, Halverson, Langendorfer, & Williams, 1979). All of these reports focused on the development of the separate components of throwing and/or on the ball velocity changes from kindergarten to seventh grade. No study has been made of the profiles exhibited by the children across components.

Data Collection

The same procedures were used each year of data collection. Children were asked to throw a tennis ball "hard" through a Roberts' (1972) velocimeter positioned three feet in front of them. The goal of each throw was to hit a wall hard approximately 30 feet away. Following three practice trials, 10 trials were filmed (64 fps) of each child simultaneously from side and rear views. A concurrent measure of the thrown ball's initial horizontal velocity was recorded by the velocimeter.

Data Reduction

Over the years, the present authors have been involved with the collection, reduction, and analysis of these longitudinal data. Either we or Dr. Halverson reduced the filmed data by projecting both rear and side views simultaneously onto a movie screen with Lafayette Analyzer™ and NAC Analysis™ step-action projectors. The Roberton (Roberton & Halverson, 1984) developmental sequences for trunk, humerus, and forearm (Table 2) were used as checklists to categorize the movements of each child on each trial for each of the five occasions. For the 39 children completing the longitudinal series, 1,946 trials were reduced in this fashion. (Each year was represented by 390 trials with the exception of ages six and seven when 389 and 387 trials were available respectively.) Inter- and intra-observer objectivity for each component were always established each year of the study by having the person reducing the data practice until he or she had achieved at least 80% exact agreement with another observer and with themselves at a later date (see, for example, Halverson et al., 1982; Roberton, 1978a).

Data Analysis

The development of the individual components from the second kindergarten filming (age six) through seventh grade (age 13) was reported in Halverson et al. (1982). These same data were re-examined for the present study; in addition, we added the data from the first kindergarten filming (age 5.7 years). We combined the separate classifications for the humerus, forearm, and trunk into a "developmental profile" for each child on each trial.

For each year studied, we counted the frequency with which every profile appeared across all the trials in the sample. We also counted the number of trials out of 10 during which each child displayed a profile. Finally, we counted the number of children exhibiting a profile at any time in their 10 trials. From this information we calculated for each year the frequency with which the profile occurred a) as a percentage of the total trials in the sample, and b) as a percentage of the number of children in the sample. For each year we also calculated an average within-child consistency or stability measure for each profile. This measure was the number of trials over which the profile occurred out of each child's 10 trials converted to a percentage and averaged across the 39 children.

To study the strength of the profiles as attractors using the data from the total group, the profiles were placed within yearly plots. These plots were formed by a) the profile's frequency of occurrence in the children that year and b) the average within-child stability with which the profile was shown. Whereas the strength of attractors in dynamic systems is defined by the frequency and stability with which they occur in *individuals*, this method allowed us to use the *group* data to see simultaneously these two aspects of attractor strength as they occurred in the *sample* rather than in an individual. We considered stronger sample attractors to be those profiles that relatively large numbers of children demonstrated with a relatively high degree of across-trial stability. Sample attractors of more moderate strength were those that had relatively moderate levels of frequency and stability or high levels of one or the other but not both. Weak sample attractors were those profiles with relatively low stability or relatively few children displaying them. Non-attractors were those profiles that were theoretically possible but never observed in the sample during the time period studied.

The action of constraints upon the appearance of the profiles was determined by assuming that each profile would have an equal probability of appearing if all constraints were operating equally at all times. If the profiles appeared non-randomly, then the investigators concluded that particular constraints were eliminating or enhancing the probability of certain profiles at that age. To determine whether the absence of profiles was a non-random event, a Bayesian analysis was used to create a posterior density function for p, the exact probability associated with n of N children not falling into X categories out of 27 when the random probability associated with each category was 1/27. The 27 categories were formed by all possible combinations of the developmental levels in each component with the developmental levels in the other components, (i.e., 3 x 3 x 3). We decided *a priori* that an exact probability of $p<.01$ would be required for us to conclude non-random behavior.

RESULTS AND DISCUSSION

Frequency in the Sample

The children in our sample exhibited only 14 of the theoretically possible 27 profiles as they developed from 5.7 years of age through 13 years of age. This event of 13 profiles never appearing in five measurement times over 7+ years is unlikely to be a chance occurrence ($p<.01$). It strongly suggests that constraints acted to discourage certain body movements from occurring in the presence of other body movements during this time period.

We also found that the 14 profiles, which did appear, occurred with considerably less frequency than do component developmental levels. No profile occurred in more than 33% of the trials at any given year. As Figure 2 indicates, only one profile, T2-H1-F1, was ever displayed by as many as 60% of the children at any measurement time. This finding is in contrast to the component developmental levels, *each* of which occurred in well over 50% of the sample at some time across the years studied (Halverson et al.,

1982). The relatively low frequency of occurrence for each profile needs to be kept in mind as we proceed to use statements like "most frequent" or "relatively strong" sample attractor.

The profiles that appeared most frequently across the 7+ years were T2-H2-F2 (block rotation of the trunk, humerus aligned but independent, forearm lag), T2-H1-F1 (block rotation of the trunk, humerus oblique, no forearm lag), and T2-H2-F1 (block rotation of the trunk, humerus aligned but independent, no forearm lag). As the children grew older, T2-H3-F2 (block rotation, humerus lags, and forearm lag), T2-H3-F3 (block rotation, humerus lags, and delayed forearm lag) and T3-H3-F3 (differentiated rotation of the trunk, humerus lags, delayed forearm lag) became more frequent. Most of the children displaying these latter profiles were boys.

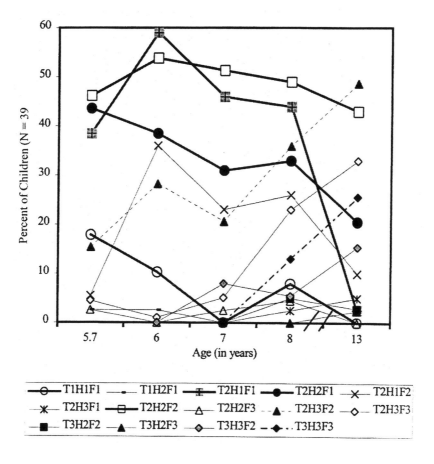

Fig. 2. The developmental course of each profile observed. All children displaying a profile at least once in 10 trials were counted. Therefore, some children are represented more than once in a given year. Also, at 5.7, 8, and 13 years, some profile symbols are masked by other symbols with similar frequencies. Significance of the four profiles with **bold lines** is explained later in the text.

Profiles as Sample Attractors

Figure 3 contains five age-graphs of the profiles as a function of their frequency in the sample at that age as well as their average stability within the children over 10 trials. These graphs give a sense of the relative "sample attractor strength" of each profile and how that strength changed over time. Figure 3(a) shows, for example, that the profiles T2-H2-F1 and T2-H2-F2 were displayed by a relatively large number (around 45%) of the 5.7-year-old children, and that these same children showed the profiles, on average, in about 65% of their trials. This combination of a relatively large number of children showing the profile with relatively high stability made T2-H2-F1 and T2-H2-F2 fairly strong attractors in the sample at that point in time. At the same time, the primitive profile of T1-H1-F1 was shown by only about 20% of the sample, but those 20% showed it on about 60% of their trials. Thus, whereas Figure 2 indicates that T1-H1-F1 was not the most frequent profile for these kindergartners, Figure 3(a) shows that it was moderately strong as a sample attractor because of its stability within some individuals.

In contrast, at 13 years of age, the profile T2-H3-F2 was highest in frequency across the sample but was shown on average in less than 50% of any child's trials (Figure 3[e]). Thus, the relative attractor strength of this

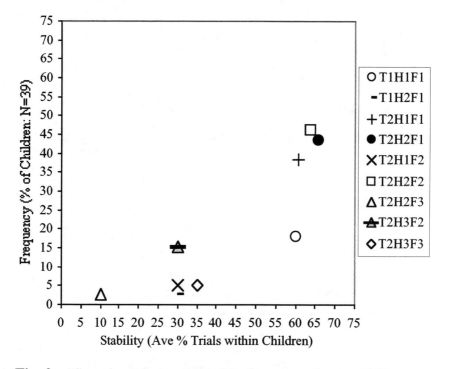

Fig. 3a. "Sample attractor strength" of overarm throw profiles at 5.7 years of age.

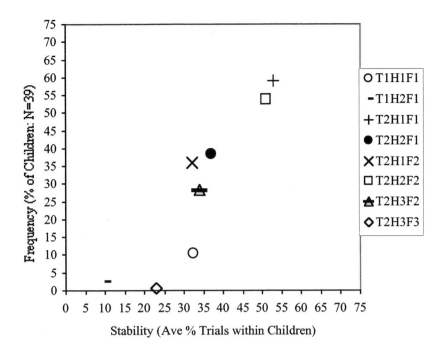

Fig. 3b. "Sample attractor strength" of overarm throw profiles at 6 years of age.

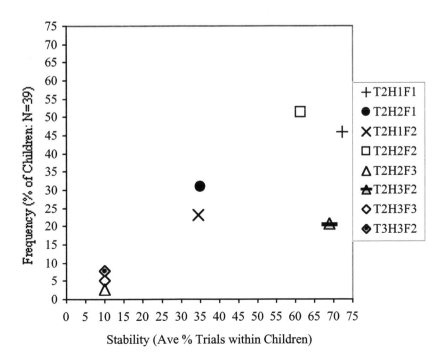

Fig. 3c. "Sample attractor strength" of overarm throw profiles at 7 years of age.

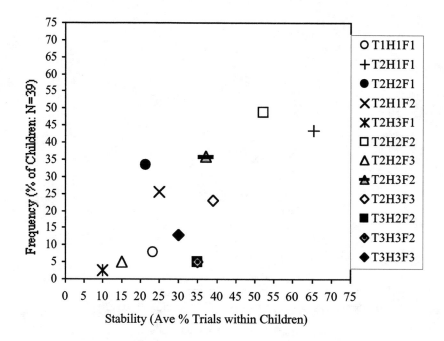

Fig. 3d. "Sample attractor strength" of overarm throw profiles at 8 years of age.

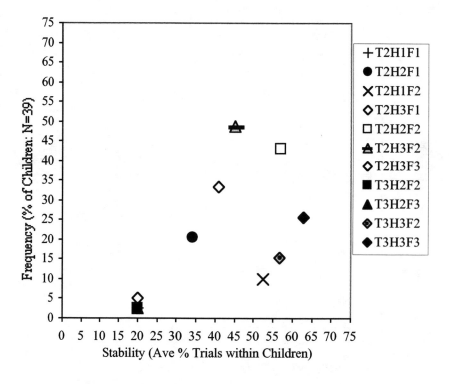

Fig. 3e. "Sample attractor strength" of overarm throw patterns at 13 years of age. The symbols for profiles T2-H1-F1 and T3-H2-F3 are masked by the symbol for T3-H2-F2.

profile was more moderate than its frequency in the sample would suggest (see Figure 2). These comparisons show the information gained by graphing the profiles as sample attractors.

Figure 3 also shows that the largest number of profiles to appear at any one time occurred when the children were eight years of age. Then 12 profiles could be observed across the 39 children. Eleven profiles still occurred when the children were 13 years old. Thus, the range of individual differences in throwing was greatest in second grade but remained large in seventh grade. It should be noted that by these ages, Wild (1938) indicated that all children would be in her Stage IV.

A few profiles were relatively strong sample attractors at each age studied. Figure 3(a) indicates that T2-H1-F1, T2-H2-F1, and T2-H2-F2 were the strongest attractors for the children at 5.7 years; T1-H1-F1 was a moderately strong attractor. At age six (Figure 3[b]), T2-H1-F1 and T2-H2-F2 were the strongest attractors. They, as well as T2-H3-F2, grew more stable as attractors at age seven (Figure 3[c]). By age eight, T2-H1-F1 and T2-H2-F2 were still the strongest attractors. The latter remained strong at age 13 when it was joined by T2-H3-F2 and T3-H3-F3 as moderately strong sample attractors.

Changing Sample Attractor Strength

In Figure 4, we depict the changing sample attractor strength of two throwing profiles across the seven+ years. Figure 4a contrasts the waxing and waning strength of T2-H1-F1 with Figure 4b that illustrates the relatively constant strength of T2-H2-F2 over the same time period. The graphs give a visual sense of how the sample was changing over the five occasions relative to its display of these specific movements.

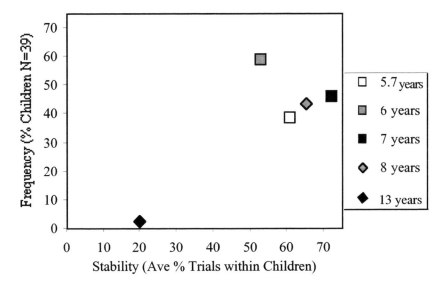

Fig. 4a. Longitudinal changes in profile T2-H1-F1

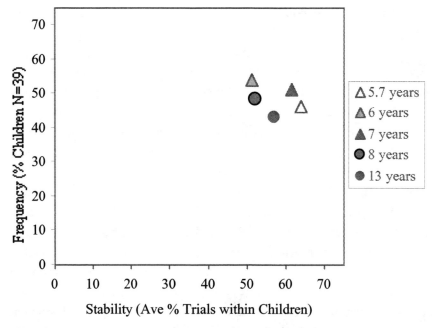

Fig. 4b. Longitudinal changes in profile T2-H2-F2

Profile T2-H1-F1 began as a moderately strong attractor for the 5.7-year-olds (see Figure 4a). Its frequency in the sample then increased substantially to age six years. By seven years, the frequency had declined to less than half the sample. At the same time, however, the profile's average stability increased to more than seven of 10 trials. Subsequently, both its frequency and stability declined slightly by eight years of age, although T2-H1-F1 remained one of the strongest attractors for the eight-year-olds. When tested the final time at age 13, only one participant threw using a T2-H1-F1 profile on just two trials. Thus, T2-H1-F1 had become a very weak attractor for these children at age 13.

In contrast, profile T2-H2-F2 (see Figure 4b) remained relatively strong over the seven-year period. Its frequency within the sample only ranged from 43-54% while its average stability varied only from 51-64%. Interestingly, this continued, relative strength in the sample was due in part to the gender differences associated with throwing development (Halverson et al., 1982). From ages 5.7-8 years, a majority of the T2-H2-F2 profile users were males, but by 13 years of age, most of the throwers displaying this profile were females. Thus, the profile remained strong as an attractive movement state for the sample as the two gender sub-groups were moving out of or into the profile over time.

Profiles as Wild's Stages

Identifying the stronger profile attractors in the sample allowed us to ask whether these attractors could be identified with one of Wild's (1938) stages. Wild's work implied that only four profiles would be strong attractors at some time in the study. Yet, likely candidates in Figure 3 were the profiles T1-H1-F1, T2-H1-F1, T2-H2-F1, T2-H2-F2, T3-H2-F3, and T3-H3-F3. The first problem we encountered in associating these profiles with Wild's stages was the global nature of her descriptions. For instance, Wild's "mature stage" did not recognize differentiated rotation as distinct from block rotation (see Tables 1 and 2). Thus, we could not identify the two strong attractors containing trunk action level 3 as a Wild stage. This fact explains why Wild (1938) claimed that 6.5-year-old boys had a "mature" throw: She did not include differentiated trunk rotation in her definition of maturity. It should be noted that the Seefeldt and Haubenstricker (1982) total body stages expanded Wild's system to include a stage characterized by sequential derotation (i.e., differentiated rotation).[1]

In addition, Wild described arm actions according to the plane in which the arm traveled (see Table 1). Her Stage I was clearly describing an oblique humerus with no forearm lag (profile H1-F1). Stages II and III are less clear: the humerus could be either oblique (Step 1) or horizontally

Table 3
Additional Stepping Actions Observed to Occur with Profiles Resembling Wild's Stages

	Age (in years)				
Profile+Step Action	5.7	6	7	8	13
T1-H1-F1+No Step (Wild I)	13	10	0	0	0
T1-H1-F1+Homolateral Step	5	10	0	5	0
T1-H1-F1+Contralateral Step	8	5	0	3	0
T2-H1-F1+No Step (Wild II)	21	36	31	18	0
T2-H1-F1+Homolateral Step	5	8	10	10	0
T2-H1-F1+Contralateral Step	18	41	28	28	3
T2-H1-F1+Long Contralateral Step	0	0	3	0	3
T2-H2-F1+ No Step	23	10	10	3	5
T2-H2-F1+ Homolateral Step (Wild III)	10	3	8	3	0
T2-H2-F1+Contralateral Step	28	33	26	23	15
T2-H2-F1+Long Contralateral Step	0	0	5	3	5
T2-H2-F2+ No Step	23	18	13	8	3
T2-H2-F2+ Homolateral Step	3	5	0	0	0
T2-H2-F2+ Contralateral Step (Wild IV)	39	49	49	44	31
T2-H2-F2+Long Contralateral Step	0	0	8	8	18

Note. Data are percentages, rounded to nearest integer (N = 39). Profiles in **bold** are those that most closely approximate the description of Wild's (1938) stages (see Table 1).

aligned but independent (Step 2). She did not address forearm action. Thus, arm profiles H1-F1 or H1-F2, and H2-F1 and H2-F2 might all fit into Stage II and III in combination with trunk block rotation (Step 2). Wild's Stage IV described the humerus action as horizontal adduction, which is Step 2 in the Roberton humerus action. Again, Wild's most advanced stage did not recognize that advanced forceful throwing is accomplished with the humerus locked onto the trunk at 90^0 to the trunk axis so that it is spatially lagging by front facing (see Table 2 for Roberton's Step 3).

At this point in the process, our best guess was that profile T1-H1-F1 was similar to Wild's Stage I and that profile T2-H2-F2 was similar to Wild's Stage IV. Wild's Stages II and III could be either T2-H1-F1 or T2-H2-F1. All had been relatively strong sample attractors in our data. However, as Table 1 indicates, Wild also included action of the feet in her whole body descriptions. Therefore, we added the foot actions that we had observed accompanying these profiles in each year of the current study. (See Table 2 for our descriptions of foot action levels.) Table 3 shows that at each age we found more stepping actions combining with each profile than Wild's stages recognized.

Lastly, we analyzed the behavior of the developmental curves associated with these four profiles. (They are **bold** in Figure 2.) We did not add the variety of foot actions observed, which would have greatly increased the number of profile combinations and decreased their occurrence percentages. We evaluated the curves "sans feet" using the criteria proposed for accurate developmental sequences by Roberton, Williams, and Langendorfer (1980). Briefly, those criteria indicate the curves should rise and fall in the order of their predicted sequence, making each curve the modal behavior of the sample at some point in developmental time. Using these criteria, we concluded that profile T1-H1-F1 (Wild's Stage I) behaved as would be expected (except for the blip at age eight) by gradually disappearing over the age range. Judging from the slope of the curve, it could possibly have been modal at a younger age. Its slope and frequency of occurrence suggested it would be the most primitive category within a four-level sequence. Profile T2-H2-F1 (Wild's Stage II or III) was also declining over the age range. Its slope also suggested that it might have been modal during an earlier age period. Its frequency over the age range placed it as second in a four-level sequence. Interestingly, T2-H1-F1 (which we would consider a less-advanced profile than T2-H2-F1) appeared to be the third level of the sequence, reaching modality at age six and then declining over the rest of the time. Wild's stage descriptions (Table 1), however, do not permit a distinction between these two profiles. If they were collapsed, they would behave appropriately as a second level in a developmental sequence. (Keep in mind Wild maintained that no stepping action occurred with Stage II. As Table 3 shows, other stepping actions occurred in our data with both profiles.) Finally, modal at every other age studied was T2-H2-F2, the most advanced of Wild's stages. While its occurrence was robust at all the ages studied, the shape of the curve gave modest support for the notion that it had grown in frequency at earlier ages.

Thus, these data showed that three or four of the stronger sample attractors in our data seemed related to Wild's stages and could be sequenced in approximately the order she reported, if we ignored the action of the feet and guessed at the arm action. As the other profiles in Figure 2 indicate, however, what Wild did was to sacrifice the information in her data on other profiles in favor of a four-"stage" sequence of stronger sample attractors. She may not have seen the rising of more sophisticated profiles at older ages, probably because she studied only two children at each age from 7-12 years. Wild primarily based her third and fourth stages on the action of the feet, missing the important changes occurring in the other components. We should point out that in our data at age 13 several profiles containing differentiated rotation increased in strength, supporting the Haubenstricker and Seefeldt (1982) addition of "derotation" to the Wild sequence.[1]

GENERAL DISCUSSION

Constraints Operating on Throwing Profiles

The authors hold a view congruent with Newell's (1984, 1986) constraints model that the movement patterns used to throw a ball emerge from various relationships that constrain the action. When qualitative changes occur in the throw, the model suggests that a shift has also occurred between person-environment and/or person-task relationships.

Our results illustrated convincingly that all throwing movement profiles were not equally likely to occur at each age and that, in fact, 13 possible profiles never occurred in the five measurement periods over the seven+ years sampled by this study. This finding was not a random event ($p<.01$). We need to emphasize that the absence of these sample attractors during this time does not mean that the profiles would never occur. Indeed, most of them are associated with a level 1 trunk, a movement more frequently seen in children younger than those studied. Their absence from ages 5.7-13, however, is consonant with the argument that constraints were reducing the likelihood of their appearance.

These results also demonstrated that those profiles that we did observe changed sample attractor strength over time. It therefore must be the case that certain constraints were operating to eliminate some profiles and to change the likelihood of others. It seems highly probable, therefore, that these constraints were shifting over the time studied.

At least one constraint can be eliminated as an explanation for these results. The procedures for collecting these data were held reasonably constant during each of the five measurement occasions. All participants were asked to throw the tennis ball "as hard as you can" or to "crash the ball against the wall." Therefore, it is improbable that a change in task goal (i.e., a task-person constraint) changed the children's developmental levels of throwing. On the other hand, participants did experience normal changes in body size (both increased mass and limb segment lengths), and many of them engaged in numerous formal and informal throwing activities over the seven+ years (see Halverson et al., 1982). Consequently, both changing body size and changing experience relative to the task may have influenced the observed movements. Subsequent studies will need to explore these latter possibilities.

The presence and absence of profiles did suggest three within-person constraints that may also have been operating at various times over the seven+ years. Newell (1984) had proposed three categories of intra-organismic constraints: (bio)mechanical, anatomical, and physiological. At least two of these could be active in the development of throwing. The first, an anatomical constraint, was suggested by the relative rarity of humerus level 3 combined with forearm levels 2 or 3 (see Table 2) even in the children at 13 years of age. Only four of the 14 profiles observed included the humerus lag/forearm lag position (H3-F2 or F3). The physical therapy literature describes two extreme joint positions, called loose-packed and close-packed (Magee, 1987). For any joint, the loose-packed position produces maximum joint laxity. In contrast, close-packed position is the position under which the ligaments, muscles, and joint capsule are maximally stretched. Interestingly, the close-packed position for the glenohumeral joint is described as occurring when the humerus is held in abduction and laterally rotated. This description describes level 3 of the humerus action combined with forearm action steps 2 or 3. It is clearly not a position assumed with ease. Because 10 of the throwing profiles observed did not contain the close-packed position, it may be concluded that children tend to assume arm positions of more comfort when throwing forcefully. Even when the close-packed position appeared, these profiles (T2-H3-F2, T2-H3-F3, T3-H3-F2, and T3-H3-F3) were weak to moderate in the sample. Thus, the oblique humerus with no lag and the horizontally adducted humerus with or without lag may reflect the relative comfort of the loose-packed position that places far less stretch on the glenohumeral joint capsule and its muscle receptors. Ironically, it is the close-packed position that ultimately allows the thrower to best exploit the inertial properties of humerus and forearm segments as well as the elastic properties of the shoulder ligaments and muscles.

A second, within-person biomechanical constraint also may have influenced throwing change. It was the connection between the rotating trunk and advanced levels of humerus and forearm action. Levels 3 of humerus and forearm were always paired with a rotating trunk (levels 2 or 3). In fact, the only profiles that emerged with a non-rotating trunk in throwing were T1-H1-F1 and T1-H2-F1. On the other hand, four profiles (T2-H1-F1; T2-H2-F1; T2-H1-F2; T2-H3-F1) showed that the lowest level of either the humerus or forearm action also could occur with a rotating trunk. Thus, trunk rotation is necessary, but not sufficient for advanced arm action. The thrower apparently needs to be able to *both* rotate the trunk *and* assume a close-packed shoulder position in order for the rotating trunk to enable spatial "lag" of the humerus.

Finally, the profiles also revealed that differentiated rotation occurred in combination with only four arm profiles (H2-F2; H2-F3; H3-F2; H3-F3). This tight confluence of arm actions with this one trunk action suggested another potential biomechanical constraint: either the differentiated trunk action enabled these arm actions or the arm actions enabled differentiated rotation. These particular arm profiles are ones that would produce the greatest functional arm segment moments of inertia. We speculate, therefore, that the moments of inertia generated by the arm segments in these profiles may actually produce differentiated trunk rotation. The arm segment inertia could act to momentarily hold back the upper spine and shoulders while the pelvis rotates forward. Again, because these same arm profiles also occurred in combination with a block rotating trunk, they are not sufficient alone to explain the occurrence of differentiated trunk rotation. An additional relationship must be operating that causes differentiated trunk rotation to emerge. Likely candidates include the spatial pathway and position of the arm segments during the backswing, the displacement and/or velocity of forward trunk rotation or, perhaps, the timing relationship between the arm backswing and the initiation of forward trunk rotation.

In addition, we cannot ignore Jensen's (1986) hypothesis that growth-related changes in segmental moments of inertia alone can cause movement changes. The critical point is that we suspect further investigation of factors related to differentiated rotation will show that this advanced movement is an emergent property of the confluence of other movements in the body and is not the result of a separate "motor program" in the brain. We suspect that the neural command to rotate the trunk results in either block or differentiated rotation, depending on the context of other body movements.

Attractive Profiles as Wild's Stages

Our data suggested that when profiles were graphed as sample attractors, several of them appeared to be relatively strong in comparison to other profiles. Further, several of these stronger attractors partially fit Monica Wild's (1938) original stage descriptions of the development of the forceful overarm throw. They were T1-H1-F1, T2-H1-F1, T2-H2-F1, and T2-H2-F2. Thus, we can conclude that certain profiles existed in her sample frequently enough that she chose to identify them as a "stage." Because we wondered why Wild did not see more of the individual differences represented by the other profiles that appeared in our data, we examined her original, three-volume dissertation (Wild, 1937). It revealed that she reduced her filmed data by describing *components*, which she called "movement features!" She then applied a scattergram technique to associate the various features with each other, coming up with the four stages used in the published article. Thus, the irony of Monica Wild's classic work is that she started with a component approach and saw individual differences even in her small sample (especially in arm action), but decided to ignore these in the published summary. Moreover, the lack of a rear view in combination with the slower film speed (48 fps) (Wild, 1937) may have masked differentiated rotation of the trunk. Alternatively, by studying only three trials of one boy and one girl at each of the ages between seven and 12 years, it may be that none of her participants displayed differentiated rotation. Moreover, nowhere in her dissertation did she indicate awareness of the significance of forearm lag. Therefore, her "mature throw" was really the "intermediate level" throw, T2-H2-F2, illustrated in Figure 1.

These comments are not meant to detract from the importance of Wild's work. Indeed, every reader should read the original article (Wild, 1938) or the original dissertation (Wild, 1937) rather than relying on secondary sources. The work is truly monumental. Our point is simply that 60 years after the publication of her article, it is time to move forward in our understanding of the probabilistic nature of *variation* in motor development as it is reflected in forceful throwing.

Profile T2-H2-F2

While the stage concept of Wild does not do justice to the variation that can be seen in throwing, the relative strength of profile T2-H2-F2 at every age in the study led us to speculate that the confluence of these intermediate levels of throwing may, in fact, be "phylogenetic." Indeed, 37 of our 39 children displayed the T2-H2-F2 profile on at least one trial at some time in the course of the study. Perhaps many children will reach this profile via one pathway or another if they receive some minimal experience in forceful throwing. Conversely, the various profiles beyond this level may be reserved for those who truly achieve skill in the throw. Perhaps these latter profiles are the "ontogenetic" aspect of throwing. As Roberton (1984) pointed out, the forceful overarm throw is a task that has been characterized in some texts as phylogenetic and in other texts as ontogenetic. It could be that both views are correct in that early levels of the throw are phylogenetic, but advanced levels are ontogenetic.

Component vs. Whole Body Approach

We wish to close by stressing again that at each age no movement profile occurred in more than one-third of the total trials across the children or in more than 60% of the sample. Moreover, the stability with which the profiles were exhibited was much less than the stability with which component levels are exhibited. Roberton (1978a) reported that these same children, on average, showed the same component (trunk, humerus, and forearm) developmental levels in 84-91% of their trials. Williams et al. (1998) recently reported high consistency for all component levels in elderly throwers. The profile variability within and between children that occurred as they linked the movement of differing body parts over time gave strong support to the component model as an accurate descriptor of throwing coordination.

The increasing number of profiles observed with time, e.g., increasing individual differences, fits with what we know about motor development over the lifespan. It does not fit with the common conclusion in the motor development literature that by age six most children have developed the "mature form" of the overarm throw. This conclusion results from a strange reluctance to move beyond a 60-year-old, cross-sectional study of 32 children. As descendants in the same academic, family tree as Monica Wild (Glassow,Wild,Halverson,Roberton,Langendorfer), we suspect she would encourage future generations to move beyond the few sample attractors she identified so many years ago.

REFERENCES

Abraham, R.H., & Shaw, C.D. (1983). *Dynamics: The geometry of behavior*. Santa Cruz, CA: Aerial Press.

Clark, J.E. (1995). On becoming skillful: Patterns and constraints. *Research Quarterly for Exercise and Sport, 66*, 173-183.

Clark, J.E., & Phillips, S. (1985). A developmental sequence of the standing long jump. In J. E. Clark & J.H. Humphrey (Eds.), *Motor development: Current selected research* (Vol. 1, pp. 73-85). Princeton, N.J: Princeton Book Co.

Gleick, J. (1987). *Chaos—Making a new science*. New York: Penquin Books.

Goldfield, E.C., Kay, B.A., & Warren, W.W. (1993). Infant bouncing: The assembling and tuning of action systems. *Child Development, 64*, 1128-1142.

Halverson, L.E. & Roberton, M.A. (1979). The effects of instruction on overhand throwing development in children. In G. Roberts & K. Newell (Eds.), *Psychology of motor behavior and sport–1978* (pp. 258-269). Champaign, IL.: Human Kinetics.

Halverson, L.E., Roberton, M.A., & Langendorfer, S. (1982). Development of the overarm throw: Movement and ball velocity changes by seventh grade. *Research Quarterly for Exercise and Sport, 53*, 198-205.

Halverson, L.E., Roberton, M.A., Safrit, M.J., & Roberts, T.W. (1977). The effect of guided practice on overhand throw ball velocities of kindergarten children. *Research Quarterly, 48*, 311-318.

Haywood, K.M. (1993). *Life span motor development* (2nd ed.). Champaign, IL: Human Kinetics.

Jensen, R.K. (1986). Body segment mass, radius, and radius of gyration proportions of children. *Journal of Biomechanics, 19*, 359-368.

Kelso, J.A.S. (1995). *Dynamic patterns*. Cambridge, MA: MIT Press.

Magee, D.P. (1987). *Orthopedic physical assessment*. Philadelphia: Saunders.

Muchisky, M., Gershkoff-Stowe, L., Cole, E., & Thelen, E. (1996). The epigenetic landscape revisited: A dynamic interpretation. In C. Rovee-Collier (Ed.), *Advances in infancy research* (Vol. 10, pp. 121-159). Norwood, NJ: Albex.

Newell, K. (1984). Physical constraints to development of motor skills. In J. Thomas (Ed.), *Motor development during preschool and elementary years* (pp. 105-120). Minneapolis: Burgess.

Newell, K. (1986). Constraints on the development of coordination. In M.G. Wade & H.T.A. Whiting (Eds.), *Motor development in children: Aspects of coordination and control* (pp. 341-360). Dordrecht, The Netherlands: Nijhoff.

Roberton, M.A. (1977). Stability of stage categorizations across trials: Implications for the "stage theory" of overarm throw development. *Journal of Human Movement Studies, 3*, 49-59.

Roberton, M.A. (1978a). Longitudinal evidence for developmental stages in the forceful overarm throw. *Journal of Human Movement Studies, 4*, 167-175.

Roberton, M.A. (1978b). Stages in motor development. In M. Ridenour (Ed.), *Motor development: Issues and applications* (pp. 63-81). Princeton, N.J: Princeton Book Co.

Roberton, M.A. (1982). Describing stages within and across motor tasks. In J.A.S. Kelso & J.E. Clark (Eds.), *The development of movement control and coordination* (pp. 293-307). New York: Wiley.

Roberton, M.A. (1984). Changing motor patterns during childhood. In J.R. Thomas (Ed.), *Motor development during preschool and elementary years* (pp. 48-90). Minneapolis: Burgess.

Roberton, M.A., & Halverson, L.E. (1984). *Developing children—Their changing movement: A guide for teachers*. Philadelphia: Lea & Febiger.

Roberton, M.A., & Halverson, L.E. (1988). The development of locomotor coordination: Longitudinal change and invariance. *Journal of Motor Behavior, 20*, 197-241.

Roberton, M.A., Halverson, LE., Langendorfer, S., & Williams, K. (1979). Longitudinal changes in children's overarm throw ball velocities. *Research *Quarterly, 50*, 256-264.

Roberton, M.A., & Langendorfer, S. (1980). Testing motor development sequences across 9-14 years. In C. Nadeau, W. Halliwell, K. Newell, & G. Roberts (Eds.), *Psychology of motor behavior and sport-1979* (pp. 269-279). Champaign, IL.: Human Kinetics.

Roberton, M.A., Williams, K., & Langendorfer, S. (1980). Pre-longitudinal screening of motor development sequences. *Research Quarterly for Exercise and Sport, 51*, 724-731.

Roberts, T.W. (1972). Incident light velocimetry. *Perceptual and Motor Skills, 34*, 263-268.

Seefeldt, V., & Haubenstricker, J. (1982). Patterns, phases, or stages: An analytic model for the study of developmental movement. In J.A.S. Kelso & J.E. Clark (Eds.), *The development of movement control and coordination* (pp. 309-318). New York: Wiley.

VanSant, A. (1997). A lifespan perspective of age differences in righting movements. *Motor Development: Research and Reviews, 1*, 46-63.

Wild, M.R. (1937). *The behavior pattern of throwing and some observations concerning its course of development in children.* Unpublished Ph.D. Dissertation, University of Wisconsin-Madison.

Wild, M.R. (1938). The behavior pattern of throwing and some observations concerning its course of development in children. *Research Quarterly, 9*, 20-24.

Williams, K., Haywood, K., & VanSant, A. (1998). Changes in throwing by older adults: A longitudinal investigation. *Research Quarterly for Exercise and Sport, 69*, 1-10.

Zanone, P., Kelso, J.A.S., & Jeka, J. (1993). Concepts and methods for a dynamic approach to behavioral coordination and change. In G.J.P. Savelsbergh (Ed.), *The development of coordination in infancy* (pp. 89-135). Amsterdam: Elsevier.

Authors' Note

We would like to thank the many people who helped collect these data over the years, especially our mentor, Lolas E. Halverson, of the University of Wisconsin-Madison. We wish to acknowledge the assistance of the Bowling Green State University Statistical Consulting Center, especially Hanfeng Chen, Maria L. Hong, and John Tisak. Precursors of this paper were presented at the North American Society for the Psychology of Sport and Physical Activity in 1993 and 1997.

Footnote

[1]Seefeldt and Haubenstricker (1982) hypothesized a five-stage sequence for the overarm throw for force, which modified and expanded the work of Wild (1938).

2

CONTROL PARAMETERS FOR THE DEVELOPMENT OF THROWING

Dan Southard

ABSTRACT

The purpose of this study was to determine if relative mass of upper limb segments and throwing velocity are control parameters that contribute to the development of throwing patterns. Forty participants (ages 5-12 years) were categorized into four levels according to throwing pattern. Each participant was required to complete 10 overhand throws at two efforts (25% of maximum and maximum) within two conditions (adult mass and normal) for a total of 40 trials per participant. For the adult condition, the throwing arm was changed so that the relative mass of segments was equal to that of an adult limb. Results indicated that the adult mass condition increased the level of throwing pattern for level 1 and 2 throwers. Increasing throwing velocity increased level of pattern for level 1, 2, and 3 throwers. It was concluded that changes in relative mass of upper limb segments and increases in effort of throw are contributing factors toward the development of a mature throwing pattern.

The term "fundamental motor skill" refers to the observable performance of basic locomotor, manipulative, and stabilizing movements, such as running, jumping, kicking, throwing, and catching (Gallahue & Ozmun, 1997). Such activities are generally thought to form the foundation for more advanced and specific movement activities (Gabbard, 1992). Much of the attention devoted toward the study of fundamental motor skills has been focused on the description of patterns of coordination. Consequently, motor developmentalists have hypothesized a developmental sequence of patterns for fundamental motor skills such as throwing (Langendorfer, 1980; Roberton, 1978; Wild, 1938), catching (Harper, 1979; Haubenstricker, Branta, & Seefeldt, 1983), running (Wickstrom, 1983), hopping (Halverson & Williams, 1985), and punting (Roberton, 1983). Relatively less attention has been spent on questions concerning the process of development. That is, where do these patterns of coordination come from and why do they evolve in time?

Clark and Whitall (1989) suggest that the evolution of motor development studies has shifted from a descriptive approach, which encompasses years 1946 to 1970, to a process-oriented period from 1970 to present. Early process-oriented approaches were steeped heavily in information processing theory (Connolly, 1970). A problem with information processing-based theories is the lack of a principled account of how central representations can serve as both feedback and feedforward mechanisms. Somehow cognitive representations must "know" not only what movements are important for given environmental conditions but also predict (in a consistent way across individuals and circumstances) developmental changes in motor patterns. Clark and Whitall indicate that a breakthrough paper by Kugler, Kelso, and Turvey (1982) presented a theory that was in distinct contrast to information processing viewpoints. Unlike information processing approaches, dynamical systems theory indicates that pattern and order can emerge from component interactions of a complex system without the need for representations or instruction (Thelen & Smith, 1994).

The dynamical systems perspective suggests that elements of the motor system are self-organizing and interact with each other along with the environment to establish motor patterns. The nervous system is but a component of the interaction and not the sole determiner of movement patterns (Kelso, 1994). There may be an infinite number of ways in which components of the system may organize into observable behaviors. However, certain relationships between elements tend to dominate the behavior of the system. Haken (1977) refers to these dominant modes as order parameters. Order parameters are capable of constraining the system to act within a limited range of possible behaviors. The many degrees of freedom exhibited by the system are not considered a nuisance; rather, behavioral variability is essential to the self-organization of the system. Without variability, systems are less likely to be attracted to new forms of movement or in dynamic systems terminology "attractor states."

Attractor states may have different degrees of stability. Very stable attractor states are motor patterns to which individuals will readily return after undergoing extreme perturbation. Thelen and Smith (1994) suggest that stable attractor states are so reliable under a variety of circumstances that it is easy to incorrectly view them as the products of "hardwired structures or programs." Developmental sequences hypothesized by motor developers may be stable attractor states that are preferred for relatively long periods of time (i.e., stages). Conversely, less stable attractor states may readily change to new coordinative patterns as a result of relatively small disturbances and go unnoticed by the observer looking for more stable patterns. Regardless of stability, attractor states are discontinuous and capable of change. Changes in any one of the system components, including biomechanical and contextual factors, can decrease stability in the system and instigate organization to a new attractor state. Anthropometric changes as a result of development, change in performance variables, or even a change in attitude could theoretically drive the system toward a new way of organizing. Those variables which instigate such changes are called control parameters. To make matters complex, control parameters may themselves change as systems move from one attractor state to another. It is important to recognize that control parameters do not represent change but rather take advantage of naturally occuring instabilities in the system (Kelso, Scholz, & Schöner, 1986). Control parameters are key variables to both understanding and instigating pattern change. Encouraging individuals to scale up on control parameters may be the best strategy for improving performance of fundamental motor skills (see Thelen & Smith, 1994 for an excellent discussion of order parameters, control parameters, and changing attractor states). Identifying control parameters is an important but difficult task. The key is to first recognize essential variables to task performance, then identify periods of developmental transitions, and finally experimentally test for control parameters, which drive the shift between attractor states (Thelen, 1989). If variables identified as possible control parameters are artificially scaled up and such changes induce conversion to a new attractor state, then there is evidence that the variables are control parameters.

Throwing is a fundamental skill that lends itself well to investigation via dynamical systems perspective. It is a complex skill that involves a large number of degrees of freedom essential for self organizing systems and potential changes in attractor states. The essential variables related to throwing center around a single mechanical concept—the kinetic link principle. The upper limb is composed of segments or links that have a base at the shoulder and a free or open end at the hand. Movement of any segment in the link affects all other segments to which it is attached. The kinetic link principle allows the upper limb to attempt conservation of angular momentum during a throwing motion (Kreighbaum & Barthles, 1990). Angular momentum is equal to moment of inertia times angular velocity (AM = Iw). For accomplished throwers, as the more proximal body segments rotate and create angular momentum, their less massive distal neighbors lag behind. Then as the proximal segment slows down, angular momentum is transferred to the less massive distal neighbor. Because the distal segment is less massive than its proximal neighbor, the distal segment increases velocity in an attempt to conserve angular momentum. This process occurs in sequence from the trunk to the hand with each distal segment increasing in velocity in an attempt to conserve momentum. This whip-like action occurs if the mass of the distal segment is less than its proximal neighbor and if the distal segment lags behind its proximal neighbor.

Descriptions of the overhand throw indicate that the degree to which performers take advantage of the transfer of angular momentum is related to developmental stages (attractor states). Roberton's (1978) component description of developmental sequences for the overarm throw show a progression from no trunk action to differentiated rotation of the trunk, no humeral lag relative to trunk to humeral lag, no forearm lag to delayed forearm lag. Each developmental step by component (including action of the feet and preparation to throw) favors an increase in the whip-like action of the body and arm segments. Whereas Roberton does not directly refer to the transfer of angular momentum in her description, Atwater (1979) describes the kinetic link principle in her biomechanical analysis of overarm throwing. She states that the sequence in which the segments of skilled throwers reach peak angular velocity is the pelvis, upper trunk, humerus, forearm, and hand. In addition, she indicates that as each segment accelerated in turn, the succeeding segment first lagged behind, then acquired the speed of the segments moving it, and then accelerated to reach an even greater angular speed while the preceding segment decelerated. It appears from descriptive analysis that when attempting an overarm throw, the motor system organizes itself around the kinetic link principle (attempts to take advantage of the transfer of angular momentum). It is hypothesized that the kinetic link principle or attempts by the system to conserve angular momentum is an order parameter for the fundamental skill of throwing. Essential variables related to the order parameter could be those elements that determine angular momentum.

Southard (1998) determined that shifts in attractor states occurred when the relative mass of upper limb segments were altered and or adult throwers performed at varying velocities. Mass and velocity are essential variables to the conservation of angular momentum. He concluded that for adult throwers, mass and velocity are control parameters for the overarm throw. Southard hypothesized four different attractor states to indicate the degree to which the system might take advantage of the kinetic link principle. He used a Watsmart infrared motion analysis system with Roberton's (1983) component analysis as a guideline for categorizing the action of the humerus, forearm, and hand. Throwing pattern was defined as level 1 when participants exhibited simple arm and elbow extension with little or no segmental lag. Segmental lag was determined by relative time to peak velocity for each segment and assessed at 200hz. Throwers were categorized as level 2 when they displayed a lag of the hand relative to the forearm but no lag of the forearm relative to the humerus. Level 3 throwers displayed segmental lag of the forearm and hand with little or no lag of the humerus to the trunk. Level 4 throwers displayed segmental lag of the humerus relative to the trunk, the forearm relative to the humerus, and the hand relative to the forearm. He found that adding mass to distal arm segments of accomplished adult throwers (level 3 and 4) decreased the degree to which participants utilized the kinetic link principle (participants went from a level 3 or 4 to a level 1 or 2 pattern). Conversely, adding mass to the more proximal segments of level 1 and 2 throwers resulted in a change to a level 3 or 4 pattern. Additionally, increasing throwing velocity resulted in increased throwing levels for level 1, 2, and 3 throwers. Such findings lead to the following question. Do anthropometric changes of the arm and increase in throwing velocity affect developmental changes in throwing pattern?

A review of the anthropometric literature (Frisancho, 1993; Jensen,

1981; Jensen, 1986; Malina & Brouchard, 1991; McConville, Churchill, Kaleps, Clauser, & Cuzzi, 1980) indicates that the human upper limb develops distal to proximal (data represents ages 5-15 years). That is, the relative mass of limb segments reaches adult proportion in the hand, followed by the forearm, and then the humerus. This is not to say that the distal segment of a child (on an absolute basis) is more massive than its proximal neighbor. Rather, the relative mass of a child's distal segment in proportion to its proximal segments is greater than the relative mass of adult distal to proximal segments. Recalling that Southard (1998) determined that adding mass to distal segments reduced the degree to which throwers utilized the kinetic link principle, it stands to reason that changes in relative mass of upper limb segments may enhance the development of the overarm throw. In dynamical systems terms, when the control parameter of mass is increased for the proximal segments relative to their distal neighbors, there is a change in attractor state that favors the kinetic link principle (conservation of angular momentum). The system is organized relative to the hypothesized order parameter; therefore, when changes in control parameters favor the conservation of angular momentum, an increase in throwing level is the predicted result. Based on previous work on adults, the purpose of this study was to determine if relative mass of upper limb segments and throwing velocity are control parameters that affect the development of throwing patterns.

METHOD

Participants

Forty children (ages 5-12 years; 23 males and 17 females) enrolled at a university laboratory school served as participants in this study. The parents of each participant completed an informed consent form before their child participated in the experiment. Participants were observed throwing during organized physical education classes (playing catch with a soft baseball size ball). Children were encouraged to throw different distances (velocities) using any preferred method. Initially, observation was used to organize participants according to level of performance. Wild's (1938) developmental stages along with Roberton's (1983) component analysis were used to identify participants as level 1, 2, 3, or 4. This initial grouping of participants was helpful in organizing participants for analysis and placement in final categories.

The final throwing categories were determined using a Watsmart motion analysis system. Each participant threw a ball five times at preferred speed (50-60% of maximum for most participants) while kinematic arm data were recorded. The classification scheme was identical to that explained earlier (Southard, 1998) and associated with the degree to which participants utilized the kinetic link principle (segmental lag of distal segment relative to its proximal neighbor). The relative position of each limb segment was digitized using a data analysis package designed by Northern Digital inc., Waterloo, Ontario, Canada. Distal segments were determined to lag behind their proximal neighbors if the difference in time to peak velocity were greater than 5 ms. The 5 ms minimum is based on minimal, but consistent, differences in segmental lag (hand to forearm) typically experienced by more accomplished throwers (Southard, 1998). It was common for subjects designated as level 1 or level 2 to exhibit arm patterns that were not defined by the classification scheme (e.g., hand and humerus together followed by the forearm). In those instances, the pattern most consistently utilized was used to classify the participant. There were no subjects that consistently (more than two trials out of five) utilized a pattern outside the classification scheme to throw the ball. There was a high correlation (r=.90) between the observational groupings and the final categories based on kinematic arm data. See Table 1 for the distribution of participants by age, gender, and level of throwing pattern. For the most part, younger participants were categorized as level 1 or 2, and older participants were categorized as level 3 or 4.

Table 1
Number of Participants within Level by Gender and Age

	Level 1	Level 2	Level 3	Level 4
Age	5 yrs	6 yrs	6 yrs	10 yrs
Gender	(1) Female	(0) Female	(0) Female	(0) Female
	(0) Male	(1) Male	(1) Male	(2) Males
Age	6 yrs	7 yrs	9 yrs	11 yrs
Gender	(2) Female	(4) Female	(0) Female	(0) Female
	(3) Male	(1) Male	(3) Male	(1) Male
Age	7 yrs	8 yrs	10 yrs	12 yrs
Gender	(2) Female	(2) Female	(0) Female	(1) Female
	(1) Male	(2) Male	(2) Male	(5) Male
Age	9 yrs	10 yrs	11 yrs	
Gender	(1) Female	(0) Female	(3) Female	
	(0) Male	(1) Male	(0) Male	
Age		11 yrs		
Gender		(1) Female		
		(0) Male		

Design and Procedure

A within-subjects design was utilized with each participant completing 10 overhand throws at two velocities (25% maximum and maximum) within two mass conditions (normal mass and adult mass) for a total of 40 trials per participant. Maximum velocity for each participant was established with the motion analysis system prior to data collection. Each trial was monitored during data collection and participants were told to increase or decrease velocity to ensure that trials were within 5% of the required percentages. Six participants required extra trials in order to meet the required percentage. Two participants required three trials or less and three participants required five extra trials in order to meet the 10 trial criterion. Four of the six participants requiring extra trials were younger participants classified as level 1 or level 2 throwers. The most common problem was perception of 25% of maximum during the adult mass condition. Most errors were made as a result of throwing faster (35-50% maximum) than the acceptable percentage. Trials outside the required percentage were not included in data analysis.

For the normal mass condition participants completed trials without altering the mass of limb segments. For the adult mass condition, the mass of each child's arm segments (humerus and forearm) were altered so that relative mass was the same as an adult arm. First, the ratio of proximal to distal segment mass was computed for the adult arm (Clauser, McConville, & Young, 1969). Then, mass of each participants' arm segments were determined using data provided by Jensen (1986). Finally, mass adjustment for each participants' segments was calculated relative to known adult proportions. Mass of arm segments was determined by multiplying the participant's total body mass by the percentage of total body mass representing each segment. Percentage values for segment mass were based on the age of participants; however, the actual mass added to segments was individually adjusted relative to the total body mass of each participant. It should be noted that participants were within the predicted mass values for children at their respective ages. Table 2 indicates the segmental mass of the upper limb segments, adult ratios, percentage increases required to reach adult proportions, and average increase in mass of each segment. Note that no increase in mass of the hand is required because the upper limb develops proportionately in a distal to proximal sequence.

Increase in segment mass was accomplished by sewing lead shot in self adhesive cloth strips. The 4 centimeter (cm) wide strips containing the additional mass were placed around the center of mass of appropriate segments. The mass conformed to the shape of the limb and remained in place during throwing trials. Participants reported no discomfort or hindrance from the cloth strips during the trials requiring the adult mass condition. Individual strips were customized for each participant in the study.

Participants completed trials by throwing a ball with a circumference of 21 cm and a mass of 100 grams to a wall four meters from the data collection point. Cushioned mats were placed against the wall to prevent the ball from rebounding back toward participants. Accuracy of throw was not a requirement for the task. The only augmented information provided participants was in reference to the required throwing velocity. Each participant was allowed five warm-up throws (normal mass and preferred velocity). Data collection trials were randomized by velocity and condition. Data were collected one participant at a time in the school's gymnasium.

Table 2
Segmental Mass, Adult Ratios, and Average Increase
to Reach Adult Proportion

		Age (years)			
	Adult	12	10	8	6
Segment Mass (% total body)					
Humerus	.035	.032	.030	.029	.028
Forearm	.016	.017	.016	.015	.015
Hand	.005	.009	.009	.009	.010
% Increase to Equal Adult Proportion					
Humerus		3.100	3.300	3.400	4.200
Forearm		1.180	1.280	1.380	1.700
Mean Increase in Mass (kg)					
Hunerus		1.127	1.050	.927	.954
Forearm		.427	.404	.377	.386

Apparatus

Data were collected at a sampling rate of 200 Hz with a Watsmart Motion Analysis System. Two infrared detectors (cameras) were mounted on tripods. The tripods were raised to a height of 2.2 meters and spaced so that cameras were three meters apart and three meters from the participant. The camera arrangement allowed for a data collection area (2 x 2 meters), which easily contained the throwing motion. The system was calibrated using a frame of known dimensions before each data collection session. Calibration was completed at the throwing height of each subject. The range of spatial error was from 2.75 mm to 4.62 mm with a mean error of 3.72 mm. The range of velocity error would be .56 cm/s to 2.23 cm/s for lower velocity throws and 5.95 cm/s to 6.69 cm/s for higher velocity throws.

Infrared emitting diodes (IREDS) were placed on the fingernail of the third finger, ulnar styloid, lateral epicondyle, gleno-humeral axis, and spinous process of the first thoracic vertebrae. The power source for the IREDS was placed at the waistband of the participants gym trunks and secured in place with self adhesive wrap. Wires from the power source to the IREDS were routed about the subject so as to minimize distraction during throwing trials. See Figure 1 for a representation of IRED placement and mass increases for the forearm and humerus.

Analysis

Trials began with the forward movement of the trunk, humerus, forearm, or hand and ended when the last segment attained peak velocity. Time to peak velocity ended when a segment reached peak velocity relative to the common starting time. Peak velocity and time to peak velocity were digitized from a phase map using commercially prepared software. Peak velocity was determined to the nearest millimeter per second and time to peak velocity to the nearest millisecond. Analysis of the throw was limited to the relationship of the trunk, humerus, forearm, and hand. The temporal relationship between adjacent segments was represented by the diffference in time to peak velocity between the hand and forearm (H - F), forearm and humerus (F - Hu), and humerus and trunk (Hu-T). The difference between subjects' peak velocities of adjoining segments (H - F, F - Hu, and Hu-T) was used to determine changes in velocity because of segmental lag.

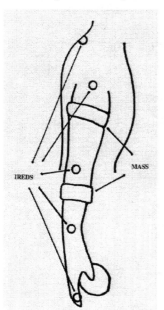

Statistical analyses served to determine, in a quantitative way, the topographical features of the throwing pattern. Separate multivariate analysis of variance (MANOVA) was performed on segmental timing and velocity variables. Significant MANOVAs ($p<.05$) were followed by univariate ANOVA to determine which dependent measures were responsible for significance. A Newman-Kuels post hoc procedure was used to determine mean scores responsible for significant ANOVAs ($p<.05$).

Fig. 1. Representation of IRED and mass placement for each segment.

RESULTS

Segmental Timing

Results regarding timing of each segment (time to peak velocity) are reported here. The Mass x Level x Velocity (2 x 4 x 2) MANOVA on time to peak velocity for each segment (hand, forearm, humerus, and trunk) revealed significant effects for mass (Hoteling's T^2=18.81), $F(4, 677)$=7.38, p<.001; level (Wilks'l = .54), $F(12,1648)$=24.74, p<.001; velocity (Hoteling's T^2 = 32.46), $F(4,677)$=14.07, p<.001; and for mass x level (Wilks'l=.64), $F(12,1648)$=13.03, p<.001, and velocity x level (Wilks'l=.78), $F(12,1648)$=8.15, p<.001, interactions. Follow-up univariate ANOVA (mass x level x velocity) indicated that there was an increase in time to peak velocity in the adult mass condition, but only the forearm reached significance. For levels, the hand, forearm, and humerus were significantly slower for level 2 than remaining levels with the humerus reaching peak velocity significantly faster at level 4 than remaining levels. For velocity, each of the segments reached peak velocity sooner at 100%, but only the hand was significantly less. The hand, forearm, and humerus were responsible for the mass x level interaction. For level 1, the hand and forearm were significantly later in reaching peak velocity (52 ms and 71 ms) during the adult mass condition. Level 2 throwers experienced significant decreases of 41 ms and 25 ms in time to peak velocity for the hand and humerus respectively. Level 3 throwers experienced significant increases of 36 ms, 62 ms, and 73 ms in the hand, forearm, and humerus when throwing with adult mass. Change in mass did not have a significant effect on the level 4 throwers. See Figure 2 for representation of mean scores for the mass x level interaction.

Each of the segments were responsible for the velocity x level interaction. Increasing velocity of throw resulted in significant decreases in time to peak velocity for the humerus (20 ms) and trunk (50 ms) for level 1 throwers. Level 2 throwers experienced a significant decrease of the hand (37 ms), forearm (28 ms) and trunk (35 ms) when throwing at 100% velocity. Level 3 throwers experienced a significant decrease in the time to peak velocity of the trunk (32 ms) when throwing at maximum velocity. Level 4 throwers experienced a significant decrease in both the hand (32 ms) and forearm (26 ms) at 100% velocity. The lower level (1, 2, and 3) throwers were more sensitive to changes in mass, particularly proximal segments, than the level 4 throwers. See Figure 3 for representation of mean scores for velocity x level interaction.

Temporal Segmental Delay

The temporal delay between segments (H-F, F-Hu, and Hu-T) provides a view of segmental lag. The mass x level x velocity MANOVA on

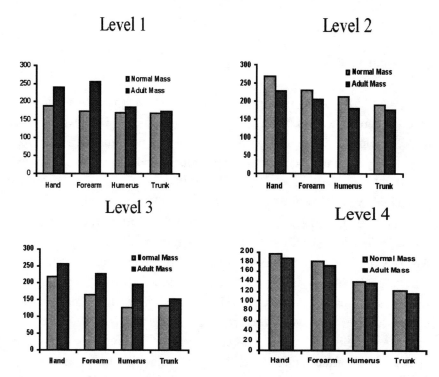

Fig. 2. Graphs representing time to peak velocity (ms) for mass x level interaction. Bars represents hand, forearm, humerus, and trunk for normal (gray) and adult (dark) mass.

differences between time to peak velocity of adjoining segments (H-F , F-Hu, and Hu-T) revealed significant effects for mass (Hoteling's T^2=20.41), $F(3,678)$=9.45, $p<.001$; level (Wilks' l=.33), $F(9,1356)$=21.64, $p<.001$; and velocity (Hoteling's T^2=16.23), $F(3,678)$=8.78, $p<.001$, with significant mass x level (Wilks'l=.57), $F(9,1356)$=12.91, $p<.001$, and level x velocity (Wilks'l=.68), $F(9,1356)$=12.23, $p<.001$, interactions. Follow-up univariate ANOVA (mass x level x velocity) indicated that each of the dependent measures was responsible for main effect by mass. H-F was significantly less in the adult mass condition with F-Hu and Hu-T significantly greater during adult mass condition. For main effect by level, level 3 was significantly greater than level 1 for H-F. Levels 3 and 4 were significantly greater than 1 and 2 for F-Hu, and levels 1 and 2 were significantly greater than 3 and 4 for Hu-T. When throwing at 100% velocity, there was an increase in segmental delay of all segment combinations but only the Hu-T was significant.

Each of the dependent measures was responsible for the mass x level interaction. For level 1 throwers there was a significant increase in segmental delay for F-Hu (19 ms) and Hu -T (25 ms) when throwing at adult mass. Level 2 throwers significantly increased delay for H-F (21 ms) and F-Hu (13ms). Level 3 throwers significantly increased delay for H-F (25 ms) and for Hu-T (20 ms). Level 4 throwers experienced no significant change in delay when throwing at adult mass compared to normal mass. See Figure 4 for representation of mean scores for mass x level interaction.

Each of the dependent measures was responsible for the velocity x level interaction. When throwers increased velocity of throw from 25% to 100%, level 1 throwers experienced a significant increase in delay of H-F (17 ms), F-Hu (18 ms), and Hu-T (24 ms). Level 2 throwers experienced a significant decrease in H-F (15 ms), and significant increases in F-Hu (12 ms) and Hu-T (25 ms). Level 3 performers experienced a significant increase in Hu-T (19 ms), and level 4 performers experienced significant decreases in H-F (17 ms) and F-Hu (26 ms). Delay changes as a result of throwing at 100% velocity resulted in segmental lag patterns that favored the order parameter at each level except for level 4. See Figure 5 for representation of mean scores for velocity x level interaction.

Segmental Velocities

The Mass x Level x Velocity (2 x 4 x 2) MANOVA on peak velocity for each segment (hand, forearm, humerus, and trunk) indicated significant effects for mass (Hoteling's $T^2=25.14$), $F(4,677)= 18.66$, $p<.001$; level (Wilks'l=.48), $F(12,1648)=63.67, p<.001$; velocity (Hoteling's $T^2=12.80$),

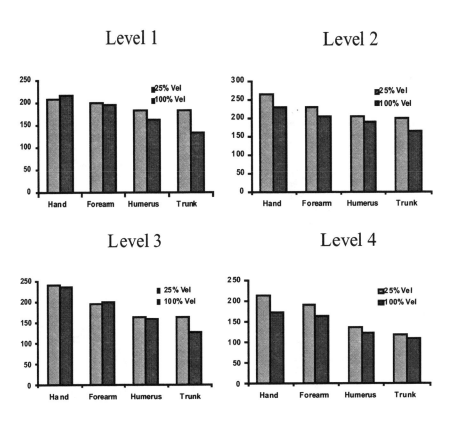

Fig. 3. Graphs representing time to peak velocity (ms) for velocity x level interaction. Bars represent hand, forearm, humerus, and trunk for 25% (gray) and 100% (dark) velocity.

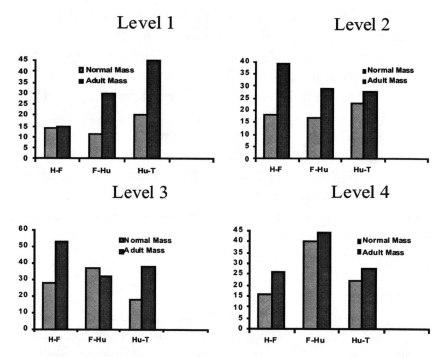

Fig. 4. Graphs representing temporal delay (ms) for mass x level interaction. Bars represent H-F, F-Hu, and Hu-T for normal (gray) and adult (dark) mass.

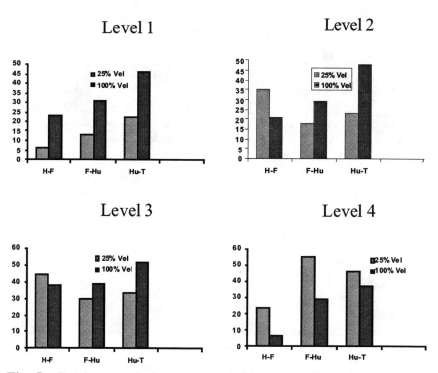

Fig. 5. Graphs representing temporal delay (ms) for velocity x level interaction. Bars represent H-F, F-Hu, and Hu-T for 25% (gray) and 100% (dark) velocity.

$F(4,677)=123.03$, $p<.001$; and for level x velocity interaction (Wilks' l=.39), $F(12,1648)=11.90$, $p<.001$. Follow-up univariate ANOVA (mass x level x velocity) revealed that increases in velocity of the hand and forearm were responsible for the main effect by condition. The hand had a significant increase of 585 mm/s, the forearm increase was significant at 542 mm/s during the adult mass condition. The humerus experienced a decrease of 266 mm/s, and the trunk decreased by 122 mm/s neither of which were significant. The differential changes in velocity of the trunk, humerus, forearm, and hand were responsible for the interaction. The hand and forearm increased velocity at 100% effort across throwing levels. For level 1, the hand increased 2,477 mm/s, and the forearm increased 1,264 mm/s, both of which were significant. For level 2, increases were 2780 mm/s and 1,935 mm/s for hand and forearm respectively. For level 3, the hand increased 1456 mm/s and the forearm by 2,055 mm/s. Level 4 throwers experienced an increase in hand velocity of 2,852 mm/s and forearm velocity of 2,629 mm/s. The trunk decreased in velocity for level 1 by 343 mm/s, remained unchanged at level 2, and increased by 530 mm/s and 976 mm/s for levels 3 and 4 respectively. The humerus remained unchanged at level 1, decreased by 1,918 mm/s at level 2, increased by 670 mm/s at level 3, and increased by 1,367 mm/s at level 4. See Figure 6 for representation of mean scores for level x velocity interaction.

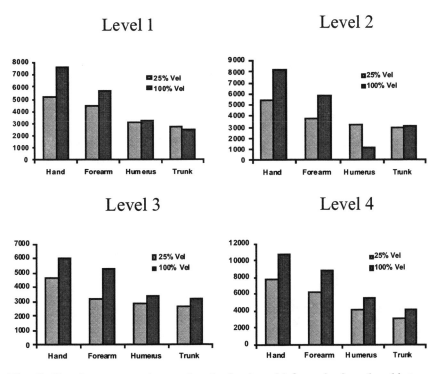

Fig. 6. Graphs representing peak velocity (mm/s) for velocity x level interaction. Bars represent hand, forearm, humerus, and trunk for 25% (gray) and 100% (dark) velocity.

Adjoining Segment Velocities

Differences in velocity between distal segments and their adjoining proximal neighbor (H-F, F-Hu, and Hu-T) is an indication of the effects of segmental lag in the attempt to conserve angular momentum. The mass x level x velocity MANOVA on differences in velocity of adjoining segments indicated significant effects for mass (Hoteling's T^2=17.00), $F(3,677)$=23.96, $p<.001$; level (Wilks'l=.84), $F(9,1356)$=20.11, $p<.001$; velocity (Hoteling's T^2=19.8), $F(3,677)$=67.14, $p<.001$; with significant mass x level (Wilks'l=.79), $F(9,1356)$=6.24, $p<.01$, and level x velocity (Wilks'l=.72), $F(9,1356)$=6.28, $p<.01$, interactions. Follow-up univariate ANOVA (mass x level x velocity) indicated that H-F, F-Hu, and Hu-T were responsible for main effects. There were significant increases in H-F, F-Hu, and Hu-T when throwing at adult mass and 100% velocity. For main effect by level, H-F was significantly less for levels 1 and 3 compared to levels 2 and 4; F-Hu was significantly greater for levels 1 and 4 than for levels 2 and 3; and for Hu-T, levels 1 and 2 were significantly greater than levels 3 and 4.

Each of the dependent measures was responsible for the mass x level interaction. For level 1 performers, there was an increase in H-F of 1,380 mm/s when throwing at adult mass. Increases in F-Hu (283 mm/s and Hu-

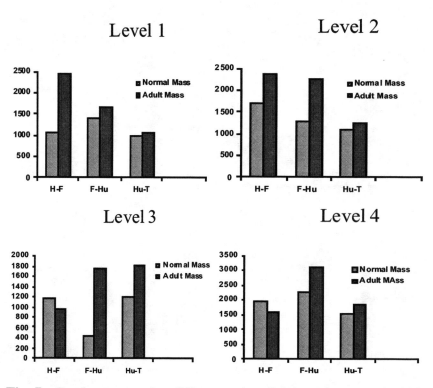

Fig. 7. Graphs representing differences in adjoining segment velocities (mm/s) for mass x level interaction. Bars represent H-F, F-Hu, and Hu-T for normal (gray) and adult (dark) mass.

T (86 mm/s) were not significant. For level 2, there was a 712 mm/s increase in differences between H-F when throwing at adult mass, F-Hu experienced an increase of 944 mm/s, and Hu-T experienced an increase of 142 mm/s, which was not significant. For level 3 there was a non-significant decrease in difference between H-F (207 mm/s) when throwing at adult mass, with significant increases in F-Hu (1,320 mm/s) and Hu-T (589 mm/s). For level 4, there was a significant decrease in H-F (361 mm/s) with significant increases in F-Hu (844 mm/s) and Hu-T (323 mm/s). The lower level throwers (levels 1 and 2) demonstrate greater differences between the more distal segments (H-F), whereas level 3 and 4 throwers register greater differences between segments F-Hu, and Hu-T. Throwing with adult mass has the effect of increasing the effects of segmental lag from distal to proximal segments. See Figure 7 for representation of mean scores for mass x level interaction.

Each of the dependent measures was responsible for the velocity x level interaction. When throwers increased velocity from 25% to 100%, level 1 participants experienced significant increases in differences across segment combinations H-F (1,213 mm/s), F-Hu (1,163 mm/s), and Hu-T (887 mm/s). For level 2, there were significant increases in differences across segment combinations for H-F (718 mm/s), F-Hu (1,296 mm/s), and Hu-T (925 mm/s). For level 3, there were significant increases for H-F (323 mm/s), F-Hu (1,534 mm/s), and Hu-T (556 mm/s). For level 4, there was a significant decrease in H-F (599 mm/s) when throwing at 100% velocity, with significant increases in F-Hu (1,262 mm/s) and Hu-T (681 mm/s). Generally, the lower level throwers (levels 1, 2, and 3) experienced increases in velocity of adjoining segments when throwing at 100% velocity compared to 25% velocity. Interestingly, level 4 throwers actually decrease in differences between the hand and forearm at 100% velocity, which indicates that the hand is slowing down relative to the forearm. See Figure 8 for representation of mean scores for velocity x level interaction.

Trajectory Data

The trajectory data reinforces the quantitative analysis. Specifically, altering the relative mass of limb segments and increasing throwing velocity results in changes in throwing pattern for levels 1, 2, and 3. Such changes favor the suggested order parameter by allowing a proximal to distal sequence of segmental lag and increasing segmental velocity. Level 4 throwers were not affected by changes in mass and actually decreased in segmental lag between the hand and forearm at 100% velocity throws. Trajectory data for normal and adult mass conditions at 25% and maximum velocities within the four throwing patterns may be found in Figure 9.

Level 1. Segmental lag is improved by both altering mass and increasing velocity. Looking across rows at 25% velocity the forearm moves

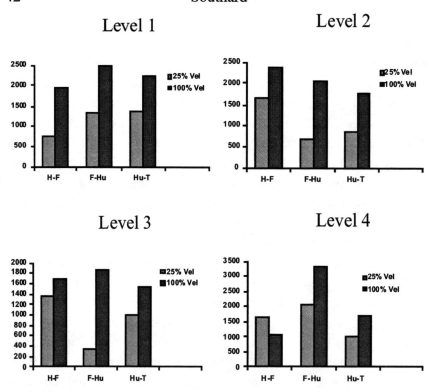

Fig. 8. Graphs representing differences in adjoining segment velocities (mm/s) for velocity x level interaction. Bars represent H-F, F-Hu, and Hu-T for 25% (gray) and 100% (dark) velocity.

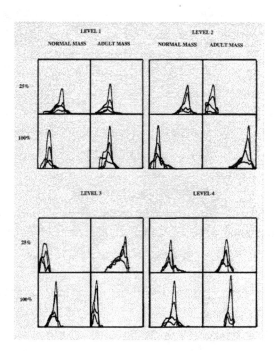

Fig. 9. Trajectory data (ordinate = velocity; abscissa = time) by mass, velocity, and level of pattern. The hand is represented by the plot with greatest velocity following in order by the forearm, humerus, and trunk. Each graph represents an individual trial from the same subject at each level.

from a position following the hand in time that which precedes the hand (in this case by 12 ms). Increasing velocity without altering mass improves the lag between the humerus and forearm, but the most dramatic changes are seen at maximum velocity with altered mass where segmental lag is similar to a pattern described here as level 4. The subject's total mass is 23.6 kg and is a six-year-old male.

Level 2. The addition of mass at low velocity improves lag between the two most proximal segments (shoulder and humerus together) relative to the most distal segments (forearm and hand together). By increasing velocity without the addition of mass, there is a noticeable lag between the humerus, forearm, and hand. The shoulder remains in time with the forearm, which prohibits the conservation of angular momentum from trunk to arm. Notice, however, at maximum velocity and altered mass, there is segmental lag for all four segments similar to a level 4 pattern. The subject's total mass is 28.1 kg and is an eight-year-old female.

Level 3. The effects of altering mass on segmental lag are more noticeable at low velocity than high velocity. There is lag between the shoulder, humerus, and forearm. An increase in velocity without altering mass does improve segmental lag between segments (particularly the forearm and hand). Unlike levels 1 and 2, when mass is altered at maximum velocity, there is no improvement in segmental lag compared to the maximum velocity and normal mass condition. The subject's total mass is 31.8 kg and is a nine-year-old male.

Level 4. There is no improvement in segmental lag as a result of altering mass. In fact, notice that at 25% velocity segmental lag is diminished between the humerus and forearm. An increase in velocity without altering mass improves lag between segments. Altering mass at maximum velocity does not change patterns as in levels 1 and 2. The subject's total mass is 36.3 kg and is a 12-year-old male.

Phase Plane Data

The phase plane data confirm that the relative position of the segments coincides with their relative time to peak velocity. The shape of the phase plane is influenced both by the velocity of the segment and its position during the throw. Phase plane data for normal and adult mass at 25% and maximum velocity within the four throwing patterns may be found in Figure 10.

DISCUSSION

Mechanical descriptions of the mature overarm throw are consistent concerning the sequence of segmental lag occurring from proximal to dis-

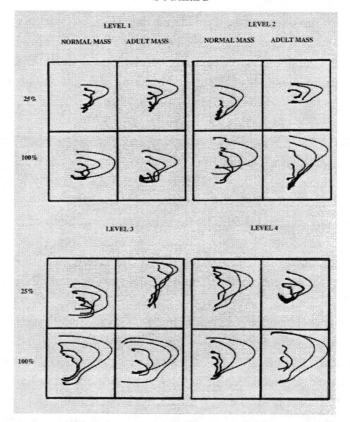

Fig. 10. Phase plane data (ordinate = position; abscissa = velocity by mass, velocity, and level of pattern. Data used to create trajectory data (Fig. 9) and phase plane data are the same. The hand is represented by the plot with greatest velocity following in order by the forearm, humerus, and trunk.

tal segments (Atwater, 1979; Joris, Edwards van Muyen, van Ingen Schenau, & Kemper, 1985). Developmental descriptions of the overarm pattern also support a pattern of proximal to distal segmental lag (Halverson, Roberton, & Langendorfer, 1982; Roberton, 1977). Data from this study indicate that altering the mass of a child's upper limb (change to adult proportion) and increasing the velocity of throw promotes this sequence of segmental lag for participants utilizing throwing patterns defined as levels 1, 2, and 3. Throwing patterns for level 4 throwers were not favorably affected by altering mass or increasing velocity of throw. Interpreting the results from a developmental standpoint, it appears that changes in the relative mass of the upper limb, as a result of normal growth patterns, may be a contributing factor toward the adoption of a mature throwing pattern. For this study, the most noticeable changes from immature to more mature patterns occurred for level 1 and 2 throwers when throwing with adult mass and at maximum velocity.

The results fit well into a dynamic systems perspective. Mass and velocity are control parameters for the development of throwing patterns. When limb segments were altered to that of adult proportion, their relative masses were scaled beyond a critical value. The system reorganized (according to its order parameter) to a higher level of throwing pattern characterized by an increase in segmental lag. Levels 1, 2, and 3 experienced favorable changes because those performers were not at what Thelen and Smith (1994) refer to as a globally stable attractor. Global stability for the hypothesized order parameter (conservation of angular momentum) would be proximal to distal segmental lag for trunk, humerus, forearm, and hand. Once this state is reached, there is no probability of entering a new attractor state that can favor an increase in segmental lag. Therefore, level 4 throwers do not change pattern even though mass of segments is altered to favor the order parameter. Growth changes that move the upper limb toward adult proportions may allow mass to reach critical values that instigate change toward a global stability. It is possible that because the level 4 throwers (older and larger participants) were closer to adult upper limb mass, the relatively smaller changes were not critical to changing existing patterns. Because control parameters and critical values may themselves change during ontogeny (Thelen, 1988), what is a critical value for one level may not be a critical value for other levels. The level 4 throwers actually experienced a decrease in temporal lag of the H-F and F-Hu segment combinations when throwing at maximum effort. Increasing velocity of the upper limb for level 1, 2, and 3 throwers improved lag of the less massive distal segment compared to its proximal neighbor. It is likely that growth and velocity are not independent factors in the influence of change. A sufficient increase in velocity at a time when growth has decreased pattern stability may be necessary to trigger a change in attractor state.

Observation alone indicates that change in relative mass is only a contributing factor regarding a shift in attractor state. This fact is exampled by older throwers (at, or closer to adult mass) that do not demonstrate global stability. Such examples are not necessarily limited by gender nor age, but appear to be more common among females than males (Langendorfer, 1980; Seefeldt & Haubenstricker, 1982). In addition, gender differences in throwing are reported to be primarily due to environmental rather than biological differences (Williams, Haywood, & Painter, 1996). Data from this study indicate that velocity of throw may be a contributing environmental factor in changing throwing pattern. Could the socialization of females away from throwing activities reduce opportunities to increase throwing velocity that may account, in part, for less mature patterns?

Results from this study indicate that an important practical step in helping individuals change throwing patterns is the identification and emphasis on control parameters during practice. Encouraging a change in attractor state toward a more mature throwing pattern may be as simple as encouraging individuals to scale up on control parameters particularly during periods of attractor instability. Future research should focus on identifying other possible control parameters and determining critical values and periods of attractor or pattern instability.

REFERENCES

Atwater, A. (1979). Biomechanics of overarm throwing movements and of throwing injuries. *Exercise and Sport Science Reviews, 7,* 43-85.

Clark, J.E., & Whitall, J. (1989). What is motor development: The lessons of history. *Quest, 41,* 183-202.

Clauser, C.E., McConville, J.T., & Young, J.W. (1969). *Weight, volume, and center of mass of segments of the human body.* AMRL Technical Report 69-70. Wright-Patterson Air Force Base, Ohio: AMRL.

Connolly, K.J. (1970). *Mechanisims of motor skill development.* London: Academic Press.

Frisancho, A.R. (1993). *Anthropometric standards for the assessment of growth and nutritional status.* Ann Arbor: University of Michigan Press.

Gabbard, C. (1992). *Lifelong motor development.* Dubuque: Wm C. Brown.

Gallahue, D., & Ozmun, J. (1997). *Understanding motor development: Infants, children, adolescents, adults.* Boston: WCB/McGraw-Hill.

Haken, H. (1977). Synergetics: An introduction. Berlin: Springer-Verlag.

Halverson, L.E., Roberton, M.A., & Langendorfer, S. (1982). Development of the overarm throw: Movement and ball velocity changes by seventh grade. *Research Quarterly for Exercise and Sport, 53,* 198-205.

Halverson, L.E., & Williams, K. (1985). Developmental sequences for hopping over a distance: A prelongitudinal study. *Research Quarterly for Exercise and Sport, 56,* 37-44.

Harper, C.J. (1972). *Learning to observe children's motor development. Part III. Observing children's motor development in the gymnasium.* Paper presented at the American Alliance for Health, Physical Education, Recreation, and Dance, New Orleans, LA.

Haubenstricker, J., Branta, C., & Seefeldt, V. (1983). *Preliminary validation of developmental sequences for throwing and catching.* Paper presented at the annual conference of the North American Society for the Psychology of Sport and Physical Activity. East Lansing, MI.

Jensen, R.K. (1981). Age and body type comparisons of the mass distribution of children. *Growth, 45,* 239-251.

Jensen, R.K. (1986). Body segment mass, radius, and radius gyration proportions of children. *Journal of Biomechanics, 19,* 359-368.

Joris, H.J.J., Edwards van Muyen, A.J., van Ingen Schenau, G.J. & Kemper, H.C.G. (1985). Force, velocity and energy flow during the overarm throw in female handball players. *Journal of Biomechanics, 18*, 409-414.

Kelso, J.A.S. (1994). The informational character of self-organized coordination dynamics. *Human Movement Science, 13*, 393-413.

Kelso, J.A.S., Scholz, J.P., & Schöner, G.S. (1986). Non-equilibrium phase transitions in coordinated biological motion: Critical fluctuations. *Physics Letters, A118*, 279-284.

Kreighbaum, E., & Barthels, K. (1990). *Biomechanics: A qualitative approach for studying human movement.* New York: McMillan Publishing Company.

Kugler, P.N., Kelso, J.A.S., & Turvey, M.T. (1982). On the control and coordination of naturally developing systems. In J.A.S. Kelso, & J. Clark (Eds.), *The development of movement control and coordination* (pp. 5-78). New York: John Wiley & Sons.

Langendorfer, S. (1980). *Longitudinal evidence for developmental changes in the preparatory phase of the overarm throw for force.* Paper presented at the Research Section of the American Alliance for Health, Physical Education, Recreation, and Dance, Detroit, MI.

Langendorfer, S. (1980). A model for overarm throwing technique. *Journal of Biomechanics, 21*, 718-724.

Malina, R.M., & Bouchard, C. (1991). *Growth, maturation, and physical activity.* Champaign: Human Kinetics Publishers.

McConville, J.T., Churchill, T.D., Kaleps, I., Clauser, C.E., & Cuzzi, J. (1980). *Anthropometric relationships of body and body segment moments of inertia.* AMRL Technical Report 80-119. Wright - Patterson Air Force Base: Ohio AMRL.

Roberton, M.A. (1977). Stability of stage categorizations across trials: Implications for the "stage theory" of overarm throw development. *Journal of Human Movement Studies, 3*, 49-59.

Roberton, M.A. (1983). Changing motor patterns during childhood. In J. Thomas (Ed.), *Motor development during childhood and adolescence.* Minneapolis: Burgess.

Roberton, M.A. (1978). Longitudinal evidence for developmental stages in the forceful overarm throw. *Journal of Human Movement Studies, 4*, 167-175.

Seefeldt, V., & Haubenstricker, J. (1982). Patterns, phases, or stages: An analytical model for the study of developmental movement. In J.A.S. Kelso, & J. Clark (Eds.) *The development of movement control and co-ordination* (pp. 309-318). New York: John Wiley & Sons.

Southard, D. (1998). Mass and velocity: Control parameters for throwing patterns. *Research Quarterly for Exercise and Sport, 69*, 355-367.

Thelen, E. (1988). Dynamical approaches to the development of behavior. In J.A.S. Kelso, A.J. Mandell, & M.F. Shlesinger (Eds.). *Dynamic patterns in complex systems.* Singapore: Utopia Press.

Thelen, E. (1989). Self-organization in developmental processes: Can systems approach work? In E. Thelen & M.R. Gunnar (Eds.). *Systems and development: The Minnesota Symposia On Child Psychology Vol 22.* Hillsdale: Lawrence Erlbaum Associates.

Thelen, E. & Smith, L.B. (1994). *A dynamic systems approach to the development of cognition and action.* Cambridge: MIT Press..

Wickstrom, R.L. (1983). *Fundamental motor patterns.* 3rd ed. Philadelphia: Lea & Febiger.

Wild, M. (1938). The behavior pattern of throwing and some observations concerning its course of development in children. *Research Quarterly, 9,* 20-24.

Williams, K., Haywood, K., & Painter, M.A. (1996). Environment versus biological influences on gender differences in the overarm throw for force: Dominant and nondominant arm throws. *Women in Sport and Physical Activity Journal, Fall,* 29-48.

3

CONSTRAINTS ON THROWING BEHAVIOR OF CHILDREN

Michelle L. Hamilton
Amanda Tate

ABSTRACT

Newell (1986) proposed that fundamental motor skill acquisition is influenced by constraints of task, organism, and environment. The purpose of this study was to determine if task factors of distance and size could be scaled using a dynamical systems approach to a critical value to influence changes in throwing patterns. Twenty-six third grade children, 14 males and 12 females, participated in the present study. Children threw at targets that were small, medium, and large and were placed at a distance that was individually scaled at two times, four times, and six times the height of each child. The results of the 3 x 3 (Distance x Size) MANOVA with repeated measures showed a significant effect for distance, Wilk's 8 = .61, F(10, 92) = 2.50, p < .01. No significant effects were determined for size or distance by size interactions. Practitioners should consider distance as a critical factor when determining developmentally appropriate tasks for children.

Throwing is a fundamental motor skill that has been the subject of interest to the field of motor development. Skillful throwing involves the simultaneous coordination and control of the upper and lower limbs, trunk, and posture. This multi-limb task is undoubtedly one of the most difficult fundamental motor skills for children and adults to acquire competence and proficiency, as it requires coordination of the whole body.

Researchers and scholars in motor development have long been interested in the question of *change*. Specifically, how is it that one moves from one pattern of throwing to another pattern of throwing? This question, first addressed by Monica Wild in her seminal paper (1938) on throwing has interested researchers for decades.

Broadly speaking, two paradigms or approaches have been used to study the question of change in motor development. These two approaches have helped to define the questions of how a motor skill changes from one pattern to another. These approaches are known as the structuralist and functionalist approaches.

The Structuralist Approach

Traditionally, motor development researchers have focused on describing the characteristics and typical throwing patterns observed in children as stages. This approach has been referred to as the *structuralist* approach to understanding movement (Beek & Hopkins, 1992; Schöner, 1994; Thelen & Ulrich, 1991, p.4). The structuralist approach has been used to explain throwing patterns that are observed in children at various stages of development (Roberton, 1977, 1978; Seefeldt & Haubenstricker, 1976; Wild, 1938). The underlying assumption of this approach is that development occurs in a linear fashion and is directed toward an endpoint that is defined by a mature pattern of throwing.

The structuralist approach has merit. Often, observable characteristics of children appear seemingly as different developmental levels. One need only to compare a unilateral and arm dominated pattern of a one-year-old child throwing to that of a proficient baseball pitcher to notice that there are apparent differences in the "levels" or "stages" the throwers that exist at different points in time.

However, several difficulties with this approach can be noted. One fundamental problem with the structuralist approach is the question of how the organism moves from one stage of throwing to another is often inadequately answered. Structuralists (e.g., stage theorists) operate under the assumption that fundamental motor skills are driven almost entirely by neurological processes. As stated by Wild (1938, p. 24), "Maturational factors are believed to be operative as the basic patterns of throwing develops." Unfortunately, this mechanistic and reductionistic view does not take into account the multiple influences of task, environment, or the individual on motor skill acquisition.

A second fundamental difficulty with the structualist approach is that it cannot account for the instability observed in everyday motor performance. A clear example of this is that we can often observe the same baseball player using both mature and less mature throwing patterns during a game. If the player clearly has the mature pattern, why then do we see apparent differences in performance?

A third difficulty with the structuralist approach is that it does not account for omissions and reversals that often occur within performance of tasks. Often omissions and reversals in motor performance are acknowledged in motor development theoretical discussion; however, they are often dismissed as unreliable data (Newell, 1986, p. 343).

The Functionalist Approach

A second more contemporary view has been to attempt to understand and define processes of change and factors that underlie this change in the motor skill patterns. In this view, motor skill development is not a fixed linear path that individual moves along in time. The *functionalist* approach, instead, focuses on the dynamics that underlie movement (Beek & Hopkins, 1992; Schöner, 1994).

A functionalist approach quickly gaining popularity in motor behavior is known as Dynamical Systems Theory (DST). According to DST, motor skills are not fixed levels or stages that we observe at a given point in time but rather are a result of the cooperation of components of the system at a given point in time. These components can be defined in terms of their morphological, environmental, or task properties (Newell, 1984; 1986; Thelen & Ulrich, 1991).

The purpose of DST is to understand change by defining components of the system in relationship to the environment or task context. The stability of a motor pattern can be evaluated by looking at the *attractor state* or preferred pattern across multiple trials and task conditions. In DST terms, the attractor state is the preferred mode of operation of the system. The attractor state is not a "fixed state" but rather a "preferred" state under the conditions of the system. This attractor state is influenced by the many components that self-organize within a system at a any given time.

By experimentally perturbing the system to another attractor state, the potential influence of *control parameters* can be identified. A control parameter can be one or more components of the system that cause it to change to another attractor state or mode of operation. When observing children's throwing patterns, these control parameters can be internal to the system (e.g., morphological or biological factors) or external to the system (e.g., task or environmental factors). To determine the influence of a control parameter, the hypothesized control parameter is scaled to a critical value. This view provides a possible alternative that may account for instability and stability and motor skill acquisition in children's fundamental motor skills.

The Task Context

For nearly three decades, researchers have discussed the importance of examining the task demands or task context in relation to the performer and the motor pattern observed (Gentile, 1972; 1987; Herkowitz, 1978; Langendorfer, 1990; Newell, 1984; 1986; Roberton, 1987; Thelen & Ulrich 1991). The task demands can be defined as the requirements of the task that are imposed on the performer, equipment used by the performer and goals that are defined by the task (Newell, 1986).

Many earlier throwing studies did not pay attention to the task or task context. Roberton (1987) was among the first to note that throwing studies were conducted in an unchanging environment or task context. According to Roberton, many of these studies make the assumption that the developmental status of the child remains unchanged across environments. In other words, developmental status was assumed to be a "fixed level" regardless of the task or condition presented to the child. This approach does not take into account the multiple influences on skill acquisition that include components of the task, environment, and individual.

A handful of researchers investigating the dynamic nature of throwing have looked at a small number of task conditions, and have demonstrated limited or no change in children's developmental status. Roberton (1987) studied the effects of a moving target and a stationary target on the throwing patterns of kindergarten-aged children. In the aforementioned study, Roberton determined that children's throwing patterns were robustly stable across the stationary and moving task conditions. The stability of motor patterns observed by Roberton, however, may have been attributed to the young age of the performer. Specifically, the children used primitive throwing patterns regardless of the moving or stationary condition of the task.

Landgendorfer (1990) examined the effects of task constraints on the developmental status of children and adults, using force and accuracy conditions. Langendorfer asked children to throw under two conditions. The first condition involved throwing for force and "crashing the ball into the wall." In the second condition, children were asked to perform a task that involved aiming and throwing at a small dot. Langendorfer concluded that the advanced performers were able to use a more advanced throwing pattern when throwing for force as opposed to accuracy under two task conditions, whereas the more primitive throwers were not able to change throwing pattern and threw for force under all conditions. In both studies mentioned, the tasks presented measured throwing performance on two dichotomous tasks (e.g., stationary vs. moving and force vs. accuracy). Although both authors looked at stability across task conditions, it is unclear as to the differences the investigators may have found if the task conditions would have been scaled. Also unclear is whether the investigators chose the most pertinent task factors to influence the developmental status of those children included in the study.

In the research reported here, we assume that critical properties (e.g., control parameters) of throwing include distance and size of the target. These control parameters represent "real world" features of a throwing task. That is to say, when one throws at a target, the target has properties of distance and size. Thus, using the dynamical systems approach we assume that: (1) task constraints influence the developmental status of throwing patterns; and, (2) distance and size parameters can be scaled to influence developmental outcomes of children's throwing patterns.

The first question of interest was to determine the stability or instability of developmental patterns across changing task conditions (e.g., distance and target size). Specifically, we wanted to determine if children's preferred attractor state as measured by the various body components would remain the same across all task conditions. This was accomplished by manipulating two possible control parameters of the skill that included both the distance and size of the target. By scaling the distance and target size, we could determine the point at which changes began to occur in the motor pattern. In the present study, the size of the target was scaled to include targets that require various levels of accuracy for the child. A small, medium, and large target were included. We proposed that distance is a relative term that is specific to the height of the individual. A child throwing a distance of 60 feet, is performing a more difficult task when compared to a much larger adult who is throwing the same distance. Distance was, therefore, scaled to the height of the performer. Distance and target size for this study are illustrated in Figure 1.

The second question of interest was to determine the significance of each of the proposed control parameters. As mentioned previously, it is possible for a system to have one or more control parameters at any given time. We wanted to determine if the factors of distance or target size would be more influential or if each control parameter was equally influential on the task of throwing. We assumed *a priori* that both control parameters would influence the throwing patterns observed and that all body components would be influenced.

The third question of interest was how would accuracy (e.g., product of movement) change across distance and size conditions? This question was of interest in particular, because children were asked in the protocol to throw the ball as hard as possible under all task conditions. The investigators assumed that both factors (distance and size) would influence the throwing accuracy across task conditions. Specifically, the assumption was made that children would become less accurate when throwing at targets that were smaller and farther away.

METHOD

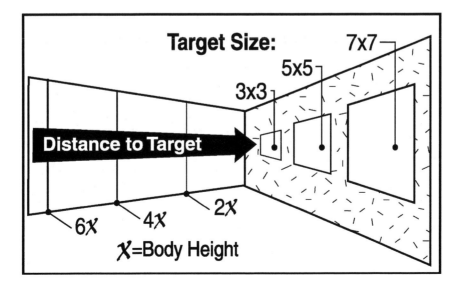

Fig 1. Small, medium, and large targets scaled to the height of the performer at two times, four times, and six times the height of the performer.

Participants

The present study was conducted in a large urban school district with a largely Hispanic population. The participants in this study included 26 third-grade children (14 males and 12 females, M age = 8.25, SD = 0.61). All parents of the study and children provide consent as required by the Institutional Review Board. Participants were measured in height to the nearest quarter of an inch, (M = 51.5", SD = 2.3").

Design and Procedure

Children were individually removed from the classroom and tested outdoors. All children were measured to the nearest quarter of an inch. Three targets were set up that varied in size (e.g., 3, 5, 7 sqaure feet). The distance from the target was scaled at two, four, and six times the height of each child. A total of nine conditions were presented (e.g., size x distance). Children threw at each of the task conditions, a block of five trials. All nine blocks (e.g., size by distance) were randomly presented to the children. Children were instructed to throw as hard as possible at each of the task conditions.

Each throw was filmed outdoors using side and rear views with cameras, placed at 90-degree angles a distance of 20 feet away from the performer. The cameras were synchronized by hand signals from the recorder that corresponded to the initiation of each trial and condition (e.g., size x distance). Two Panasonic wide-angle telephoto lens cameras with high-speed 1/1000 shutter recording movement at 30 fields per second were used.

Data Reduction and Analysis

All trials of the overarm throw were viewed on a JVC slow motion projector with variable tracking. All data were analyzed using the developmental movement component checklist (Roberton, 1977, 1984; Roberton & Halverson, 1984; Roberton & Langendorfer, 1980). The movement component list identifies the essential criteria for the foot, forearm, backswing, humeral action, and trunk action. The criteria for each of the developmental steps have been published in previous studies and are summarized in Table 1.

Inter-rater and intra-rater reliability were established by exceeding the 80% exact agreement criteria for each component. A total of 1,170 trials were available for analysis. The modal value for each block was chosen for statistical analysis. The authors chose to use the modal value at each block, because it best represented the developmental pattern that was predominantly used for each task condition.

To determine accuracy, all trials were recorded as a hit or miss based on the number of trials each participant hit out of the five trials in task condition. The trial was scored as a "hit" if any portion of the target was hit by the ball. Each participant received a score that ranged from 0 to 5.

Table 1
Developmental Sequences for the Overarm Throw

Foot Action Component

Step one:	No step
Step two:	Ipsilateral step
Step three:	Short contralateral step
Step four:	Long contralateral step

Trunk Action Component

Step one:	No trunk action/trunk flexion
Step two:	Block rotation
Step three:	Differentiated rotation

Humerus Component

Step one:	Humerus oblique
Step two:	Humerus aligned but independent
Step three:	Humerus lags

Forearm Component

Step one:	No forearm lag
Step two:	Foream lag
Step three:	Delayed forearm lag

Backswing Component

Step one:	Backswing
Step two:	Elbow and humeral flexion
Step three:	Circular, upward
Step four:	Circular downward

RESULTS

The independent variables in this study were distance and target size (3 x 3). The dependent variables in this study were determined by rating score data of each of the five body parts using Roberton's scale (1978) and submitted to a MANOVA with repeated measures.

The results of the 3 x 3 (Distance x Size) MANOVA with repeated measures showed a significant effect for distance, Wilk's $8 = .61$, $F(10, 92) = 2.50$, $p < .01$, Eta squared $= .21$. No significant differences were determined using the MANOVA test for size or distance by size interaction.

Univariate tests were conducted on each of the five body parts to determine the statistical significance for each body part for distance, size, and distance by size interactions. Significant body components for the factor of Distance were determined for the components of the foot, humerus, and trunk respectively using Greenhouse-Geisser are $F(1.58, 26) = 7.12$, $p > .002$;

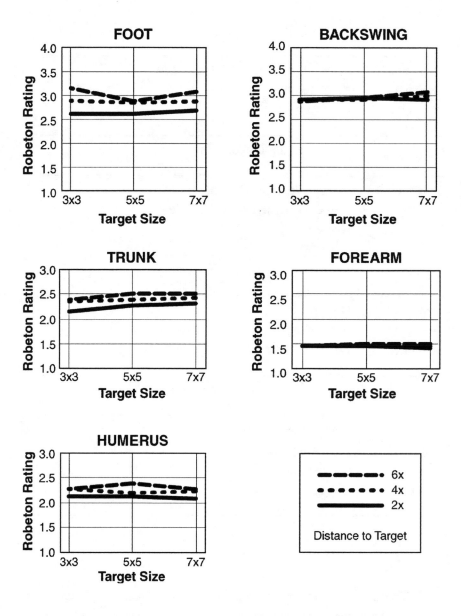

Fig, 2. Developmental status according to distance and size of target.

Table 2
Means and Standard Deviations for Task Conditions

Distance	Foot 3 x 3		5 x 5		7 x 7	
	M	*SD*	*M*	*SD*	*M*	*SD*
2 x Height	2.62	1.06	2.62	.98	2.69	1.12
4 x Height	2.88	.91	2.85	.88	2.88	.99
6 x Height	3.15	1.43	2.96	.87	3.08	.80

	Trunk					
	M	*SD*	*M*	*SD*	*M*	*SD*
2 x Height	2.15	.88	2.27	.78	2.31	.88
4 x Height	2.35	.85	2.38	.80	2.42	.86
6 x Height	2.38	.80	2.50	.71	2.50	.71

	Humerus					
	M	*SD*	*M*	*SD*	*M*	*SD*
2 x Height	2.12	.86	2.12	.77	2.08	.88
4 x Height	2.27	.78	2.19	.75	2.23	.82
6 x Height	2.27	.72	2.38	.70	2.50	.76

	Backswing					
	M	*SD*	*M*	*SD*	*M*	*SD*
2 x Height	2.92	.89	2.92	.92	2.92	.98
4 x Height	2.92	.89	2.96	.89	2.96	.89
6 x Height	2.88	.86	2.96	.86	3.00	.87

	Forearm					
	M	*SD*	*M*	*SD*	*M*	*SD*
2 x Height	1.46	.65	1.46	.65	2.92	.64
4 x Height	1.46	.65	1.46	.65	2.96	.65
6 x Height	1.46	.65	1.50	.71	3.00	.71

$F(1.49, 26) = 6.39, p < .008$, and $F(1.66, 26) = 7.54$, $p < .003$. Means and standard deviations across each task condition (distance x target size) are represented in Figure 2 and in Table 2.

Accuracy Data

Although the primary purpose of this study was to look at developmental form, accuracy data for each of the conditions was collected for this study. Means and standard deviations for each task condition are represented in Table 3.

An inspection of the means on the number of times that each participant hit the target demonstrated an expected pattern of less "hits" from distances that were increasingly farther away. The researchers anticipated that participants would hit the target less often as they were required to move back. Another finding was that participants also hit the larger targets more frequently than the smaller targets.

To determine the significance of the accuracy results for distance and size, A 3 x 3 (Distance x Size) MANOVA with repeated measures was determined for Distance, Wilk's $8 = .31$, $F(2, 23) = 2.64$, $p > .000$, Eta squared $= .039$ and Distance x Size Wilk's $8 = .46$, $F(4, 21) = 6.04$, $p < .002$, Eta squared $= .53$. Size of target was not determined to be statistically significant in this study.

DISCUSSION

The present study was an exploratory study conducted in a real world context designed to determine the effects of distance and size on the throwing patterns of young children. The first question of interest in this study was to determine if the throwing patterns that children used would remain robust across all task conditions.

If one believes that motor skills are stage driven (e.g., structuralist perspective), few differences would be expected across various task condi-

Table 3
Means and Standard Deviations of Target Hits

Distance	3 x 3		5 x 5		7 x 7	
	M	*SD*	*M*	*SD*	*M*	*SD*
2 x Height	3.25	2.25	3.56	2.04	4.20	1.60
4 x Height	2.96	1.76	3.08	1.93	3.36	1.93
6 x Height	.96	1.51	1.28	1.76	2.12	1.98

tions. An examination of the means and standard deviations clearly showed that there were differences across task conditions for various body parts. The means of the individual body components were all greater in conditions that required increased distance. The instability in these patterns across task conditions shows that children are influenced by task factors.

The second question of interest was to determine the influence of the factors of distance and size on developmental status of each body component. The investigators in this study hypothesized that both size and distance would be control parameters in the throw. In this study, however, distance from the target was determined to be statistically significant for the components of trunk, foot, and humerus. Size of the target was determined not to be statistically significant.

It is interesting that a statistically significant change did not occur in all of the body parts measured as distance was increased. The changes that were identified could be partly attributed to the scaling factors that were used and their effect on the various body parts used to produce the necessary pattern at the required distance. For instance, it may be necessary to make changes in the stepping pattern without making corresponding changes in the backswing or forearm pattern in order to achieve the goal. We hypothesized that an individual coordinates the dynamics of the body pattern with the task that is provided (e.g., distance and target size).

Some motor development theorists might argue that force is the "real" control parameter, not distance. One critical feature of this study is that children were asked to throw for force in all task conditions. The distances that children were required to throw in this study ranged from 8 -27 feet. The investigators did not believe that force alone could explain the differences in children's throwing patterns in the short distances that were required. Instead, it is proposed that by increasing the distance required in a throwing task, children "self-organize" their throwing patterns to accommodate the task. This self-organization provides the best explanation for the qualitative differences observed in children's motor patterns.

One plausible explanation for these results might be throwing various distances requires perception of the target close and far away. The authors hypothesize that perception may play a larger role in adjusting throwing patterns to various distances than previously considered. Perception, on the other hand, may have played less of a role in the size of the target. Because children in this study were asked to throw as hard as possible under all task conditions, perceptual factors may not have been influenced by target size. A three-foot-square target is large when considering the distances from which children threw.

The accuracy data were contradictory to our expectations. We anticipated that the participants would become less accurate as distance to the target was increased and size of target was decreased. However, this was not the finding. Rather, there were no significant differences for target size.

This may have been because of the relatively large targets used in each of the task conditions, and that children were not really forced to throw under accurate conditions as a three-foot-square target is not very small. Future studies should examine the effects of throwing using a smaller target.

The findings of the present study are exploratory. It appears from inspection of the data that both the factors of distance and size could be varied across a larger scale. Although size was not a control parameter in this study, it is not clear which patterns or body parts would have been affected if targets would have been smaller or distances would have been longer.

The authors also questioned whether they would have found greater differences across task conditions if they had not asked the participants to throw for force. Future studies should allow children to "naturally" determine the amount of force that they would need to accomplish this goal and determine if larger scaling distances would present similar findings.

Another question that was left unanswered in this study is how children of various ages and developmental levels are affected by scaling distance and target size. Although the authors chose not to study a group of primitive throwers or adults in this study, it may be that distance and size operate differently as control parameters at different times in development.

There are some important practical implications that can be drawn from this study. The teacher, coach, and practitioner should consider the desired outcome of the throwing task (e.g., process or product). If it is desirable to improve developmental form of the child, it is helpful to move the child farther back when performing throwing tasks. Throwing at greater distances increases the likelihood that a child's most mature pattern will be demonstrated. In this study, the size of the target appeared to be less of an influential factor on the developmental form than did distance. However,the authors interpret this factor cautiously, as smaller sizes of targets may have been used to possibly elicit greater differences in the developmental form exhibited.

REFERENCES

Beek, P.J. & Hopkins, B. (1992). Four requirements for a dynamical systems approach to the development of social coordination, *Human Movement Science, 11*, 425 – 492.

Gentile, A.M. (1972). A working model of skill acquisition with application to teaching. *Quest Monograph XVII,* 3-23.

Gentile, A.M. (1987). Skill acquisition: Action, movement, and the neuromotor processes. In J.H.Carr, R.B Shepherd, J.Gordon, A.M Gentile, & J.M. Hinds (Eds.), *Movement Science: Foundations for physical therapy in rehabilitation* (pp. 93-154).

Herkowitz, J.H. (1978). Developmental task analysis: The design of movement experiences and evaluation of motor development status. In M.V. Ridenour (Ed.). *Motor Development: Issues and Applications.* Princeton, NJ: Princeton Book Company.

Langendorfer, S. (1990). Motor-task goal as a constraint on developmental status. In J. Clark & J. Humphrey (Eds.), *Advances in motor development research* (Vol. 3. pp. 16-28). New York: AMS Press.

Newell, K.M., (1986). Constraints on the development of coordination. In M.G., Wade & H.T.A Whiting (Eds.), *Motor development in children: Aspects of coordination and control* (pp. 341-360). The Netherlands: Martin Nijhoff.

Roberton, M.A. (1977). Stability of stage categorizations across trials: Implications for the "stage theory" of overarm throw development. *Journal of Human Movement Studies, 3,* 49-59.

Roberton, M.A. (1984). Changing motor patterns in childhood. In J.R. Thomas (Ed.), *Motor development in childhood and adolescence* (pp. 48-90). Minneapolis: Burgess.

Roberton, M.A. (1987). Longitudinal evidence for developmental stages in the forceful overarm throw. *Journal of Human Movement Studies, 4,* 161-175.

Roberton, M.A. (1987). Developmental level as a function of the immediate environment. In J.E. Clark & J.H. Humphrey (Eds.) *Advances in motor development research,* Vol. I (pp. 1-15). New York: AMS Press.

Roberton, M.A., & Halverson, L.E. (1984). *Developing children: Their changing movement.* Philadelphia: Lea & Feiber.

Roberton, M.A., & Langendorfer, S. (1980). Testing motor development sequences across 9-14 years. In C. Nadeau, W. Halliwell, K. Newell, & G. Roberts (Eds.), *Psychology of motor behavior and sport*-1979 (pp. 269-279). Champaign, IL: Human Kinetics.

Schöner, G. (1994). Dynamic theory of action-perception patterns: the time before contact paradigm. *Human Movement Science 13,* 415-439.

Seefeldt V., & Haubenstricker, J. (1976). *Developmental sequence of throwing.* Rev. ed. Unpublished manuscript, Michigan State University, East Lansing.

Thelen, E., & Ulrich, B.D. (1991). Hidden skills. *Monographs of the Society of Research in Child Development, 56,* Serial No. 223.

Wild, M.R. (1938). The behavior pattern of throwing and some observations concerning its development in children. *Research Quarterly, 9* (3), 20-24.

4

EXAMINING DEVELOPMENTAL CHANGES IN THROWING

Clersida Garcia
Luis Garcia

ABSTRACT

This study qualitatively examines developmental changes in the over-hand throw using the five stages of the developmental sequence of throwing, known as the Total Body Approach, proposed by Haubenstricker, Branta, & Seefeldt, 1983. Participants were randomly selected and included six children (three boys and three girls) whose ages ranged from 1 year 9 months to 5 years. The children were observed for two years during their enrollment in a motor development program. The participants individually performed between 368 to 843 throws during class and testing sessions. All throws were videotaped and a total of 3,469 throws were analyzed. Field notes were gathered to describe the activities, and brief interviews were conducted to document how learning occurs in the context of the overhand throwing activity. The results of the study indicate that children move backward and forward to adjacent and nonadjacent stages, in contrast to the proposed sequence of linearity in the development of overhand throwing. From the field notes, three main themes appear. The themes have a dynamic symbiotic interaction that helps to explain the process of learning the overhand throw. Motivation, body awareness, and learning context affected the number of trials, understanding, and movement toward mature forms of throwing and skill stabilization.

The overhand throw has been studied extensively by many investigators. From a qualitative perspective, previous studies suggested that the development of the overhand throw pattern follows an orderly linear sequence. Wild s (1938) classic study identified several stages of throwing development and suggested that the development of throwing follows a linear sequence from immature to mature forms. In 1978, Roberton proposed a different strategy for studying throwing development where longitudinal evidence was presented for developmental stages within the humerus, forearm, and trunk components of the forceful ovearm throw. In this approach, known as the Component Approach, Roberton emphasized that the components (humerus, forearm, and trunk) change from low levels to higher levels of development, describing a linear sequence within components of the body. In 1983, Haubenstricker, Branta, and Seefeldt presented preliminary validation of the developmental sequence of throwing using the Total Body Approach. The investigators described points in time, which they called stages, consisting of specific configurations that involve the whole body (arm, trunk, and legs). They proposed that these stages follow a hierarchical sequence from lower to more advanced levels of development.

Linearity in the sequence of throwing refers to a hierarchical progress in the sequence without regression to immature forms (invariant order). According to stage theorists (Kolhberg, 1963; Turiel, 1969; Inhelder, 1971), there could be changes in the sequence but only to adjacent stages. The literature clearly suggests that the development of the overarm throw pattern over time proceeds in an orderly and linear fashion (Roberton, 1998; Haubenstricker, Branta & Seefeldt, 1983; Wild, 1938). In addition, the literature shows that these developmental sequences of throwing are based on longitudinal investigations during which children were tested at different times during the year (i.e., every three, six, and 12 months). None of these studies reported on data collected between testing times.

The present study examines how children develop the overhand throwing pattern when involved in an instructional motor skill program with frequent observation. This study challenges the order and linearity of the developmental sequence of throwing. Following a dynamical system perspective, developmental change is seen as nonlinear. At the micro-level of analysis, development is also nonlinear, qualitative, messy, highly variable, context-sensitive, function-driven, and emergent from interactions. The conclusions of previous research that development is orderly and linear may be because of infrequently long-term observations. Development may be more tentative and variable when observed more often and in different contextual situations (Thelen & Smith, 1994). In previous investigations, children have been tested sporadically; thus researchers may have missed more subtle continuous and discontinuous changes in the body configurations. This information can be very significant to teachers and researchers who observe children s developmental changes in more frequent fashion (daily, biweekly, etc.).

There are still a number of developmental questions without answers, such as how children change their throwing patterns on daily or weekly bases as compared to changes over long periods of time. Do they change their throwing patterns in a sequential order? Is there linearity in the throwing sequence using the Total Body Approach? How do the individual goals or motivations, teaching context/environment, and the task change these patterns of movement? The proponents of the dynamical system approach have attempted to explain the development of human movement, arguing that the system self-organizes, suggesting that body components could interact in infinite ways to create many combinations of their parts, and insinuating that the system is not linear, as it changes over time (Thelen & Smith, 1994). According to the dynamical system perspective, development emerges from the interaction of the organism with the outside world, and it is not guided by an intrinsic design. Patterns of movement are likely to change as children are exposed to more social contexts, as their body size and proportions change, as peer and adult interactions increase, and as their intentions for action change (Thelen & Smith, 1994).

The dynamical systems perspective has challenged our knowledge base, traditions, and research approach to the study of developmental change. Therefore, one of our tasks as developmental specialists is to examine closely how the process of developmental change occurs, and in particular, how the overarm throw develops. This study attempts to observe young children in real life phenomena in action within their environment (an instructional motor program, filled with instructors and peers in continuous interaction). We have concluded that dynamical systems approach could enhance our understanding of the complex but fascinating processes that engender developmental change, thereby providing important information to practitioners and investigators.

In this investigation, a closer observation of changes in the throwing patterns of children took place over a period of two years. Daily and weekly changes in the throwing patterns of six young children were examined, tracing the actual course of individual developmental change over time. In this way, variability and individual differences, as well as contextual and motivational variables, were taken into account as part of the data. According to Clark (1997), studying individual patterns of change may lead to a more accurate understanding of the global process of developmental change than examining group or average data. It is also advised by Thelen and Smith (1994) that by welcoming variability and individual differences as part of the data, rather than seeing it as noise, we can begin to understand the complexities of developmental change.

METHODS

Participants

The participants in this investigation were six children, three boys and three girls. Their ages at the beginning of the study ranged between 1year 9 months and 5 years. The average age of the girls was 1 year and 3 months younger than the average age of the boys. They were involved in an ongoing motor development research program at Northern Illinois University. Parents were required each year to sign informed consent forms allowing their children to participate in the study.

The six participant children were randomly selected from a population of 39 longitudinal children (18 boys and 21 girls) who had regularly attended the program for at least two consecutive years. The selection of six children out of a larger number of longitudinal cases was done for reasons of feasibility. During this period, each selected child performed between 368 and 843 throws. A brief description of each participant follows:

Participant # 1 (P1). This participant is a girl, the youngest child in the motor development research program. Her age at the beginning of the study was 1 year and 9 months. She is strong, agile, and did not to talk much. Although young for the program, she was willing to be a participant, perhaps because her older brother was also enrolled in the program. Initially, handedness was not well defined.

Participant # 2 (P2). This participant is a girl and began attending the program when she was 3 years, 7 months of age. Her older brother was also in the program during the first year of the study. Initially, P2 was shy and hesitant to try new things. Physically, she is a tall girl with long limbs and little muscle mass, her movements appeared uncoordinated and she evidenced delayed language development. P2 seemed to be unsure of her preferred hand.

Participant # 3 (P3). This participant is a girl and began in the program when she was 4 years, 2 months of age. During the first year, P3 was quiet and reserved. She listened to directions and tried to follow them but did not talk much. She is strong and seemed to prefer using her right hand.

Participant # 4 (P4). This participant is a boy and who began the program when he was 3 years, 8 months of age. He is the brother of P1. He was very observant and a little timid at the beginning of the study, and he spoke very clearly. P4 was affectionate, patient, and helpful to his sister. He is right-handed.

Participant # 5 (P5). This participant is a boy and began in the program when he was 4 years, 9 months of age. During the first semester, P5 was strong, very outgoing, and talkative. He is also right-handed.

Participant # 6 (P6). This participant is a boy and began in the program when he was 5 years of age. He has low muscle tone with mild planus feet and left internal rotation of the tibia. He has agenesis of the corpus callosum, a condition that makes any transfer of information between the right and left hemispheres of the brain very difficult. While in the program, P6 was also diagnosed as having attention problems and hyperactivity; however, he performed most of the activities, although he got distracted at times, usually while waiting or during explanation times. P6 was talkative and handedness was not well defined.

All participant throws were analyzed using the developmental sequence of throwing, referred to as the Total Body Approach (Seefeldt and Haubenstricker; 1976; Haubenstricker et al., 1983). For a description of the developmental sequence, see Table 1.

This developmental sequence has withstood preliminary validation with the use of a mixed longitudinal sample (Haubenstricker et al., 1983). In addition, a qualitative description of the way children move their different body segments and the environmental and behavioral factors participating in these actions were added to the analysis.

Table 1
Developmental Sequence for Throwing: Total Body Approach

Stage	Description
1	The throwing motion is essentially posterior-anterior in direction. The feet usually remain stationary during the throw. Infrequently, the performer may step or walk just prior to moving the ball into position for throwing. There is little or no trunk rotation in the most rudimentary pattern at this stage, but children at the point of transition between Stages 1 and 2 may evoke slight trunk rotation in preparation for the throw and extensive hip and trunk rotation in the follow-through phase. In the typical Stage 1, the force for projecting the ball comes from hip flexion, shoulder protraction, and elbow extension.
2	The distinctive feature of this stage is the rotation of the body about an imaginary vertical axis with the hips, spine, and shoulders rotating as one unit. The performer may step forward with either an ipsilateral or contralateral pattern, but the arm is brought forward in a transverse plane. The motion may resemble a sling rather than a throw due to the extended arm position during the course of the throw.
3	The distinctive pattern in Stage 3 is the ipsilateral arm/leg action. The ball is placed into a throwing position above the shoulder by a vertical and posterior motion of the arm at the time that the ipsilateral leg is moving forward. This stage involves little or no rotation of the spine and hips in preparation for the throw. The follow-through phase includes flexion at the hip joint and some trunk rotation toward the side opposite the throwing arm.
4	The movement is contralateral, with the leg opposite the throwing arm striding forward as the throwing arm is moved in a vertical and posterior direction during the wind-up phase; thus, the motion of the trunk and arm closely resembles the motions of Stages 1 and 3. The stride forward with the contralateral leg provides for a wide base of support and greater stability during the force production phase of the throw.
5	The wind-up phase begins with the throwing hand moving in a downward arc and then backward as the opposite leg moves forward. This concurrent action rotates the hip and spine into position for forceful derotation. As the contralateral foot strikes the surface, the hips, spine, and shoulder begin derotation in sequence. The contralateral leg begins to extend at the knee, providing an equal and opposite reaction to the throwing arm. The arm opposite the throwing limb also moves forcefully toward the body to assist in the equal and opposite reaction.

Note: From Haubenstricker, Branta, & Seefeldt, (1983); Seefeldt and Haubenstricker (1976, 1982); Seefeldt, Reuschlein, & Vogel, (1972). Material reprinted with permission.

The Motor Development Program

This program is offered to the community during fall and spring semesters. The program runs for 10 consecutive weeks per semester and meets two times per week for a period of one hour. A total of 20 to 24 children are enrolled each semester. The children participate in large group activities at the beginning and end of each session before being divided into four groups to participate at different learning stations with a ratio of two teachers to six children. Each learning station addresses different motor skills, movement concepts, and health/fitness concepts. The learning stations continue for 10 minutes, followed by discussion/reflection time (one to two minutes) at the end of each session. Physical education students who are enrolled in the teacher preparation program provided developmental instruction at each learning station. Throwing, a fundamental motor skill taught regularly each semester, consists of approximately 10 lessons per semester. The curriculum is designed and supervised by the director of the program and follows a developmental perspective.

The Task and Set-Up

The task and set-up for throwing activities varied slightly throughout the semester and the study. Footprints, carpet squares, ropes, and pretend bugs were used to aid stepping in the task. Initially, children were given spots on which to stand, so they knew where to be in the space, and they were asked to step onto the footprint, step over the rope, or step off the carpet square, until no aid was provided for the stepping. They were given the freedom to begin their throw where they felt most comfortable. Some chose to throw from far away, while others chose to throw from closer distances. Later in the semester, we also asked them to go and pick up balls and come back to throw, making them move before their throws. This strategy was most often applied when a participant displayed a straddle stiff position, with the intent to create more dynamic throw activities. As children became more aware of their space and the tasks, the activities became less static and more dynamic. Some lessons focused on trunk rotation, which was initiated by stationary swings with scarves, balls inside scarves, and ribbons, where the children were asked to twist their trunks to make the scarves fly. Trunk rotation was then added to the throw with regular balls or objects. Arm motion, from beginning stages to the more advanced level, was also the focus of some lessons; however, this was probably the most difficult component for the children to incorporate into their throws. The targets were colorful and were placed at different heights and distances. When hit, many targets produced noise (i.e., cans with beans inside, milk jugs with bells inside, etc.) or fell down. Other targets were big containers that swallowed the balls. The balls or objects to throw varied in texture,

weight, color, and shape. The set-up was attractive and colorful, and it varied throughout the semester.

Data Collection Procedures

Participants were videotaped during all regular throwing activities
and during the testing session in the fall and spring of two consecutive
years. All throws performed by each individual child during the instructional time and testing time were videotaped from a sagittal view. A
Panasonic VHS video camcorder (Model AG-188u) was used with a shutter speed of 1/250 s. Videotaping took place inside a large gymnasium as
children participated in their regular throwing activities with other children, except for the regular testing sessions at the beginning and end of
each semester when children took individual turns to throw. Videotapes
were reviewed in regular speed and slow motion using a Super VHS editing system. A total of 3,469 throws were available for analysis.

Field notes describing in detail the actions and interactions among the
participants and teachers, the context of the activity and children s intentions,
and responses or feelings about the tasks at hand were also taken during the
throwing activities. In addition, brief interviews of the participants took place
after each session, and their verbalizations and actions were documented.

Data Reduction and Analysis

Videotaped throwing trials were played back on the videocassette
recorder in regular speed and slow motion and were classified using the
Total Body Approach (Haubenstricker et al., 1983). The authors have training and experience in the categorization of stages using the Total Body
Approach, with an inter-rater objectivity of 90% agreement with the proponents of this approach. Each author independently categorized the trials;
one author categorized all trials and the other categorized a random selection of 20% of each child s activities across semesters. The objectivity of
the investigators in the categorization of the Total Body Approach throwing sequences was established by achieving at least 80% agreement.

The authors viewed the tapes and coded the stages of development,
making notes of any other behavior, task, or environmental information
observed during the trial. Special color markers and letters were used to
indicate any behavioral, environmental, or body configuration change not
included in stages. Each child s trial was analyzed and recorded on a special form; individual patterns of change were examined and additional notes
were taken during the analysis of the stages. These notes were attached to
each form. Individual data were plotted in a graph reflecting the number of
times each pattern was repeated and changed over time. Another table was
created to show how many trials each child performed at different stages of

development during the years they were in the study. Finally, the notes were analyzed against the stages, to check behavioral, task, environmental, and contextual information that helped explain some of the observed changes. Some commonalties were found across notes on the children, and observed changes in the stages of development and themes emerged from these analyses.

RESULTS

Individual profiles of the six participants are described below. Figures 1- 6 graphically show the throwing profiles of each individual participant.

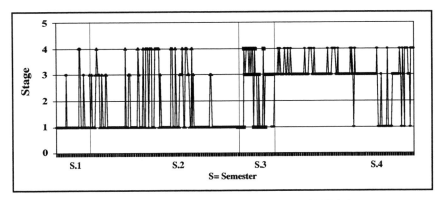

Fig. 1. Throwing Performance per Semester (P1), 368 Trials

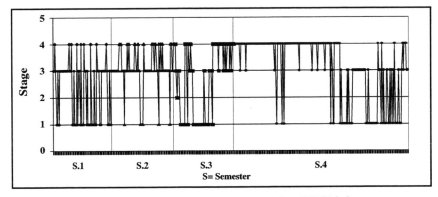

Fig. 2. Throwing Performance per Semester (P2), 473 Trials

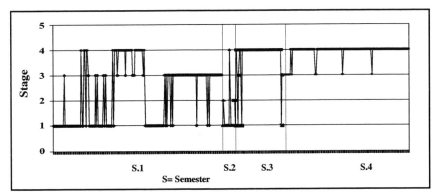

Fig. 3. Throwing Performance per Semester (P3), 439 Trials

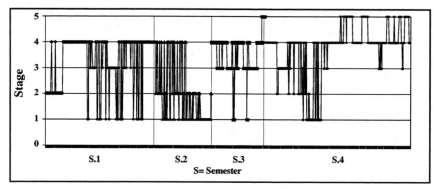

Fig. 4. Throwing Performance per Semester (P4), 843 Trials

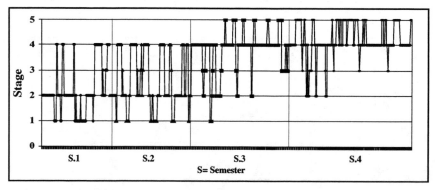

Fig. 5. Throwing Performance per Semester (P5), 643 Trials

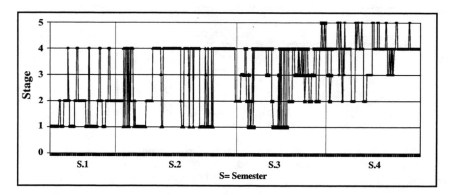

Fig. 6. Throwing Performance per Semester (P6), 703 Trials

In Tables 2-7, the frequencies of the throwing stages are reported. A review of Figures 1-6 would seem to indicate that the linearity of the throwing sequence described by the Total Body Approach does not hold when using frequent observations. Children moved back and forth across the spectrum of stages from semeser 1 to 4. In fact, children moved to nonadjacent stages, (i.e., from Stages 1 to Stage 3, skipping Stage 2). Therefore, the classical notions of stage theory (Inhelder, 1971; Roberton, 1982) that behavioral development is a universal sequence is challenged by these data.

If we look at Tables 2-7 in which frequencies of the throwing stages through each semester are reported, one can observe that children have greater frequencies of modal stages at the lower level and then move to greater frequencies of modal stages at the higher level. However, P2 and P4 were exceptions. P2 moved from Stage 3 (the modal Stage) during the first semester (50%) and second semester (72%) to greater frequency at Stage 1 (62.8%) during the third semester. Similarly, P4 moved from Stage 4 (61.2%) during the first semester to Stage 1 (45.1%) during the second semester. Some possible explanations for this lack of linearity are (a) all

Table 2
Participant #1

	Sem. 1	Sem. 2	Sem. 3	Sem. 4	Total
1	30 (88.2%)	117 (72.6%)	13 (35.2%)	20 (14.7%)	180 (48.9%)
2	0 (0.0%)	0 (0.0%)	0 (0.0%)	0 (0.0%)	0 (0.0%)
3	2 (5.8%)	21 (13.1%)	15 (40.5%)	89 (65.4%)	127 (34.5%)
4	2 (5.8%)	23 (14.3%)	9 (24.3%)	27 (19.9%)	61 (16.6%)
5	0 (0.0%)	0 (0.0%)	0 (0.0%)	0 (0.0%)	0 (0.0%)
Total	34	161	37	136	368

Table 3
Participant #2

	Sem. 1	Sem. 2	Sem. 3	Sem. 4	Total
1	29 (39.2%)	4 (4.4%)	71 (62.8%)	39 (20.0%)	143 (30.2%)
2	0 (0.0%)	0 (0.0%)	1 (0.9%)	0 (0.0%)	1 (0.2%)
3	37 (50.0%)	66 (72.5%)	15 (13.3%)	36 (18.5%)	154 (32.5%)
4	8 (10.8%)	21 (23.1%)	26 (23.0%)	120 (61.5%)	175 (36.9%)
5	0 (0.0%)	0 (0.0%)	0 (0.0%)	0 (0.0%)	0 (0.0%)
Total	74	91	113	195	473

throws performed by young children during instructional times were observed and thus reflected the child's attempt to find solutions to the tasks and contextual variables that were intervening at different rates and times, and (b) it is possible that the sequence does not prescribe linearity but rather common patterns observed at different times in the development of throwing.

Common themes emerged as the whole corpus of data were analyzed, such as children's motivation to participate, body awareness, and learning context (i.e., peer observation, teacher instruction, teacher verbal cues, teacher perceptual cues, words of encouragement, equipment set-up,

Table 4
Participant #3

	Sem. 1	Sem. 2	Sem. 3	Sem. 4	Total
1	76	9	4	0	89
	(41.3%)	(81.8%)	(7.1%)	(0.0%)	(20.3%)
2	0	1	2	0	3
	(0.0%)	(9.1%)	(3.6%)	(0.0%)	(0.7%)
3	73	0	3	18	94
	(39.7%)	(0.0%)	(5.3%)	(9.6%)	(21.4%)
4	35	1	47	170	253
	(19.0%)	(9.1%)	(84.0%)	(90.4%)	(57.6%)
5	0	0	0	0	0
	(0.0%)	(0.0%)	(0.0%)	0(0.0%)	(0.0%)
Total	184	11	56	188	439

Table 5
Participant #4

	Sem. 1	Sem. 2	Sem. 3	Sem. 4	Total
1	25	55	4	25	109
	(9.8%)	(45.1%)	(3.2%)	(7.4%)	(12.9%)
2	37	42	0	15	94
	(14.5%)	(34.4%)	(0.0%)	(4.4%)	(11.2%)
3	37	0	51	36	124
	(14.5%)	(0.0%)	(40.5%)	(10.6%)	(14.7%)
4	156	25	64	206	451
	(61.2%)	(20.5%)	(50.8%)	(60.6%)	(53.5%)
5	0	0	7	58	65
	(0.0%)	(0.0%)	(5.5%)	(17.0%)	(7.7%)
Total	255	122	126	340	843

children's goals, and task). These themes may explain some of the variability observed. They evolve as the time passed and therefore will be presented across semesters.

COMMON THEMES

The analysis of data from this study resulted in the emergence of three themes as important variables that influence the developmental change

Table 6
Participant #5

	Sem. 1	Sem. 2	Sem. 3	Sem. 4	Total
1	25	23	3	0	51
	(19.4%)	(16.5%)	(2.0%)	(0.0%)	(7.9%)
2	77	59	15	8	159
	(59.7%)	(42.4%)	(9.4%)	(3.7%)	(24.7%)
3	4	7	20	11	42
	(3.1%)	(5.0%)	(12.6%)	(5.1%)	(6.5%)
4	23	50	99	124	296
	(17.8%)	(36.1%)	(62.2%)	(57.4%)	(46.0%)
5	0	0	22	73	95
	(0.0%)	(0.0%)	(13.8%)	(33.8%)	(14.8%)
Total	**129**	**139**	**159**	**216**	**643**

Table 7
Participant #6

	Sem. 1	Sem. 2	Sem. 3	Sem. 4	Total
1	58	61	25	0	144
	(42.3%)	(26.1%)	(15.6%)	(0.0%)	(20.5%)
2	68	28	27	17	140
	(49.6%)	(12.0%)	(16.9%)	(9.9%)	(19.9%)
3	0	9	36	20	65
	(0.0%)	(3.8%)	(22.5%)	(11.6%)	(9.2%)
4	11	136	68	107	322
	(8.1%)	(58.1%)	(42.5%)	(62.2%)	(45.8%)
5	0	0	4	28	32
	(0.0%)	(0.0%)	(2.5%)	(16.3%)	(4.6%)
Total	**137**	**234**	**160**	**172**	**703**

in throwing patterns. They were motivation, body awareness, and learning context. They are influenced by the level of throwing children have or do not have, and they also change constantly as time, exposure, instruction, practice, and experience on the throwing skill increases. These variables are in constant interaction with each other. It is only for the sake of clarity that they are presented separately in this paper. It was hard to maintain the separation, as they are in constant interaction. The authors hope that the reader will keep track of this relationship. The information about these themes will be presented by semester to provide a time line for organization.

Motivation

This theme refers to the disposition of the children toward the activity and their willingness to try the activity. It also includes their enjoyment as well as their intensity in the activity. Their facial expressions, verbal comments, intentions, and overall participation were observed. There were gender differences in motivation, and motivation changed through the semesters.

Semester 1. The girls (P1, P2, and P3) showed different motivation at the beginning of their experience in the throwing activities. P1 was highly motivated to participate and do all activities as her older brother did. P1 (1 year and 9 months) moved slowly and did a total of 34 throws (see Table 2). P2 was shy and hesitant to try the activities. She also had an older brother in the program. She seemed bored and uninterested in participating. Sometimes P2 sat out, thus showing low motivation. P2 threw 74 times (see Table 3). P3 was quiet and reserved. Although P3 threw 184 times (see Table 4) she seemed uninterested and appeared to have a low level of motivation. At the beginning of the semester, P3 threw many balls rapidly as though she was merely complying with the teacher's request (see Figure 3). As the semester progressed, P3 sat out several times during the activities, saying she felt sick, had a stomach ache, or needed to go to the bathroom, and she said, "I do not like to throw." All of the girls showed a positive disposition to listening to the teacher and following direction. They also showed a great degree of concern for order in the station. They liked to organize the objects in the setting; all of them seemed excited (moving quickly and showing smiling faces) when picking up objects, setting pins back up, or putting balls back in buckets. They seemed to explore the setting with their eyes, looking at the balls and especially the spider balls (colorful rubber balls with black elastic filaments coming out of them). In general, these girls at the beginning of the study appeared to like exploring and organizing the equipment (i.e. picking up and setting equipment in place) more than participating in the throwing activities. They tended to spend time exploring equipment or the space, thus wasting practice time; they moved slowly; and, on occasions, P2 and P3 dropped out of the throwing activity voluntarily.

The boys (P4, P5, and P6) on the other hand, demonstrated mostly high motivation in the throwing activities of the program. P5 loved to hit the target; he called the teachers to tell them about his success. P5 did a total of 129 throws (see Table 6). P4 also showed high motivation. P4 did a total of 255 throws (see Table 5). He was eager and happy to participate. P6's motivation varied; he was generally involved and active, but at times looked distracted and did some exploring of the equipment. P6 did a total of 137 throws (see Table 7). The boys in general wanted to exhibit force and sometimes speed (P4, on occasions, grabbed the ball so hard that the ball did not come out of his hands). Also, the boys did not appear to listen well to instruction. They seemed to want to knock the target down, they were anxious to begin the activity, and they also showed competition among themselves. For instance, P5 threw all the balls in his bucket as fast as possible so he would finish before the other children.

Semester 2. During this semester, the girls' motivation was similar to the previous semester. P1 showed total engagement in the throwing activities (she did a total of 161 throws), whereas P2 and P3 continued showing low motivation. P2 sat out on her own, seemed bored, looked around, playing with balls in her hands, and walked to targets to knock them down with the ball in her hand. Upon teacher encouragement, P2 threw all balls at once or one in each hand, as if she were trying to finish the task quickly. P2 did a total of 91 throws (see Table 3). P3 sat out more times during this semester. She continued feeling sick during throwing activities, had stomach aches, and took bathroom trips, and she again verbally expressed, "I do not want to throw." P3 did only 11 throws during this semester (see Table 4).

The boys seemed very happy participating in the activities. They were very much into throwing; in general their level of motivation was consistently high. They said to teachers, "Watch me, watch me" as they threw the ball. They used such force during throws that on occasion it turned them around and the ball went in the opposite direction. This is particularly true of P4, who threw very forcefully and wanted to hit the target, but the ball went in the opposite direction. The total number of throws made by P4 was 122, less throws than in the previous semester; but P4 still seemed highly enthusiastic about it (see Table 5). P5 loved to aim at the objects (targets) and he kept track of his success in hitting them (i.e., P5 would say, "I hit 16 in a row!"). He also loved to show his thumb up to teachers and on occasion said, "Yes!" P5 did a total of 139 throws (see Table 6). P6 showed high interest and enthusiasm in the throwing activities this semester. P6 did a total of 234 throws (see Table 7). On a couple of occasions, he removed himself from the throwing activity and played with cones and balls, but then came back and continued throwing. Later in the semester, he expressed that he loved baseball.

Semester 3. During this semester, some changes were observed in the girls' motivation. At the beginning of the semester, P1 did not want to participate because she was placed in a different group, not with her brother. She refused to throw, sat out, and was unhappy (crying). After she was switched back to her brother's group, her motivation was high again and she was happy (smiling), trying to do all the activities her brother did. P2 and P3 began to demonstrate more comfort in the throwing station; they appeared to be happier (smiling) and demonstrated enjoyment as they threw. P2 threw a total of 113 times (see Table 3). P2, however, still sat out at times and showed some concern with order. P3 appeared motivated by stickers, footprints, and teacher encouragement. P3 threw a total of 56 times (see Table 4). Teachers used stickers to indicate stepping feet, or to praise the girls' work. P3 appeared more interested and did not express verbal rejection during this semester.

During this semester, the boys' motivation continued to be high, showing great involvement in throwing activities. The number of throws for P4 (126) and P5 (159) increased (see Tables 5 and 6). P6 made 160 more throws than did P4 and P5, but less than in the previous semester (see Table 7). They appeared confident and eager to do better in each trial. They continued throwing forcefully and they liked to demonstrate to the teacher. They also could say what they did when they threw. P6 became more outspoken and his throw flowed much better. He consistently responded when asked and was willing to participate in the discussion about throwing.

Semester 4. During this semester, all the girls were more highly motivated. P1 showed great motivation for the throwing activities. She threw a total of 136 times, 99 more times than in the previous semester (see Table 2). P2 also improved her motivation as evidenced by her active participation. She made a total of 195 throws (see Table 3), 82 more throws than in the previous semester. P2 also showed smiling facial expressions during throwing activities. It seemed that she wanted to throw and that she was happy. P3 showed more interest in throwing, appeared happy, and participated diligently, paid attention and tried to do as the teacher said or showed her. P3 smiled more and performed a total of 188 throws, 132 more trials than in the previous semester (see Table 4). All the girls improved in the number of trials performed when compared to the previous semester (see Tables 2, 3, and 4). They also showed happiness (smiling faces) when hitting targets.

All the boys seemed excited and happy to get to the throwing station. Boys' motivation was still very high. They were very active and involved. P4 did a total of 340 throws, P5 did 216, and P6 threw 172 times (see Tables 5, 6, and 7). P4 and P5 mentioned that they liked to throw hard. They all liked to hit the target. P6 looked confident, wanted to hit the target, and expressed that he liked baseball and wanted to be a baseball player.

Body Awareness

This theme refers to the ability of the child to identify their body parts and their actions, the ability to incorporate information into their body actions, and the ability to understand and recognize their body actions. Body awareness changed through the semesters.

Semester 1. In general, during the first semester of the study, all the children lacked body awareness. However, the girls lagged behind in awareness of both the upper and lower body (arms, trunk, and legs) in the throwing action. The boys were more aware of the arms (had a general idea), but were unaware of the action of the legs and trunk. The girls were so unaware of their body actions that even with teacher manipulation (holding their arm and assisting the motion of arm and leg) they appeared not to be aware of what body part the teacher touched or moved, and the ball could fall out of their hand without their even realizing. When asked about what they do when they throw, they looked at the teachers and said nothing. It was clear that they had no idea what their body was doing. They seemed to get their cues more visually, in particular by watching other children, rather than from teacher manipulation or verbal feedback (e.g., P1 would watch her brother first and then throw).

Only one boy (P6) showed lack of awareness of the arms and legs; however, this boy had agenesis of the corpus callosum, a condition which makes any crossing of information between the right and left hemisphere of the brain very difficult. When asked about throwing, boys did say that they knew how to throw, and they liked to show it; but they could not talk about it, showing that they lacked body awareness.

Semester 2. During the second semester, little variation in body awareness was observed in the girls. However, the youngest girl, P1 (2 years, 3 months), who was very motivated, began to show change in her body awareness, as she appeared more aware of what the legs were supposed to do. She stepped and staggered her legs (locking the legs in that position) and threw with a broken, slow pattern. It seemed that she wanted to control her body. This pattern was also observed in two boys, who began to change from showing a lot of variation to showing the step-straddled position. They did several throws in that position, then changed to either leg and stepped to throw, but now appeared more concerned about how to move their legs. This pattern seemed to be deliberate, indicating the beginning of body awareness and control. The beginning of body awareness seems to be positively related to high motivation, since all the motivated children began to show willingness to control their body movements. It looked as if they wanted to control their bodies and were more aware of what their bodies were doing. All the boys added force to their throws, pushing and rotating their trunks. One of the boys (P6) still showed erratic motions in both arms and legs, but exhibited great improvement in his throwing pattern (see Table 7, and The Learning Context session of Semester 2). The other two boys began to mention that they "step" when they throw, thus showing a little more awareness of what their legs do when they throw.

Semester 3. In this semester, the girls (P2 and P3) began to show more awareness of their bodies. P2, who was approximately 4 years and 6 months of age, began to show stiffness after stepping, so she step-straddled her legs and then moved her arms while her legs did not move, doing more than one throw in this position. The arms were still erratic. It seems that she gained more awareness of her legs and tried to control her body by freezing movement of her legs. The other girl, P3, who was 4 years, 2 months of age, was now able to verbally respond to teacher questions such as, "What do the legs do when we throw?" She said, "Step," and, when asked what hand she used, she showed her left hand. However, she used her right hand to throw; but even so, she was more aware than she had been the first two semesters. Her arm movements were still erratic, with some strange motion at the wrist level. The youngest girl, P1, participated very little this semester; she planted her foot and threw with a broken, delivered pattern. However, she did step with each throw, thus showing less stiffness than in the previous semester. All the girls showed improvements in their throwing patterns (see Table 2, 3, and 4).

The boys became more conscious and aware of their arm and leg actions (showing opposition of arm and leg). For instance, P4, who was approximately 4 years, 1 month of age, after throwing with his left hand and left foot, stopped, seemed to be thinking, and corrected himself, moving to a contralateral pattern of throwing. Although he lost the motion, he began showing the ability to monitor his body actions and correct himself, thus demonstrating greater awareness of his body actions. P4 demonstrated variation across stages with approximately 50% of his attempts in Stage 4, and he did seven throws in Stage 5 (see Table 5). Another boy, P5, was also more consistent in throwing, using a contralateral throwing pattern and seeming more aware of what he was supposed to do. When the teacher asked questions about throwing, he was able to demonstrate what the arms and legs were supposed to do and was able to explain verbally what the body does when one throws. P5 demonstrated 62% of his throws in Stage 4 and made 22 throws in Stage 5 (see Table 6). Although the boys may have shown some variability in the body motions, they seemed more aware of their bodies and their actions. P6, although he did not progress quite as much as the other boys, was also able to verbally express what the legs were supposed to do. P6 demonstrated approximately 42 % of his throws in Stage 4, and he did four throws at Stage 5 (see Table 7). He also showed greater awareness of his body, variability across stages, and progress in skill development. His answer to the teacher's question was "I step and throw," and he tried to explain what the arm did, although he was not sure.

Yet he still showed arm inconsistency, his steps were short, and the throwing action was segmented or broken.

Semester 4. During the fourth semester, all the girls showed greater awareness of their body motion. What they did and what they said more accurately matched reality, providing a clear indication of awareness. The girls began to release their staggered frozen legs position, stepping with either foot as they threw, sometimes ipsilaterally, others contralaterally. However, they became more able to incorporate information (feedback) provided by the teachers, either verbal or kinesthesic (verbal cues, gentle touches on arm or leg); they immediately responded and corrected their motions after any of this information was provided. When teachers assisted, they were able to move to higher stages in their throws. They continued imitating peers, but paid more attention to teachers as role models. P1's steps to throw were small, but she stepped most of the time, a total of 116 out of 136 throws (see Table 2). P2 showed less erratic arm movement and right hand dominance. She was also more able to incorporate teacher feedback into the throwing motion. She used contralateral steps in 120 out of 195 throws (see Table 3). P3 decreased erratic arm movement and began to monitor herself. For instance, when she began to throw ipsilaterally, she paused, thought, looked insecure, and was able to correct herself and throw contralaterally. If she began to throw ipsilaterally, she looked unsure and changed several times until she used the contralateral pattern and seemed to realize that that was the right feel. She used the contralateral pattern 170 times out of 188. P3 began to show stability at Stage 4 (see Table 4). She also became more able to use teacher feedback immediately, and she looked for teacher assurance (a smile or an assenting signal with head) after correcting herself. She became more conscious of what leg and arm to use when throwing.

The boys' self-awareness of their body motion was evident (i.e., their motion matched better than before what they said their bodies did). They also added more vocabulary to their descriptions of the throwing motion; they typically said, "I step, bring my arm back, and throw," but P6 said, "Body rotation." All the boys were observed stopping and correcting themselves. They became more consistent in their throwing patterns, especially P4 and P5, throwing mostly with opposition and showing a nice flow at times. P4 showed Stage 4 or 5 in 264 out of 340 throws. P5 showed Stage 4 or 5 in 197 out of 216 throws (see Tables 5 and 6). They also were able to correct themselves and adjust to the changes in the environment while maintaining their consistency (see Figures 4 and 5) and were able to respond quickly to teacher feedback. For P6, contralateral opposition in throwing was more consistent, as he showed Stage 4 or 5 135 times out of his 172 throws (see Table 7), and the length of his steps varied, sometimes big (thus uncomfortable), others relatively smooth. He also showed more consistency in handedness. All the boys showed improvement in their body awareness. It is important to remember that P6 is the boy with agenesis of the corpus callosum, and the boy who had the least body awareness at the beginning of the study. His improvements are highly significant given his special condition.

Learning Context

This theme refers to the aspect of the learning environment that appears to create changes in children's throwing patterns through the semesters. The observed changes from stage to stage, or variation of the different movements of the body parts, and how the learning context (instruction, peers, task and environment) affected these changes will be addressed. This theme could be considered the result of the combination of different levels of motivation with different levels of body awareness, and the impact of instruction, practice, task, and experience on the child's developmental level of performance.

Semester 1. During this semester, the girls varied mostly between Stages 1 and 3, skipping Stage 2, an adjacent stage (see Figures 1, 2, and 3). They did perform Stage 4, but with less frequency, showing that the linearity of the throwing sequence does not hold. This was particularly true for P2 and P3. The youngest participant, P1, had very little variation, performing at Stage 1 most of the time (see table 2). P1 performed stages 3 and 4 when physically guided by the teacher and after observing her brother's motion. The girls' throwing motion was soft and slow. Their arm movement, especially that of P2 and P3, looked uncoordinated and varied a great deal. P3 twisted her wrist, brought her arm out and threw, or tried a twisted underhand action and also brought her arm up outside. She also twisted her wrist and then dropped the ball anywhere. P2 threw back and forth with both hands with arms moving in many ways. P1 limited herself to moving her arm up and throwing with a sort of pushing-the-ball action. Changes from stage to stage were observed when the following occurred: (a) they observed other children and copied them (e.g., P1 observed her brother and changed her pattern from Stage 1 to 3), (b) the teacher guided their bodies, and (c) stickers and footprints were used to aid stepping, particularly true with P3. Changes also randomly happened, seeming unintentional. Most of the contralateral steps observed were small; they threw a lot without steps and they stepped more ipsilaterally than contralaterally. Their stepping looked uncomfortable, as if unstable, almost falling. They moved from Stage 1 to Stages 3 and 4 and quickly changed back (see Figures 1, 2, and 3). The graphic lines spike up and immediately down, indicating a short visit to the upper stages and back to Stage 1.

The boys' variation among stages was wider; they went from Stage 1 to Stage 4, with the greatest frequency observed in Stage 2 (see Tables 5 and 6). Their throwing motion was mainly characterized by a block rotation. All boys seemed to be exploring their body motions. P4 demonstrated more of Stage 4 (see Table 4); however, he seemed confused, as if exploring, unsure how to best move his legs, and he staggered his legs in many throws. P5 also seemed to be exploring with his legs. Footprints on the floor seemed to guide his leg action, aiding his change to opposition of legs in the throwing pattern. P6 also appeared to be exploring, showing a lot of changes moving from Stage 1 to 2 to 4; footprints and teacher assistance helped with his leg movement. The boys all seemed to be searching for a better way to move their bodies, and in the process they jumped around from stage to stage. On occasion, after teacher instructions, the boys' throws became very broken or segmented, as if they were thinking and unable to do as they were told or were just confused. Their arms showed different patterns, from a lateral swing to a high wind-up with hyperextension and flexion of the trunk, to making arm circles before throwing. All the boys brought with them a forceful intention as demonstrated by their motions, facial expressions, and speech. This forceful intention on occasions helped move all of the body in unison and on others distorted their throwing mechanics. The girls never showed forceful throws, even after seeing the boys do so.

Semester 2. During the second semester, the children continued to move to nonadjacent stages and back and forth between stages. Among the girls, P1 and P2 showed more Stages 3 and 4 than during the first semester. Thus, they varied more this semester. Although for P1, the most frequent stage observed was still Stage 1, P2 repeated Stage 3 the most. The other participant, P3, was not willing to participate and only performed 11 throws, with the greatest frequency (9 throws) in Stage 1.

P1's changes occurred mostly after she observed her brother or other children in her group. For instance, one time she observed her brother, who threw at Stage 4, and she then threw at Stage 3; immediately after, she saw another boy throwing at Stage 1 and she changed back to Stage 1. It was clear that she was watching their leg action. Watching her brother stepping made her step (ipsilaterally), and after this step, her throws were very slow and broken (she planted her foot, then paused, and then very slowly moved her arm). P2 was very playful and performed the task as if she did not really care for it; teacher encouragement, the use of footprints, and redirection of her actions after each trial appeared to be helpful and encouraged her to try more. It appears that the use of visual aids such as footprints facilitates the motion of legs and the shifting of body weight. Even though P3 did not want to participate, one time while participating she changed her throw after observing a boy tossing a ball; she changed her throw to a toss, too. In relation to arm movements, P2 continued switching arms and P3 showed erratic rotations of the throwing arm. Overall, similar to the boys in the first semester, they seemed to be exploring different ways of throwing. In general, the girls liked to take their time, look around, and arrange things in the setting; and when contralateral steps were observed they were small, and the ipsilateral steps varied from small to very big steps. On occasion, they almost lost balance.

The boys in this semester continued showing great variability, moving back and forth among Stages 1 to 4. However, Stage 3, an adjacent stage, was less often observed (see Tables 4, 5, and 6). P5 and P6 demonstrated Stage 4 more often than in the previous semester, but their motion appeared to be segmented and broken, and they also planted their foot and threw without stepping but showing opposition. They also did a significant number of throws with no step (Stage 1). For instance, P4 showed a significant drop in his frequency in Stage 4 and an increase in frequency in Stage 1. He became very inconsistent in particular with his stepping. It appeared that he chose not to step in an attempt to better hit the targets. P4 also applied too much force to his motion, so his body rotated and the ball trajectory went in another direction. P5 was also concerned with hitting the targets. At times, he seemed confused as to how to move his body; he tried stepping ipsilaterally, not stepping, stepping and freezing his legs, moving only arms, using contralateral opposition, and so on. It appeared that instruction did not reach them as they were on their own agenda. Even when teachers emphasized the form of the throw, they continued focusing on the target. P4 and P5 constantly continued throwing forcefully. P6, on the other hand, began to pay more attention to teacher instructions and seemed more interested in throwing. He began to show more step-throw motion with the assistance of footprints and teachers' cues, thus showing more stability in Stage 4: his arm showed a back swing motion and his body showed a small rotation. Toward the end of the semester, P4 and P5's stepping improved, but not their arm motion. P4 and P5 continued showing a poorly defined arm motion, still exploring (i.e., using a side-arm motion, circular action, or an aiming and pushing motion). Hitting the target was very important for P4 and P5 during this semester.

Semester 3. In the third semester, the girls' variation continued among stages 1, 3, and 4. During this semester, visual aids such as footprints, stickers, eye contact, body touch, smiles, and encouragement appeared to have an impact on their motivation and throwing motion. It could also be the effects of exposure to throwing activities that made them more familiar with the skill. All of them showed a desire to throw. They continued copying others, in particular P1. Her role model continued to be her brother, and she observed him a lot, even after teacher demonstrations. P1's throws were still broken; she planted her foot and then threw. All the girls showed improvement but not stability; P1 and P3 did more of stages 3 and 4 than Stage 1 (see Tables 2 and 4). P2 began to show stiffness after stepping, freezing her legs in that position and moving only her arms, showing more frequency in Stage 1, whereas in the second semester she showed Stage 3 more often (see Table 3). When she stepped, her steps were small and she still did not seem sure about handedness, so she constantly changed arms and legs, showing great inconsistency in handedness. However, she knew that she was supposed to step before throwing. P3 was more responsive than in previous semesters; in the small group discussion, she raised her hand to explain and demonstrate how to throw, showing both more confidence in herself on this skill and more knowledge about it. She also seemed more sure about the stepping than the handedness. When she demonstrated in the small group, she used a different hand than the one she preferred to use when she threw in the practical activity. She still showed erratic arm actions, but with less frequency; she appeared to be moving to a more stable pattern (Stage 4).

Overall, the girls seemed to be more ready to follow teacher cues and feedback, and they also seemed to enjoy teachers gently praising, smiling, and giving stickers or reassuring signals; they actually looked for teacher approval as they threw. All the girls continued executing Stage 4, but none with forceful actions or verbal expressions of force; their bodies moved slowly.

During this semester, instruction appeared to have a major impact on the boys' performance. Teacher corrections and encouragement, together with children's better attention, understanding, and self-monitoring, appeared to bring about the best levels, as changes were observed after teaching intervention. Their variability this semester was among all stages; now their throw stages ranged from Stages 1 to 5 (see Figures 4, 5, and 6). For the first time, Stage 5 was observed, and all the boys showed it. Stage 4 was the modal stage for all the boys, and Stages 1 and 2 were seen less often, especially for P4 and P5. However, P6 showed Stage 1 and 2 several times (see Tables 5, 6, and 7).

The boys continued throwing with a forceful intention, and they often challenged themselves by choosing to throw to targets that were higher and farther away. The boys also started to appear more conscious about their body motion (they were observed correcting themselves and adjusting their bodies to what the teacher indicated). They still observed and copied other children's performance; however, it seems that they did it less often and were also better able to judge their performance, thus correcting their performance after copying (P4 observed another boy, who was left-handed, and then changed his side, and after copying he corrected himself quickly). P5 was more consistent in his contralateral pattern; however, early in the semester he went back and performed ipsilaterally, not stepping at all, or with a block rotation. As the semester went on, he showed mostly Stages 4 and 5 (see Table 6 and Figure 5). He could also demonstrate in small group discussion and talked about it, and his actions and wording represented what he did mostly in practices (Stages 4 and 5). P6 still showed great variability and mobility among all stages (see Table 7 and Figure 6). He seemed concerned with doing things fast, and when doing so, his throw deteriorated. In small group discussion, he knew that he was supposed to step. In practice, when in contralateral motion, his steps were small. Overall, the lower stages (Stage 1 and 2) were still present but less often observed. Toward the end of the semester, the boys varied more among mostly higher stages (Stages 3, 4, and 5). In general, their throwing motion flowed better this semester, showing at times Stage 5 of throwing.

Semester 4. During the fourth semester, P1 and P3 were more consistent in showing stages 3 and 4. However, P1 still showed Stage 1, although less often than the others, and P2 showed Stage 1 more often than Stage 3 (see Tables 2, 3, and 4). During this semester, instruction appeared to have a major impact on the girls' performance (the use of visual aids, teacher cues, and demonstrations were related to notable changes). On several occasions, P1, P2, and P3 moved to higher stages after the teacher gently touched their leg to step with. This semester they were more rushed to throw; it was as if they wanted to finish first, throwing all the balls in their buckets. They showed a lot of back and forth motion, particularly with stepping (there was a constant change from ipsilateral to contralateral); they tended to stabilize on the contralateral position after teachers reminded them how to do the motion. They also did better when they were instructed to slow down. P2 and P3, upon slowing down, appeared to be self-conscious and were able to correct themselves (e.g., on occasion, they stepped ipsilaterally, then realized it, went back, and did the throw with opposition). Although P3 did most of her throwing in opposition, her throwing pattern seemed to be broken, deliberate, and slow. Two of the girls (P2 and P3) added a sound to their motion, suggesting the use of more force.

This semester, several context variables were modified: the footprints were taken away to determine whether the children would remember to step, the targets were higher and farther, the children needed to use more force, and the children were also required to move to get the ball and then throw. It was noticed that without instructions, P1 threw at Stage 1, and when rushing also threw at Stage 1. With footprints, not teacher assistance, she threw at Stage 3. When the teacher instructed her before she threw, and especially when the teacher assisted (i.e., the teacher gently touched the opposite leg of the throwing arm before the throw), then she moved her throw to Stage 4. P1's steps were very small.

P2 was more definite about handedness, using her right hand more; she also regressed to Stage 1 more readily when there were no footprints and went to Stage 4 when footprints were on the floor or the teacher provided verbal cues. Her Stage 4 was also broken and slow. P2 and P1 interestingly showed more of Stage 1 toward the end of the semester (see Figures 1 and 2). This was the time in which the setting (context) changed. The lessons required the children to move before they threw (run to pick up a ball behind the throwing area and come back to throw) and also throw farther, higher, without footprints, and over obstacles. These lessons could have confused their throwing motions.

P3 also had a little difficulty at the beginning with the contextual changes, using a big ipsilateral step at the beginning; then the teacher corrected her by touching her opposite foot. On another occasion without footprints she did a contralateral step, then seemed unsure, changed in her next throw to an ipsilateral step, then corrected herself again and showed a contralateral step (Stage 4). P3 was able to show Stage 4 consecutively without footprints. When moving more than one step to get the ball, her throws changed to ipsilateral, but upon the teacher's verbal reminder of opposition, she changed back to a contralateral step. P3 seemed more conscious of how she was supposed to move to throw the ball and more able to pick up verbal cues from the teacher than she had been in previous semesters.

During this semester, the boys' throws varied from Stage 2 through Stage 5. Stage 1 was only observed in one participant, P4. However, Stages 2 and 3 were still present in all participants. The modal stage was Stage 4, followed by Stage 5 (see Tables 5, 6, and 7 and Figures 4, 5, and 6). The boys showed their greater stability when visual aids and teacher assistance was provided (when footprints were removed, regression to Stage 3 was observed). For instance, P4 initially showed very good opposition but was disturbed by the removal of the footprints, thus throwing ipsilaterally. However, he was able to get back quickly to contralateral steps with teacher verbal cues. He became much more conscious of opposition as the semester went on and was able to correct himself immediately after verbal feedback. P5's stages 2 and 3 occurred mostly early in the semester; when he moved too close to the target, he changed to an ipsilateral step or side swing. After these early adjustments, most of his throws were in opposition. As the context of the environment changed (e.g., footprints were removed), and he moved to get the ball, his throwing performance was still stable, showing consistency in opposition, and showing Stage 5 on several occasions.

P6's stepping in opposition was more stable, especially toward the end of this semester. Early in the semester, he took big steps that looked uncomfortable, but other times his pattern was very smooth. He also added rotation and low wind-up to his throws. He was also disturbed a bit at the beginning with the changes in the context, but with teacher verbal cues he was able to adjust to the changes quickly.

All the boys continued showing self-consciousness about their motions; they were able to correct themselves immediately after the teachers' quick reminders (i.e., they realized that they were stepping ipsilaterally, stopped, went back, and stepped with opposition). The boys continued throwing with forceful intention. Stage 5 was more visible as the boys showed force and distance, and their bodies' forward rotation was noticeable; in contrast, when they returned to Stage 4, it appeared that their intensity was lower.

CONCLUSIONS

This study was highlighted by the long-term observation of a group of young children who provided rich information that may be missed in studies utilizing periodic testing. The study supports Clark's (1997) suggestion that examining individual patterns of change rather than group or average data may lead to a more accurate understanding of the global process of developmental change. Smith and Thelen's (1993) findings also support the inclusion of variability and individual differences as part of the data. The analysis of the data is tedious and a long process, but an understanding of the developmental process of change in throwing gained by using this approach is highly rewarding.

This study demonstrated that development from a close-up view is non-linear, highly variable, context sensitive, function driven and emergent from the interaction of the body with its surrounding (Thelen & Smith, 1994). The variability observed was the result of exposure to different activities, their changes in body awareness, peer and teachers interaction, and motivations or intentions for actions. Although all these children began in the program at different times, had different individual characteristics, and showed tremendous variability between and among trials, all of them showed progress in the development of the throwing pattern after receiving instruction, especially after the first year of instruction.

Instruction can perturb the system and initially may have created more variability, but variability seems to represent a search for new forms of movements, allowing the child's movements to progress toward more mature forms. Variability was daily and even within the same task and conditions; the range of possibilities observed was enormous. However, all children showed progress and increasingly reduced the number of throws in lower stages and increased the number of throws in higher stages, independent of the children's individual characteristics.

Although children seemed to have throwing patterns that are more often used, the individual variability between trials can be enormous (see Figures 1-6). Children vary their throwing patterns even after having a session in which they performed all of the throws at one stage. Observing daily changes in children's throwing patterns creates awareness about expected individual variability in young children's movements. Children can vary their movements from the early stages to the more advanced forms in one session. This information reminds us of the importance of exposure to movement experiences in the younger years when the system seems so flexible to accommodate, expand, and explore the best solution to the movement problems faced, thus creating a repertory of movement and movement combinations. These findings seem to support Langendorfer's (1990) proposition that throughout the developmental course of a skill, degrees of freedom are expanded until a maximal number are available and able to be coordinated.

During the first year of this study, none of the children, who were 2-5 years of age, performed a Stage 5 throw. After the third semester of instruction, and approximately 260 or more trials per child, the boys performed some throws at Stage 5. None of the girls performed at Stage 5 during the time of this study. However, it is important to keep in mind that overall the girls were younger than the boys, and for different motivational issues, did an average of 256 less throws than the boys did. The authors believe that, given more time, the girls would have reached the same levels as the boys.

Stage 2 throwing, which involved a block rotation of the trunk with an all-out force, was mostly observed in the throw trials of the boys, and very rarely in the girls. Maybe the girls needed to use more force or to go through this action of block rotation to then use some rotation in more advanced forms. It was also noticed that girls did not throw using all of their force; thus, they seemed to want to control the amount of force they used. Maybe this is the reason why they rarely performed at Stage 2. There were more Stage 3 performances in their trials than for the boys, where accuracy, stability and speed are more easily controlled. In addition, it was noticed that at some point in their development, the girls in this study began to avoid throwing activities and enjoyed them again showing it by their smiling faces at participation time and verbal expressions in small group discussions. This aspect of the study clearly suggests that the intentions for the action play an interactive and dynamic role between gender, force, experience, and developmental levels of the skill.

These findings imply that some developmental instruction and exposure are needed to advance the development of throwing patterns. Both boys and girls benefited from instruction in throwing. Neither boys nor girls in this study achieved stability at the most mature or more efficient form of throwing (although boys still showed some Stage 5 in their throws). Instruction and practice seems to be a key factor for continued development of the throwing pattern. This supports the findings by Halverson, Roberton, Safrit & Roberts, (1977); Halverson and Roberton (1979), Luedke (1980); indicating that instruction plays a significant role in the development of throwing patterns in young children. This study also showed that development of mature throwing patterns is a slow process that requires a lot of trials in a variety of environmental conditions. Furthermore, this study showed the dynamic relationship of the multiple system interacting in the development of a motor skill. Following are more specific conclusions addressing the different themes observed in this study.

Motivation

Motivation is an important aspect of the development of overhand throw, because high motivation leads to more willingness in children to participate in physical activities (Papaioannou & Goudas, 1999; Sarrazin & Famose, 1999; Theeboom, De Knop, & Weiss, 1995). Because differences in children's motivation seem to fall along gender lines (Garcia, 1994; Roberton & Konczak, 2001), it is particularly important for teachers to understand the differences between boys' and girls' dispositions toward throwing, and to know how to motivate children so that both boys and girls can benefit from instruction. The more teachers are able to motivate boys and girls to participate, the more the children will participate, and the more opportunity teacher instruction will have to bring about improvement in children's abilities.

In our study, motivation to participate in the throwing activities was always high in boys, but during the first two semesters it was low in girls, with the exception of P1, who was highly motivated by her brother. Our observations indicate that motivation seems to be directed by and positively related to the number of throw trials. Low motivation resulted in a low number of attempts to do the task (number of throws), and high motivation resulted in a high number of throws. For instance, comparing P2 and P3 in semesters 2 and 4, when lowly motivated, P2 did 91 and P3 did 11 trials, and when highly motivated, P2 did 195 and P3 did 188 trials.

The girls initially seemed to be more motivated by a desire to please the teachers than a desire to participate in the throwing activity, and they were often distracted from the activity. Instead of showing a desire to throw, the girls showed an initial interest in order and exploring the environment, and they also showed a consistent pattern of looking for excuses to drop off the throwing activity. However, this behavior changed after the second semester and was completely absent during the fourth semester. Conversely, the boys were highly motivated during the whole study; they did not drop off the activity, and they liked to demonstrate force. Their motivation reached such high levels that it was hard for them to listen; they were very anxious to get to the balls. The targets thrilled them and they wanted to hit them. In fact, during the first two semesters, this motivation interfered with the teaching, since they could not hear or pay attention to the teachers, and they had a hard time following directions. However, the boys made significant changes after the third semester: they became better followers of the teachers' instruction and showed concern for how to more properly execute the skill.

Differences in girls' and boys' motivation in relation to interaction with teachers were evident as well. The girls seemed to be more interested than the boys in teacher encouragement through stickers, smiles, and interaction with the teacher in general; even only eye contact with the teacher appeared to be reassuring to them. Meanwhile, the boys seemed to be more motivated by the context (targets, balls, and sound). Boys judged their performance by their ability to hit the targets and tell the teacher and others about their success. In contrast to the girls, the boys were initially very vocal in their attempts to gain the teachers' attention.

It is clear that the teacher became a fundamental part of the process as children at this young age started to learn the fundamental skills. This has a great implication for people working with children at early ages if they are not aware of this important fact. When motivation is high, more repetitions of the movement are done. High motivation is not an indication of high performance; but high motivation resulted in more trials (practice time). Therefore, teachers have a great opportunity to affect children's motor skill development if motivation is high.

Body Awareness

Body awareness is another important aspect of the development of children's overhand throw. In our study, the girls and boys initially were not aware of their body motions. The girls appeared not to have awareness of leg, trunk, and arm motion, whereas the boys seemed to have some general awareness of the arm motion, but not of the leg or trunk. Their initial process of developing awareness was done more by watching other children than by following the teacher's instruction. Both boys and girls changed significantly after the third semester, during which instruction appeared to have an impact on their learning.

Initially, the children started throwing in their own natural way, and, as time passed, they realized that they needed to step, move their arms in a particular way, and rotate their bodies. A sequence of events developed as they tried to adjust or control their bodies. The step is the part that appears to have had the most initial impact on their learning. They went from not stepping to step-straddling and staying in the position and throwing, to taking small steps, to changing back and forth between small and big steps, to changing back and forth from ipsilateral to contralateral steps. Finally, during the fourth semester, more stability on contralateral steps was observed in both boys and girls.

The arm motion was very difficult for the girls to control. They became aware that they needed to bring their arm back after the third semester; they chose, as a preferred motion, to bring their arm up backward as the initial motion, and the throw looked like a push. The boys had a more lateral initial backward motion, even though they did not know how to explain what their arm was doing. They became more aware and showed consistency in what their bodies did and what they said after the third semester; this was more evident during the fourth semester. Body rotation was observed only with the boys as they reached Stage 5; only one boy showed evidence of awareness of body rotation as he indicated and performed it.

The development of arm and leg motion awareness appears to start by first copying others, and later by paying more attention to the teacher's instruction and demonstration. The use of visual aids and touch play an important role in the development of awareness of what the body parts are supposed to do. This is important to realize because high body awareness of the pattern, which was facilitated by these visual aids and touch in our study, increased the ability of the children to self-correct themselves and to further assimilate teacher feedback.

Children started talking about their body motion in the first semester. But it was during the third semester that what they said started matching what they did. After the third semester, they also had a greater understanding of teacher corrective feedback; children were able to quickly correct themselves. Thus, it seems that high body awareness and high motivation are the ideal conditions for children to learn the fundamental skill of throwing. When children have low or no body awareness, their performance is less predictable, as if it occurred by chance.

The children in this study demonstrate that, independent of their entry level of performance, as they became aware of their bodies, they passed through a period of freezing their body parts, thus controlling and slowing their motion. Then, they moved with hesitation (too big or too little steps), until they tune their actions and can reproduce the motion in a natural way with a sound mechanical pattern. Yet, just going through the motion with a general idea, without body awareness, seems to be helpful for later development of the skill. This was evidenced by the performance of the boys in the study, as they all showed mature forms at some point during the study and at the beginning had little awareness of what their bodies were supposed to do.

Thus, the influence of instruction in instilling awareness in young children appears to go from a phase in which teaching is not clearly reaching children, to a transition phase of understanding and not understanding, to a clear understanding of what the teacher means. This process plays a significant part in children's improvement of motor skills. The development of the throwing pattern appears to be the result of a symbiotic relationship between the child's motivation, body awareness, instruction, and the context of the activity.

The Learning Context

The learning context is a key aspect for teachers to understand how young children develop the overhand throw. Rather than progressing through the stages in a linear fashion, the girls and boys in this study moved not only to nonadjacent stages, but also back and forth among stages. This variation is not an indication of failure on the part of the students or the teachers; it is apparently an inevitable part of the learning process.

The girls initially started shifting back and forth from Stage 1 to 3, and later they shifted among Stages 1, 3, and 4. Finally, they tended to find stability between stages 3 and 4. They skipped Stage 2 and did not show Stage 5. Boys, on the other hand, initially started to shift among Stages 1, 2, and 4. Later they shifted among Stages 1, 2, 3, and 4. Finally, they tended to stabilize in Stages 4 and 5. Stage 3 was the least visited stage for the boys.

The arm motions observed in the girls varied a great deal: they consisted of a simple drop of the ball with almost no arm motion, a throw with the arm moved up and elbow out, a twisted wrist motion, an underhand motion, a side arm motion, a throw with two hands, a throw with the elbow up to the side, a hand to chin motion, a half underhand back swing with arm up, and an underhand back swing. The boys showed more lateral swings, moved the whole body with the arm, moved the arm up and back, and used an underhand halfway backward swing or an underhand back swing.

In body rotation, only boys were observed showing rotation of the trunk before the action of the throwing arm. The step is the part that appears to have had the most initial variation in children's learning of the skill. They went from not stepping to step-straddling and staying in the position and throwing, to taking small steps, to changing back and forth between small and big steps, to changing back and forth from ipsilateral to contralateral steps. During the fourth semester, variation was reduced to a more stable pattern in both boys and girls.

This study shows that variation is good and should be expected to happen, because children will eventually pass the critical point of becoming aware, and learning of the skill will later start to stabilize.

SUMMARY

This study qualitatively examined how young children change their throwing patterns on daily or weekly bases as compared to changes over long periods of time. More specifically, this study tested the linearity in the sequential development of the throwing skill, using the Total Body Approach (Haubenstricker, Branta & Seefeldt, 1983) and asked what aspects involving the individuals and the environment affect developmental changes in the throwing sequence. The participants were six randomly selected children (three boys and three girls, whose ages ranged from 1 year, 9 months to 5 years) who were involved in an instructional motor skill program. All throws performed during instructional and testing time were videotaped and analyzed. In addition, field notes describing in detail the actions and interactions among participants in the study were taken during instructional and testing times.

This study demonstrated that the development of throwing is not linear, is highly variable and emerges from the interaction of the body, the intentions for the action, the motivational drives of the participants, and the context of the task. One of the unique features of this study was the micro-level of analysis provided by the frequent observations, which allowed the investigators to capture weekly variations in the development of the throwing skill.

We observed that instruction plays a critical role in the learning and development of this particular skill. Instruction can create variability. However, over the long term, instruction seems to facilitate the development of more mature patterns. Variability may be a natural response in the search for new forms of movements, allowing the children to fine tune within their body capabilities, contextual, motivational issues, and task constraints. However, all children, independent of their individual characteristics, showed a great deal of progress. For instance, P1, P2, P3, and P6 are excellent examples of the incredible possibilities younger children have when they are exposed to developmental instruction.

Furthermore, this study also showed that the development of the mature throwing patterns is a long-term process requiring considerable practice in a variety of environmental conditions. It also requires understanding the interaction between the motivational, body awareness, and learning context. These emerged as common threads in all children and throughout the whole study, and they changed as time, exposure to instruction, practice and experience in throwing skills increased. Motivation was an important aspect of the development of the overhand throw because it led to more practice of the task and a willingness of the children to incorporate teachers' instruction into the task, therefore bringing improvement in children's abilities. However, in this study, boys and girls had different levels of motivation, and they were motivated by different conditions. Since motivation seems to fall along gender lines, it is important for teachers to understand the differences between boys and girls and to find out how to motivate children so that both boys and girls can benefit from instruction.

Body awareness was an important aspect of the development of children's overhand throw and highly related to motivation. Young children came into this study with little or no awareness of their body motions. Thus, it was very difficult for them to incorporate the teacher's instructional information. However, instruction and exposure, together with visual observation of movements, or visual references, seems to initiate the development of awareness. The influence of instruction in instilling awareness of the body's movements in young children plays a significant part in children's improvement of motor skills. Increased body awareness allowed children to more easily incorporate instruction and feedback that in turn gives them the ability to self-monitor and self-correct their body movement.

Learning context was another key theme identified in this study. It refers to the aspects of the learning environment, such as instruction, peers, and the context of the task that created changes in the throwing motion. Several aspects were observed that affected the children's throwing movements, for instance the observation of peers, the setting of the activity, the teacher interaction and modeling, and static vs. dynamic tasks. All of these aspects created variability in children's throwing motion.

In conclusion, this study showed that the development of the throwing pattern was highly variable and that there was an interdependent relationship among motivation, body awareness, and learning context. Children moved to adjacent and nonadjacent stages, and they moved back and forth among stages. This variation appeared to be an inevitable part of the learning process and was not an indication of failure on the part of the children or the teachers. On the contrary, variation appeared to be a positive indicator of progress and should be expected in the developmental process. Variation allowed motor development and exploration of movement possibilities to occur so that children can fine-tune their movements toward more advanced and stable forms of throwing.

REFERENCES

Clark, J. E. (1997). A dynamical system perspective on the development of complex adaptive skills. In C. Dent-Read & P. Zukow-Goldring (Eds.), *Evolving Explanations of Development: Ecological Approach to Organism-Environment Systems* (pp. 383-406). Washington, DC: American Psychological Association.

Garcia, C. (1994). Gender differences in young children's interactions when learning fundamental motor skills. *Research Quarterly for Exercise and Sport, 65*, 213-225.

Halverson, L. E., & Roberton, M. A. (1979). The effects of instruction on overhand throwing development in children. In G. Roberts & K. Newell (Eds.), *Psychology of Motor Behavior and Sport-1978* (pp. 258-269). Champaign, IL.: Human Kinetics.

Halverson, L. E., Roberton, M. A., Safrit, M.J., & Roberts, T. W. (1977). Effect of guided practice on overhand-throw ball velocities of kindergarten children. *Research Quarterly, 48*, 311-318.

Haubenstricker, J., Branta, C., & Seefeldt, V. (1983). *Preliminary validation of the developmental sequences for throwing and catching.* Paper presented at the Annual Conference of the North American Society for the Psychology of Sport and Physical Activity. East Lansing, MI.

Inhelder, B. (1971). Criteria of the stages of mental development. In J. Tanner & B. Inhelder (Eds.), *Discussions on Child Development* (pp. 75-107). New York: International University Press.

Kohlberg, L. (1963). The development of children's orientations toward a moral order. I. Sequence in the development of moral thought. *Vita Humana, 6*, 11-33.

Langendorfer, S. (1990). Motor task goal as a constraint on developmental status. In J.E. Clark and J.H. Humphrey (Eds.) *Advances in Motor Development Research, 3,* 16-28.

Luedke, G. C. (1980). *Range of motion as the focus of teaching the overhand throwing pattern to children.* Unpublished doctoral dissertation, Bloomington IN: Indiana University.

Papaioannou, A. & Goudas, M. (1999). Motivational climate of the physical education class. In Auweele, Y.V., Bakker, F., Biddle, S., Durand, M., & Seiler, R.(Eds.), *Psychology for Physical Educators* (pp. 51-68). Champaign, IL: Human Kinetics.

Roberton, M. A. (1977). Stability of stage categorizations across trials: Implications for the stages theory of overarm throw development. *Journal of Human Movement Studies, 3,* 49-59.

Roberton, M. A. (1978). Longitudinal evidence for developmental stages in the forceful overarm throw. *Journal of Human Movement Studies, 4,* 167-175.

Roberton, M.A. (1982). Describing "stages" within and across motor tasks. In J. A. S. Kelso & J. E. Clark (Eds.), *The Development of Movement Control and Coordination* (pp. 293-317). New York: John Wiley & Sons.

Roberton, M.A. & Konczak, J. (2001). Predicting children's overarm throw ball velocities from their developmental levels in throwing. *Research Quarterly for Exercise and Sport, 72,* 91-103.

Sarrazin, P. & Famose, J.P. (1999). Children's goals and motivation in physical education. In Auweele, Y.V., Bakker, F., Biddle, S., Durand, M., Seiler, R.(Eds.), *Psychology for Physical Educators* (pp. 27-50). Champaign, IL: Human Kinetics.

Seefeldt, V., & Haubenstricker, J. (1976). *Developmental sequence of throwing* (rev. ed.). Unpublished manuscript, Michigan State University, East Lansing, MI.

Seefeldt, V., & Haubenstricker, J. (1982). Patterns, phases, or stages: An analytical model for the study of developmental movement. In J. A. S. Kelso & J. E. Clark (Eds.), (pp. 309-318). *The Development of Movement Control and Coordination.* (pp. 309-318). New York: John Wiley & Sons.

Seefeldt, V., Reuschlein, P., & Vogel, P. (1972). *Sequencing motor skills within the physical education curriculum.* Paper presented at the Annual Conference of the American Association for Health, Physical Education, and Recreation, Houston.

Smith, L., & Thelen, E. (1993). *A dynamical system approach to development: Applications.* Cambridge, MA: MIT Press.

Theeboom, M., De Knop, P.D., & Weiss, M.R. (1995). Motivational climate, psychological responses, and motor skill development in children's sport: A field-based intervention study. *Journal of Sport*

Psychology, 17, 294-311.

Thelen, E., & Smith, L. (1994). *A dynamical system approach to the development of cognition and action*. Cambridge, MA: MIT Press.

Turiel, E. (1969). Developmental process in the child's moral thinking. In P. Mussen. J. Langer & M. Covington (Eds.). *Trends and issues in developmental psychology* (pp. 92-133). New York: Holt, Rinehart & Winston.

Wild, M. (1938). The behavior pattern of throwing and some observations concerning its course of development in children. *Research Quarterly, 9*, 20-24.

5

THE INFLUENCE OF INSTRUCTION ON THE DEVELOPMENT OF CATCHING IN YOUNG CHILDREN

Jacqueline D. Goodway
Mary E. Rudisill
Nadia C. Valentini

ABSTRACT

The purpose of this study was to examine the nature of change in the components of catching resulting from instruction. Two independent motor skill interventions, using different instructional approaches, were used to investigate: (1) whether the interventions resulted in significant changes in catching performance from pre-to post-intervention, and (2) what elements of catching form changed as a result of the intervention. The participants included disadvantaged preschool (Intervention 1) and developmentally delayed kindergarten (Intervention 2) children. The results showed positive significant pre-to post-intervention changes in the components of catching performance as compared to control groups. Different patterns of change in the elements of catching form were found for Intervention 1 and 2. It was concluded that environmental constraints had a strong influence on the pattern of emergence of catching behaviors.

Fundamental motor skills (FMS) are commonly considered the building blocks to more advanced movement skills and specific sport skills (Gabbard, 2000, Haywood & Getchell, 2001, Payne & Isaacs, 2001). Despite public perception, these skills do not naturally "emerge", rather are the result of many factors that influence the child's motor skill development (Gabbard, 2000; Haywood & Getchell, 2001; Wickstrom, 1983). Newell (1984, 1986) suggests that motor skill performance is based upon the interaction between constraints from the *task*, the *organism*, and the *environment*. He recommends that developmental researchers consider a constraints perspective in the study of fundamental motor skill development. This approach would suggest that fundamental motor skills emerge within a system consisting of a task, performed by a mover, in a specific environment. The type of task the child is asked to complete will influence the performance of the skill. For example, catching with one hand as opposed to two hands results in a very different pattern of movement. There are also many factors that are inherent in the organism, namely the learner, which will influence motor skill performance. For example, motivation, types of experiences, neurological development, and fine motor control are just a few of these many factors. The environment is the third area acting as a constraint on performance. Environmental considerations include factors such as equipment and instructional strategies. For example, catching a beach ball will result in a different motor pattern than catching a bean bag. This study will examine the task of two-handed catching from a constraints perspective. The review of the literature will consider issues related to the task of catching, the learner, and the environment in order to better understand how fundamental motor skills, specifically catching, develop from a constraints perspective.

Task of Catching

Catching has been defined as the action of bringing an airborne object under control using the hands and arms (Payne & Isaacs, 2001) or a coincident timing task that involves the complex interplay of coordinating visual information and motor behavior to a single point of interception (Gabbard, 2000). The goal of catching is to retain possession of the object one catches (Haywood & Getchell, 2001).

A number of researchers have outlined the emergence of catching behaviors across time, concluding that as children mature, their ability to proficiently catch a ball improves (Deach, 1950; Gutteridege, 1939; Haubenstricker, Branta & Seefeldt, 1983; Kay, 1970; Strohmeyer, Williams, & Schaub-George, 1991). First attempts at catching an arial ball are typified by a more passive approach with the child trapping the ball against the body (Haubenstricker et al., 1983; Kay, 1970; Strohmeyer et al., 1991). Deach (1950) found that novice four-year-old catchers turned their head away from the ball, closed their eyes, and leaned away from the ball. The typical young catcher in Deach's (1950) study presented the arms in front of the body acting as a scoop for the ball. Kay (1970) found that two-year-old children had no general strategy for catching a ball and demonstrated delayed reactions. By age five, children began to demonstrate limited ability to anticipate the flight characteristics of the ball and retain control of the ball with poor timing and coordination (Kay, 1970).

As the child learns to catch, the more skilled learner responds with a series of coordinated movements involving highly precise forms of spatial adjustment and coordinative action (Haubenstricker et al., 1983; Kay, 1970; Strohmeyer et al., 1991). Although many aspects of mature catching behavior are related to the specific catching task, Wickstrom (1983) indicated that in general moving the hands into an effective position to receive the ball, and grasping and controlling the ball with the hands are two characteristics of a mature catcher. Kay (1970) found that mature catchers, by age 15, could precisely predict the flight characteristics of the ball and successfully retain control of objects in varying spatial orientations. Bruce's (1966) study of 480 children among grades 2, 4, and 6 found that unlike younger children, sixth-grade children were capable of successfully catching a ball projected at varying velocities. Hellweg (1972) found that successful catchers appeared to track the ball until it was contacted, whereas unsuccessful catchers closed their eyes prior to contact. In their textbooks in motor development, Haywood and Getchell (2001) and Payne and Isaacs (2001) concluded that proficient catching behavior is exemplified by three behaviors: (1) being able to absorb the force of the ball by "giving" with the arms and hands, (2) being able to move the body in space to orient the body to ball flight, and (3) having adjustable position of hands dependent on the location of the ball being caught.

Two studies have proposed developmental sequences for catching behavior. The study by Haubenstricker et al. (1983) used a mixed longitudinal sample of children to identify developmental sequences of catching. This study used a total body approach identifying five stages of catching behavior. Stage 1 of the developmental sequence portrays a child with a delayed reaction to the ball and an attempt (often unsuccessful) to secure the ball against the chest using the arms. In contrast, the mature (stage 5) stage of catching was exemplified by being able to catch the ball with hands only and move the body to the spatial characteristics of the ball. A second study that suggested developmental sequences was conducted by Strohmeyer and colleagues (1991). They used Roberton's (1977, 1978) component approach to identify catching sequences and examine task constraints on catching performance. The hypothesized catching sequences consisted of three levels of the hand component, four levels of the body component, three levels of the preparation arm component, and five levels of the reception arm component. This study conducted a prelongitudinal screening (Roberton, Williams, & Langendorfer, 1980) of the catching performance (three catching conditions) of 72, 5-12 year-old subjects. Data evidenced that the three-level developmental sequence for the hand component was valid. The four-level body component was revised to three levels and validated to meet the Roberton et al. (1980) criterion for developmental sequences. However, the sequences for the arm component did not meet the criteria outlined for developmental sequences (Strohmeyer et al., 1991). The authors suggested combining the two arm components, which was later adopted by Haywood and Getchell in 2001.

In summary, the literature on catching indicates that there are developmental sequences for catching performance (Haubenstricker et al., 1983; Strohmeyer et al., 1991). It is also possible to identify the typical characteristics of both novice catchers and skilled catchers (Bruce, 1966; Deach, 1950; Haubenstricker et al.,1983; Hellweg, 1972; Kay, 1970; Strohmeyer et al., 1991).

The Learner

Newell (1984, 1986) suggests that it is critical to consider constraints imposed by the learner in the development of fundamental motor skills. From a developmental constraints perspective, it is important to examine the motor skill pattern demonstrated relative to the participants being studied. The populations of interest in the present studies are those young children identified as disadvantaged and/or motorically delayed young children. Clearly, from an organismic standpoint there may be many factors in these children's lives that will constrain the development of motor skills. For example, disadvantaged children have been found to demonstrate developmental delays in object control and locomotor skills (Goodway-Shiebler, 1994; Hamilton, Goodway, & Haubenstricker, 1999). Although these children demonstrated developmental delays at the start, research has shown that systematic intervention will result in substantial improvements to fundamental motor skill performance (Goodway-Shiebler, 1994; Hamilton, Goodway, & Haubenstricker, 1999; Valentini, 1997, 1999). Several studies (Goodway-Shiebler, 1994; Hamilton, Goodway & Haubenstricker, 1999; Valentini, 1997, 1999) have shown that young disadvantaged and/or delayed children have improved from below the 20th percentile to above the 75th percentile on locomotor and/or object control skills as a result of systematic instruction. This might suggest that the children were "ready to learn" but had not received the type of instruction and practice necessary to improve fundamental motor skill performance. Thus, appropriate practice would be critically important in intervening with these populations.

Environment

As indicated previously, constraints in the environment also influence motor skill performance. Practitioners and researchers find these environmental factors to be of utmost importance in promoting motor skill development in children. The essence of good instruction is the manipulation of the environment to facilitate motor skill learning. For example, a teacher may manipulate the size of the ball or the distance apart in a partner catching activity to individualize skill practice. There is a need to better understand the types of strategies and tasks that will promote motor skill development in young children.

Halverson (1963) suggested that we need to carefully develop "environmental situations in which the child is challenged enough to grow in motor maturity and skill, but not frustrated by over challenge." There have been a number of studies which have attempted to do this and intervene in the motor skill development of young children. These motor skill interventions have taken a variety of approaches. Williams (1992) found that seven days of varied instruction promoted the performance of one-handed ball catching in an eight-year-old child. Goodway-Shiebler (1994) and Kelly, Dagger, and Walkley (1989) utilized a direct-instruction approach with at

risk and typically developing preschoolers to positively influence fundamental motor skill (FMS) development. Both studies found significant pre-
and post-intervention differences in object control and locomotor skills resulting from the direct instruction approach. Hamilton, Goodway, and
Haubenstricker (1999) used parent-assisted instruction to promote development of FMS in at risk preschoolers. Hamilton et al. concluded that an
instructional program using parents as instructional assistants could bring
about significant changes in object control skills from pre- to post-intervention. Valentini (1997, 1999) used student-directed instructional approaches, resulting in significant improvements in FMS development with
motorically delayed kindergarten children. In this study, students were free
to chose among a variety of developmentally appropriate tasks and were
able to set the level of task difficulty and the amount of time spent at each
activity. All of these studies demonstrate that improvements in motor skill
development were a product of instruction and that it was not a function of
time (Goodway-Shiebler, 1994; Hamilton, Goodway, & Haubenstricker,
1999; Valentini, 1997, 1999; Williams, 1992).

　　　These studies provide strong support for the positive changes in motor
skill development, which resulted from instruction. However, it is not clear
from these data the nature of the changes that occurred within the specific
patterns of the fundamental motor skills examined. For example, what elements of form in a skill were influenced by the instruction provided, and
did children who experienced the same or different instruction demonstrate
similar patterns of developmental change in motor skills? Such information would be of great value to practitioners as they develop instructional
strategies and tasks for young children. More specific data is required about
the nature of change in FMS performance if practitioners are to correctly
sequence instructional tasks, provide developmentally appropriate feedback, and guide the teaching-learning process.

　　　The purpose of this study was to examine the nature of change in the
motor skill patterns of catching, resulting from instruction. Two independent motor skill interventions, using different instructional approaches were
used to investigate this purpose. The following questions were asked: (1)
Did the motor skill intervention result in significant changes in catching
performance from pre- to post-intervention? (2) What elements of catching
form changed as a result of Intervention 1 or Intervention 2? It was hypothesized that both interventions would bring about significant change in catching performance. It was also hypothesized that the environment (type of intervention) would constrain the emergence of specific elements of catching form.

METHODS

　　　Catching data from two intervention studies were used to determine
the influence of instruction on the elements of catching form. The first

study (Intervention 1) was part of a larger project that examined the influence of a 12-week motor skill intervention on 12 FMS of disadvantaged preschool children. The second study (Intervention 2) examined the influence of a 12-week motor skill intervention on 12 FMS of kindergarten children identified as developmentally delayed in motor skills.

Participants

Intervention 1. Participants (n = 59) were chosen from a compensatory pre-kindergarten program in a large urban midwestern school district. The pre-kindergarten served African American, four-year-old children who were identified as at-risk of becoming educationally disadvantaged and/or developmentally delayed. Participants were enrolled in four intact classes within this program. Eligibility for the program was based on identification of state defined at-risk factors (Office of Compensatory Programs, 1991a) and a composite score on an objective-referenced preschool readiness test (Office of Compensatory Programs, 1991b). The children selected for the program were those with the lowest preschool readiness test score and the greatest number of risk factors. Once identified, the children participated in a half-day compensatory pre-kindergarten program. Informed consent was obtained for all participants.

Two of the four intact classes were identified as the Motor Skill Intervention (MSI-1) group with the remaining two classes constituting the Control-1 group. There were 15 girls and 16 boys in the MSI-1 group; and 14 girls and 14 boys in the Control-1 group. The participants in the Control-1 group (n = 28) represented a suitable comparison group for the MSI-1 group (n = 31), because (a) the eligibility requirements for the prekindergarten program were the same for all children, (b) the children in the Control-1 group were selected from the same community with the same types of risk factors and family demographics, and (c) teachers and parents reported that children from the MSI-1 and Control-1 groups were drawn from the same community.

Intervention 2. The eligible participants of this study originally included 331 kindergarten children from an early education center located in a small urban city in the Southern region of the United States. Forty participants, with the lowest gross motor functioning, were selected to participate in a motor skill intervention program (MSI-2 group). Selection was based upon individual scores on the Test of Gross Motor Development (TGMD) by Ulrich (1985). The MSI-2 group was randomly split into two separate groups consisting of 20 students per class. A second group of children was selected as a Control-2 group (n = 20). In order to identify a suitable comparison group, similarly low-motor functioning children were selected for the Control-2 group. There were 25 girls and 15 boys in the MSI-2 group; and 15 girls and 5 boys in the Control-2 group. Informed consent for the study was obtained. Table 1 provides participant demographic information for both Interventions 1 and 2.

Design and Implementation of the Motor Skill Interventions

Both motor skill interventions were developed via a formal and informal process of program design. Teachers, developmentalists, administrators, and parents of children were part of this process. The motor skill interventions were designed to provide developmentally appropriate instruction and meaningful activities. For the purpose of brevity, a brief overview of each of the interventions will be supplied. Then, specific content relative to the task of catching will be provided.

Table 1
Demographic Information for the Participants
by Group and Intervention

Variable	Group	%	M	SD
Intervention 1				
Age (years)	MSI-1		4.74	0.29
	C-1		4.74	0.33
Risk Factors	MSI-1		5.29	1.29
	C-1		5.79	2.13
Preschool Readiness				
Test Score (0-20)	MSI-1		6.03	4.05
	C-1		4.18	2.16
Receive Welfare	MSI-1	71		
	C-1	89		
Intervention 2				
Age (years)	MSI-2		5.43	0.56
	C-2		5.65	0.49
Free/ Reduced Lunch Program				
	MSI-2	60		
	C-2	40		
Pre-TGMD Scores				
Locomotor (0-26)	MSI-2		5.01	1.41
	C-2		7.05	1.73
Object Control (0-19)				
	MSI-2		8.85	2.03
	C-2		8.95	1.82

Note: MSI-1 = Motor Skill Intervention-1 (n=31), C-1 = Control-1 Group (n=28), MSI-2 = Motor Skill Intervention-2 Group (n=40), and C-2 = Control-2 Group (n=20).

Intervention 1. A motor skill intervention (MSI-1) was developed from a preschool physical education curriculum designed for all preschool students (Dummer, Connor-Kuntz, & Goodway, 1995). The intervention goals were developed via formal and informal processes of program design that took place over the period of one school year involving teachers, paraprofessionals, and administrators. The goal of the MSI-1 was to demonstrate improvement in the performance of FMS. Eight skills were selected for instruction. The number of skills that were selected was based upon the philosophy of exposing the children to a variety of introductory experiences in skills that were considered most critical to their ability to engage in games and sports. Participants were taught the mature elements of form, but given their age, mastery of all elements of form were not necessarily expected. This philosophy reflects data on young children (Seefeldt & Haubenstricker, 1982) indicating mature performance of FMS is not typical for preschool children. Instructional time for skill development was allocated as follows: (a) hopping and galloping–50 minutes, (b) jumping–80 minutes, (c) ball bouncing–90 minutes, (d) striking–100 minutes, (e) kicking–110 minutes, and (f) catching and throwing–120 minutes.

The MSI-1 consisted of 24 instructional sessions during a 12-week period. Each instructional session lasted 45 minutes and was comprised of (a) one 10-minute period of sustained activity such as running games and moving to music, (b) three 10-minute periods of skill instruction during which time each group rotated to different skill stations, and (c) a three-minute closure of the lesson plan emphasizing key components of the skills learned that day. Two minutes were allowed for transition time. At each of the three skill stations, five to six children worked with the instructor (first author, teacher, or paraprofessional) in a variety (three to four) of activities. Children rotated around all three skill stations during the lesson experiencing instruction from each instructor. For example, at a catching station the children might tap a balloon in the air and catch it, toss a bean bag and catch, and catch a tossed eight-inch foam ball. All children had their own equipment. The first author was the lead teacher for the intervention. Prior to each instructional session, the first author, teacher, and paraprofessional went over the lesson plan for the day and discussed key elements of instruction (cue words, relevant feedback, etc.) At the end of the lesson, the investigator reviewed the activities with the teachers and made instructional decisions for the next lesson based on their feedback from that lesson. For a detailed description of the intervention and lesson plans, refer to Goodway-Shiebler (1994).

The instructional activities specific to catching consisted of twelve, 10-min instructional sessions resulting in 120 minutes of catching instruction. Catching activities were developed from an array of developmental tasks that reflected a general task analysis of the skill of catching. For example, children progressed from catching a rolling ball, to catching a slow moving object such as a balloon, to catching a tossed bean bag and large ball. After each instructional period, the teachers and investigator identified the next appropriate level of catching tasks for the children.

The subjects in the Control-1 group received the regular pre-kindergarten program, which did not include physical education instruction. The first author spent an equal amount of time (one hour, two times per week) with the MSI-1 and Control-1 groups during the 12-week period. Time spent with the Control-1 group included varied activities such as assisting with centers (blocks, sand, science, etc.) or reading in the classroom.

Intervention 2. A three-step procedure was implemented to develop the Motor Skill Intervention 2 (MSI-2), which was designed to promote mastery motivation (Ames,1992; Theeboom, Knop, & Weiss, 1995; Valentini, 1997). The first step involved developing strategies consistent with a mastery motivational approach along six instructional dimensions (Ames, 1992; Valentini, Rudisill, & Goodway, 1999; Valentini, 1997). The MSI-2 was centered around the following premises: 1) variety of activities; 2) opportunity to chose tasks; 3) participant-established rules; 4) shared decision making between the participant and teacher; 5) self-paced, independent practice, and; 6) ongoing private evaluation of progress and effort. For a detailed description of the intervention strategies and lesson plans, refer to Valentini (1997, 1999). Step two incorporated this motivational approach into strategic motor skill intervention lesson plans for each daily instructional period. These lesson plans were consistent with a mastery motivational structure. Step three incorporated an ongoing assessment of program effectiveness and participant progress.

The MSI-2 program consisted of 24 sessions during a 12-week period (two per week) with a total instructional time of 840 minutes. Each session lasted 35 minutes, consisting of a three-minute introduction, 30-minute skill instruction, and two-minute closure. The introduction consisted of an explanation of the critical elements of the skills the students would perform that day. Then, the students were free to participate in the seven or eight skill activity centers that were established for the day. During the 30 minutes of skill activity, the students could move freely from center to center. The closure reinforced the critical elements of the skills identified during the introduction. The instruction and closure time was 115 minutes (five minutes for each session for 23 lessons). The total time of skill practice was 690 minutes (30 minutes for each session for 23 lessons), averaging approximately 60 minutes of practice for each of the 12 (run, hop, gallop, leap, jump, slide, skip, catch, throw, bounce, kick, strike) FMS. The last day of the intervention program was spent in celebration activities. The second and third authors were the lead teachers for this intervention. There was a 20 to 2 student to teacher ratio (2 groups of 20 students with each group meeting twice per week).

The 60 minutes of catching instruction was developed based on the children's initial TGMD analysis. Similar to Intervention 1, the children were involved in a variety of catching tasks (rolling ball, tossed ball, self-toss, etc.) with an array of different objects (beanbags, varying size balls, scarves, balloons, foam balls, etc.) All children in the MSI-2 group participated in the MSI-2 intervention in addition to the mandated 30 minutes of school physical education per day. The Control-2 group participated only in the mandatory 30 minutes of school physical education per day. The mandatory school physical education curriculum reflected the state curriculum with a variety of instructional goals including fundamental motor skill development. There was a 36 to 2 student to teacher ratio for physical education classes.

Instrumentation

Both Intervention 1 and Intervention 2 used the same assessment for the analysis of catching. All children were videotaped performing three trials of catching using standardized equipment and assessment protocols as per the TGMD protocol (Ulrich, 1985). The catching task for the TGMD consisted of catching a six- to eight-inch ball tossed from 15 feet away.

Component analysis of catching. A component analysis was conducted on the catching performance of all participants in both studies. The developmental sequence of catching was selected from Haywood and Getchell's (2001) motor development text. Table 2 describes the catching sequence which consists of three components: a 4-level arm component, a 3-level hand component, and a 3-level body component. The hand and body action components were those validated by Strohmeyer et al. (1991) in their study of children between 5 and 12 years of age. The arm action component was developed from a mixed longitudinal study conducted by Haubenstricker et al. (1983). All participants were evaluated on these three components of catching form via videotape analysis.

Inter-rater reliability. All authors were experienced in the developmental assessment of children. Inter-rater reliability had previously been determined between the authors. Authors one and two had a reliability coefficient of 0.88 (Goodway, Hamilton, & Rudisill, 1996) and authors two and three reported a reliability coefficient of 0.87 (Valentini, 1997).

Procedures

The procedures were the same for both studies. Children were administered the catching protocol (Ulrich, 1985) in small groups. For each study, component analyses for catching were conducted by the primary investigators using videotape analysis and notes taken during the motor skill testing.

RESULTS

The results are divided into two sections. The first section addresses the research question: (1) Did the motor skill intervention result in significant changes in catching performance from pre- to post-intervention? The second section addresses the research question: (2) What elements of catching form changed as a result of Intervention 1 or Intervention 2?

Table 2
Developmental Sequence of Two-Handed Catching

Component and Level	Description of Movement
Arm Action Component	
Level 1-Little Response.	Arms extend forward, but there is little movement to adapt to ball flight; but usually ball is trapped against chest.
Level 2-Hugging.	Arms are extended sideways to encircle the ball (hugging); ball is trapped against the chest.
Level 3-Scooping.	Arms are extended forward again but move under object (scoop); ball is trapped against the chest.
Level 4-Arms "Give".	Arms extend to meet object with the hands; arms and body "give"; ball is caught with hands.
Hand Action Component	
Level 1-Palms Up.	The palms of the hand face up.
Level 2-Palms In.	The palms of the hands face each other.
Level 3-Palms Adjusted.	The palms of the hands are adjusted to the flight and size of the oncoming object. Thumbs or little fingers are placed close together, depending on the height of the flight path.
Body Action Component	
Level 1-No Adjustment.	No adjustment of the body occurs in response to the ball's flight path.
Level 2-Awkward Adjustment.	The arms and trunk begin to move in relation to the ball's flight path but the head remains erect, creating an awkward movement to the ball. The catcher seems to be fighting to remain balanced.
Level 3-Proper Adjustment.	The feet, trunk, and arms all move to adjust to the path of the oncoming ball.

Note: From Haywood and Getchell (2001)

Changes in Catching Performance from Pre- to Post-Intervention

Several steps were undertaken to determine if there were significant changes in catching performance from pre- to post-intervention. First, a chi square analysis was conducted for each of the three components (arm, hand, body) in order to examine if there were between group (MSI and Control) differences in pre-intervention catching performance. Second, three separate (arm, hand, body) chi-square analyses were then conducted to examine between group (MSI and Control) differences following the intervention. If significant, a follow-up Contingency Coefficient was reported to indicate the strength of the relationship of the variables. The final statistical analyses were conducted to examine if within group differences occurred in catching performance from pre- to post-intervention using a Friedman test. The Friedman test was conducted on each catching component (arm, hand, body) for each group (MSI-1, Control-1, MSI-2, Control-2) resulting in six analyses. An adjusted alpha level of $p<.025$ (.05 divided by two groups) was calculated for the Friedman analyses.

Between Group Differences in Pre-Intervention 1. The three chi square analyses demonstrated that there were no statistically significant pre-intervention differences between the MSI-1 and Control-1 groups on the arm ($p=.72$), hand ($p=.55$), and body ($p=.92$) components.

Between Group Differences in Pre-Intervention 2. There were no statistically significant pre-intervention differences between the MSI-2 and Control-2 groups on the arm ($p=.36$) and hand ($p=.71$) components. It was not appropriate to calculate differences between groups for the body component because the expected cell counts for two cells were below five. However, all 60 participants, except for five, demonstrated a level 1 (no adjustment) performance. Although not statistically supported, the findings indicate that the groups demonstrated similar performance.

Between Group Differences in Post-Intervention 1. The chi-square analysis for the post-intervention arm component indicated significant differences between groups, $P^2(2, N = 59) = 25.25, p < .001$. The reported Contingency Coefficient was .55, $p < .001$. Significant differences between groups were also found for the hand component, $P^2(1, N = 59) = 13.37, p < .001$. The reported Contingency Coefficient was .43, $p < .001$. However, the expected cell counts for level 3 (hands adjustable) were below five, thus levels 2 and 3 of the hand component were combined for this chi square analysis. The combination of levels 2 and 3 were theoretically justified because four-year-old children rarely demonstrate this level of the arm component (Deach, 1950; Hellweg, 1972; Kay, 1970; Strohmeyer et al., 1991). The chi-square analysis for the body component found significant post-intervention differences between groups, $P^2(1, N = 59) = 24.31, p < .001$. The reported Contingency Coefficient was .54, $p < .001$.

Between Group Differences in Post-Intervention 2. It was not possible to conduct the chi square analyses between groups in the post-intervention arm and body components due to problems with expected cell counts below five. Significant differences between groups were found for the hand component, $P^2(1, N = 60) = 17.71, p < .001$. The reported Contingency Coefficient was .48, $p < .001$. The expected cell counts for level 1 (palms up/down) were below five, thus levels 1 and 2 (palms in) were combined in order to undertake this analysis.

Within Group Differences in Post-Intervention 1. A Friedman test was undertaken on the pre- and post-intervention ranks of the three catching components for each group separately. The MSI-1 group demonstrated significant changes in the arm component from pre- (rank = 1.13) to post-intervention (rank = 1.87), $P^2(1, N = 31) = 23.00, p < .001$. The Control-1 group did not demonstrate significant pre- (rank = 1.54) to post-intervention (rank = 1.46) changes in the arm component. Significant hand component changes were found for the MSI-1 group, $P^2(1, N = 31) = 10.00, p < .01$. The mean rank for the MSI-1 group changed from 1.34 to 1.66 across the intervention period. The Control-1 group did not demonstrate significant pre- (rank = 1.54) to post-intervention (rank = 1.46) changes in the hand component. The MSI-1 group also demonstrated significant pre- (rank = 1.27) to post-intervention (rank = 1.73) differences in the body component, $P^2(1, N = 31) = 14.00, p < .001$. The control group did not significantly change from pre- (rank = 1.55) to post-intervention (rank = 1.44) for the body component.

Within Group Differences in Post-Intervention 2. The MSI-2 group demonstrated significant changes in the arm component from pre- (rank = 1.17) to post-intervention (rank = 1.83), $P^2(1, N = 40) = 24.14, p < .001$. The Control-2 group did not significantly change from pre- (rank = 1.33) to post-intervention (rank = 1.67). In addition, significant hand component changes were found for the MSI-2 group, $P^2(1, N = 40) = 32.00, p < .001$. The mean rank for the MSI-2 group improved from 1.10 to 1.90 across the intervention period. The Control-2 group did not demonstrate significant pre- (rank = 1.38) to post-intervention (rank = 1.63) changes in the hand component. Both the MSI-2 and Control-2 groups did not significantly change from pre- to post-intervention for the body component. The ranks for pre-intervention were 1.46 for the MSI-2 group and 1.50 for the Control-2 group. The ranks for the post-intervention body component were 1.54 and 1.50 respectively.

Change in the Elements of Catching Form

The findings from the chi square and Friedman analyses indicated that a closer analysis of catching performance was warranted. In order to examine which elements of catching form changed from pre- to post-intervention, frequencies for each of the three catching components by group were calculated. Percentages were generated from each of the groups' pre- and post-intervention frequencies for arm, body, and hand catching components. Figures 1-6 graphically illustrate the percentages of participants from each group who demonstrated a specific level of a component prior to and following the intervention.

Elements of Arm Component Form from Pre- to Post-Intervention 1. The pre-intervention modal component for the MSI-1 group was level 3 (scooping), although a large number of MSI-1 participants also demonstrated hugging (level 2) behaviors (Figure 1). The Control-1 demonstrated both hugging and scooping as the modal arm action at the pre-intervention. By the post-intervention, scooping was still the modal behavior for the MSI-1 group, but a number of participants also showed the ability to catch the ball with the hands (level 4). In contrast, the Control-1 group showed little change with hugging as the modal behavior at the post-intervention.

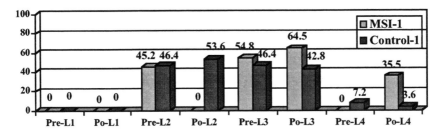

Fig. 1. Pre- and Post-Arm Component Percentages by Group for Intervention 1

Elements of Hand Component Form from Pre- to Post-Intervention 1. The majority of MSI-1 and Control-1 participants demonstrated palms-in (level 2) hand action at the pre-intervention (Figure 2). The remaining participants showed a palms-up (level 1) action. Following the intervention, more of the MSI-1 participants showed a palms-in action than prior to the intervention. The modal hand component for the Control-1 group after the intervention was level 1, with a large number of level 2 also.

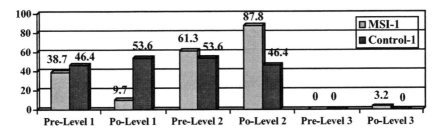

Fig. 2. Pre- and Post-Hand Component Percentages by Group for Intervention 1

Elements of Body Component Form from Pre- to Post-Intervention 1. The MSI-1 and Control-1 groups showed similar pre-intervention percentages of body actions (Figure 3). Both the MSI-1 and the Control-1 groups demonstrated level 2 (awkward adjustment) as the modal pre-intervention level. The remaining participants exhibited level 1 body action (no adjustment). Following the intervention period, all of the MSI-1 group were performing a level 2 body action. There was little body component change for the Control-1 group over the intervention period.

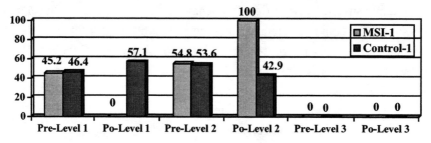

Fig. 3. Pre- and Post-Body Component Percentages by Group for Intervention 1

Elements of Arm Component Form from Pre- to Post-Intervention 2. Prior to the intervention period, all four levels of catching arm components were demonstrated by both MSI-2 and Control-2 participants (Figure 4). Following the intervention, the majority of the MSI-2 participants showed a level 4 arm action (arms give), with only a small number showing a scooping (level 3) arm action. Similarly, the Control-2 group showed some hugging (level 2) and scooping (level 3) behaviors at the post-intervention, but a larger number of level 4 (arms give) action.

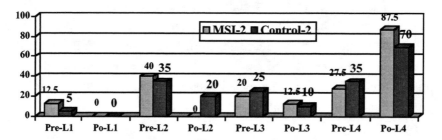

Fig. 4. Pre- and Post-Arm Component Percentages by Group for Intervention 2

Elements of Hand Component Form from Pre- to Post-Intervention 2. A substantial hand component change occurred for the MSI-2 group from the pre- to post-intervention period (Figure 5). Level 1 (palms up) hand action was widely used prior to the intervention, with a lesser number of participants demonstrating palms-in (level 2) hand action. By the end of the intervention a large number of the MSI-2 participants were able to demonstrate adjustable palms (level 3). The post-intervention modal hand component for the Control-2 group was palms-in (level 2), a change from the palms-in (level 1) pre-intervention modal component.

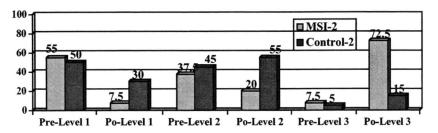

Fig. 5. Pre- and Post-Hand Component Percentages by Group for Intervention 2

Elements of Body Component Form from Pre- to Post-Intervention 2. There was little body component change for both the MSI-2 and the Control-2 group from pre- to post-intervention (Figure 6). The majority of participants demonstrated a body action of no adjustment (level 1) across the intervention period.

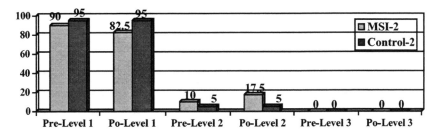

Fig. 6. Pre- and Post-Body Component Percentages by Group for Intervention 2

DISCUSSION

The purpose of this study was to examine the nature of change in the motor skill patterns of catching, resulting from two independent motor skill interventions. The following discussion will address the results of the study based upon the hypotheses. First, it was hypothesized that both interventions would bring about significant change in catching performance from pre-to post-intervention. Second, it was hypothesized that the environment (type of intervention) would constrain the emergence of specific elements of catching form.

Changes in Catching Performance from Pre- to Post-Intervention

Pre-Intervention Catching Performance. The pre-intervention catching performance of the participants in Intervention 1 and 2 reflect the catching performance described in the literature (Deach, 1950; Haubenstricker et al., 1983; Kay, 1970). The characteristics of young novice catchers in the literature and in the present studies portray a child with arms in the front of the body acting as a scoop, little visual tacking, and poor timing and coordination.

As expected, there were no differences between the MSI and control groups in the two interventions. It is logical to assume that because the MSI and control groups demonstrated comparable catching performance, similar constraints may be operating within the learner and the environment. The preschool-aged participants in Intervention 1 were identified as at risk for school failure and/or developmental delay and came from a homogeneous racial, cultural, and socioeconomic background. All participants enrolled in this compensatory program were accepted based upon the same eligibility criteria of at-risk factors and low preschool readiness scores. It is interesting to note that learner and environmental constraints acting on these children appeared to influence pre-intervention catching performance, even though motor performance was not a selection criteria in identifying these children. In contrast, participants for Intervention 2 were more heterogeneous in racial, cultural, and socioeconomic backgrounds, but selection for the study was based upon motor skill delays so the similarities in catching performance are of no surprise.

When comparing the catching characteristics of the two interventions, it is apparent that participants in Intervention 2 demonstrated more variability across the levels of the arm and hand components than those in Intervention 1. There are a number of possible constraints that may account for this finding. The children in Intervention 2 were older, had more opportunities for practice in and out of school, and came from more diverse backgrounds,whereas children in Intervention 1 were younger, had little or no opportunity to practice in and out of school, and came from similar backgrounds. The present findings in Intervention 1 and 2 support the need for early intervention with respect to enhancing the development of catching. Halverson, Roberton, and Harper (1973) suggested that it is critical to understand the child's development before designing instructional interventions. As a result of the pre-intervention data, instructional activities and strategies were developed to promote the development of catching in these children. Intervention 1 identified hand catching, tracking the ball, and moving the body to intercept the ball as instructional foci of the intervention. Intervention 2 identified a strong focus on catching with hands, along with force absorption of the ball once caught.

Changes in Pre- to Post-Intervention Arm Component. Both Intervention 1 and Intervention 2 resulted in significant pre- to post-intervention changes in the arm components. Specifically, Intervention 1 yielded notable changes in the arm component as a result of the intervention with

75% of all MSI-1 children improving at least one level. Prior to the intervention the children had been more passive recipients when the ball was tossed to them. By the end of the intervention, the MSI-1 participants were "scooping" the ball or demonstrating "arms give" while catching with hands. As a result of instruction, the children became more proactive anticipators of ball flight. Interestingly, the Control-1 group showed a slight regression in arm action over the intervention period. From observations during testing, this change may be attributed to the absence of instruction and a trial and error approach to using the arms to catch.

Intervention 2 also yielded substantial changes in the arm component with 67.5% of MSI-2 participants improving at least one level. The MSI-2 group demonstrated an attractor state of "hugging" to "arms give" across the intervention period. The Control-2 participants also demonstrated "arms-give" at the end of the intervention period, but these pre-post-intervention changes were not significantly different. It should be noted that both the MSI-2 and the Control-2 participants received daily physical education in which catching was part of the curriculum; thus, it is not surprising to see changes in both group's performance.

The environment (intervention) seemed to have a powerful influence with respect to promoting positive developmental change in arm action. Both the MSI-1 and MSI-2 children were provided with instructional activities that facilitated more advanced arm actions. For example, balloons were used to provide children with a slower moving object so they could practice reaching out and intercepting the object in the air. Cue words were systematically incorporated into instruction to emphasize the important elements of the catching skill. These cue words were reinforced throughout each instructional period. Intervention 1 reinforced "hands ready" and "reach and catch." Intervention 2 highlighted "ready hands", "soft fingers", and "bend elbows." The cuing of ready hands in both interventions facilitated arm preparation for catching as illustrated in the arm component results. In Intervention 1, "reach and catch" was also emphasized. The number of participants who exhibited "scooping" and "arms give" behaviors reflects this emphasis on anticipating ball flight. However, many of these young children were not able to absorb the force of the ball upon reception. In contrast, almost all of the MSI-2 participants were capable of absorbing the force of the ball upon reception reflecting the cue word "bend elbows."

Changes in Pre- to Post-Intervention Hand Component. Although significant, only 29% of MSI-1 participants improved one level or more in the hand component from pre- to post-intervention. The attractor state for the hand component was "palms in" (level 2) both prior to and following the intervention. However, at the end of the intervention the "palms in" hand action was a much stronger attractor state for this group. The investigators believed the modeling of hand catching, use of the cue word "ready hands", and instructional activities would bring about the desired changes in hand action in Intervention 1; however, this was not the case. The focus on "ready hands" seemed to have more influence on arm action rather than hand action. It is not clear whether instruction or a system operating within the individual children were the rate limiters in this situation. The proximodistal law of developmental direction may be one possible explanation with the hands being the last component to change. Another consideration was the children's ability to attend to all of the appropriate aspects of the task. It is possible that the children were attending more to the arm action of the skill than receiving the ball in their hands.

Unlike MSI-1, 83% of the MSI-2 group improved 1 level or more in the hand component. The majority of the MSI-2 participants shifted from "palms up" (level 1) at the pre-intervention to "palms adjusted" (level 3) by post-intervention. The Control-2 group also showed an improvement in the hand component from a modal level of "palms up" to "palms in"; however, this was not a statistically significant change. The MSI-2 results reflect the heavy emphasis placed on hands throughout the intervention. Cue words, feedback, models, and a variety of instructional tasks all highlighted the importance of hand action to successful catching performance. In contrast to Intervention 1, Intervention 2 specifically talked about "soft fingers", which may account for the greater amount of change found for the hand component in this intervention. Another explanation may be that the older children in Intervention 2 were more "ready to learn" and able to benefit from the instruction provided.

Change in Pre- to Post-Intervention Body Component. For Intervention 1, 45% of the participants showed a change of one level or more in the body component. Prior to the intervention, the participants demonstrated a combination of "no adjustment" and "awkward adjustment." After the intervention, a strong attractor state of "awkward adjustment" was exhibited by the MSI-1 participants. By the end of the intervention, it appeared that MSI-1 children could track the flight of the ball and begin to move the trunk in relation to ball flight. Again the control group showed no significant change.

Many of the instructional tasks in Intervention 1 encouraged children to attend to the path of the ball. For example, the ball was rolled along the ground and children had to position their body behind the ball to retrieve it. Another example of an activity to emphasize body adjustment was to give a child a specific verbal and visual cue as to where he or she had to move in order to receive the ball. Although there was an emphasis on proper body adjustment, the participants demonstrated "awkward adjustment" indicating an awareness of ball flight but an inability to execute the temporal aspects of adjusting the body to the path of the oncoming ball. Again, organismic constraints such as neurological development may have had an influence here.

Only 12.5% of the MSI-2 group demonstrated an improvement of one level or more exhibiting "no adjustment" for the post-intervention body component. The lack of significant change found for the body component may be associated with the testing protocol and/or the lack of instructional emphasis on this component during the intervention. In most instances, the ball was tossed directly to the child and thus did not require spatial adaptations of the child's body to the ball. Based on this limitation, it was difficult to determine whether the children were capable of "awkward" or "proper" adjustment. Furthermore, the instructional activities and cue words in the intervention did not emphasize adjusting the body to ball flight. In hindsight, it may be the participants in Intervention 2 could have accomplished proper body adjustment had the environment and the task demanded this behavior.

The Coupling of the Elements of Catching Form

These data from Intervention 1 support the emergence of a pattern of developmental coupling in the change associated with the three components of catching. The three components in Intervention 1 were coupled in the following order: Arm   Body   Hand. That is, more children (75%) improved one level or more in the arm component. The next component that changed the most was the body (45%), followed by the hand (29%). As we examined this pattern of developmental coupling, we were unsure whether this pattern was more influenced by environmental constraints (the intervention) or subsystems operating within the organism. It was interesting to note that there was less change associated with the hand component compared to the arm and body. One possible explanation is that organismic constraints drive the development of hand catching behaviors with hand catching being influenced by the cephalocaudal and proximodistal law of motor developmental. This perspective would suggest that neurological development acts as a rate limiter that restrains the influence of instruction and practice. Another perspective is that the pattern of developmental coupling is influenced by environmental constraints (the intervention provided). By analyzing these data from Intervention 2, we were better able to examine the role of constraints in the emergence of catching behaviors.

These data from Intervention 2 showed a different pattern of developmental coupling. The three components appeared to be coupled in the order of hand, arm, body. That is, hand accounted for most change (83%), followed by arm (67.5%), and then the body (12.5%). After reviewing both data sets, it was clear that environmental constraints had a strong influence on the pattern of developmental coupling. The focus of the instructional activities and feedback provided by the interventions seemed to constrain the emergence of the elements of catching form. This does not imply that environmental constraints are the only factors associated with developmental coupling, but that they appear to play a major role. Future research should examine the extent to which environmental and organismic constraints influence the emergence of catching behaviors.

CONCLUSIONS

In line with the motor skill intervention literature (Goodway-Shiebler, 1994; Hamilton et al., 1999; Kelly et al., 1989; Valentini, 1997, 1999), the present findings suggest that the two catching interventions were effective in bringing about substantial change in catching performance. Both the direct-instruction approach (Intervention 1) and the student-directed approach (Intervention 2) helped the MSI-1 and MSI-2 participants move toward the characteristics of a proficient catcher. Proficient catching performance has been described as the ability to visually track the object, adjust the hands and body position to the flight of the object, and then to absorb the force of the object by giving with the arms and hands (Haubenstricker et al., 1983; Haywood & Getchell, 2001; Hellweg, 1972; Kay, 1970; Payne & Isaacs, 2001; Wickstrom, 1983). It is clear from these findings that developmentally appropriate motor skill interventions resulted in significant improvements toward the development of catching, despite a fairly short period of instructional time spent on this skill.

The notion of instructional time is important to practitioners. As teachers develop annual physical education plans, they must assign specific amounts of instructional time to a particular motor skill. There is very little empirical support to guide teachers in making these curricular decisions. The present study suggests that in a minimal amount of instructional time, children can become fairly proficient catchers. In only 120 minutes of instruction, considerable change occurred in catching for disadvantaged four-year-old children. Based upon data from a larger study (Goodway-Shiebler, 1994), these children did not have any other opportunities to practice motor skills. Kindergarten-aged participants in the MSI-2 group received 60 minutes of catching instruction during the intervention. They also received 30 minutes of quality physical education instruction per day, which incorporated some catching activities. These findings are very promising from an early intervention perspective in that children who were disadvantaged or developmentally delayed were capable of making such progress in such a short period of time. Despite these promising findings, we caution practitioners and researchers in directly applying the instructional time used in these studies to their specific situation. The amount of time necessary for motor skill development will vary depending upon the characteristics of the children being served and the environment in which they are raised and taught.

In accordance with Newell's (1984, 1986) constraints model, the findings from this study show how the environment can constrain the emergence of catching performance. It was apparent that instructional activities, feedback and cue words shaped how catching emerged. These data have implications regarding the instruction of catching for young children. Practitioners need to recognize the importance of providing appropriate tasks, cue words, and feedback in facilitating a specific motor pattern within a skill. Specifically, practitioners need to target the behavior they desire to change, identify cue words for the behavior, design precise instructional strategies to bring about this change, and reinforce this behavior with feedback and the cue words. Future research should incorporate Newell's constraints model to further examine the relationship between the environment (instruction), the task, and organism in motor skill development.

REFERENCES

Ames, C. (1992). Achievement goals, motivational climate, and motivational processes. In G. C. Roberts (Ed.), *Motivation in sport and exercise* (pp. 167-176). Champagne, IL: Human Kinetics.

Bruce, R. D. (1966). *The effects of variation in ball trajectory upon the catching performance of elementary school children.* Unpublished doctoral dissertation. University of Wisconsin, Madison.

Deach, D. (1950). *Genetic development of motor skills in children two through six years of age.* Unpublished doctoral dissertation, University of Michigan, Ann Arbor.

Dummer, G. M., Connor-Kuntz, F. J., & Goodway, J. D. (1995). A physical education curriculum for preschool and preprimary impaired students. *Teaching Exceptional Children, 27* (3), 28-43.

DuRandt, R. (1985). Ball catching proficiency among 4-, 6-, and 8-year old girls. In J.E. Clark & J.H. Humphrey (Eds.), *Motor development: Current selected research* (pp. 35-44). Princeton, NJ: Princeton Book.

Gabbard, C. P. (2000). *Lifelong motor development* (3rd ed.). Madison Dubuque, IA: Brown & Benchmark.

Goodway, J. D., Hamilton, M. L. & Rudisill, M. E. (1996, October). *What's in a number: Investigating change resulting from motor skill interventions.* Paper presented at the Annual Motor Development Research Consortium, Indiana University, Bloomington, IN.

Goodway-Shiebler, J. D. (1994). *The effects of a motor skill intervention on the fundamental motor skills and sustained activity of African-American preschool children who are at-risk.* Unpublished doctoral dissertation. Michigan State University, East Lansing.

Gutteridege, M. (1939). A study of motor achievements of young children. *Archives of Psychology, 244,* 1-178.

Halverson, L. (1963). *A guide to curriculum building in physical education elementary schools.* Curriculum Bulletin No. 28. Issued by Angus B. Rothwell, State Superintendent, Madison, WI. R1000-186; R1000-216.

Halverson, L. Roberton, M. A., & Harper, (1973). Current research in motor development. *Journal of Research and Development in Education, 6(3)*, 56-70.

Hamilton, M. , Goodway, J., & Haubenstricker, J. (1999). Parent-assisted instruction in a motor skill program for at-risk preschool children. *Adapted Physical Activity Quarterly, 16*, 427-428.

Haubenstricker, J., Branta, C., & Seefeldt, V. (1983, June). *Preliminary validation of developmental sequences for throwing and catching*. Paper presented at the annual conference of the North American Society for the Psychology of Sport and Physical Activity, East Lansing, MI.

Haywood, K.M. & Getchell, N. (2001). *Lifespan motor development* (3rd ed.). Champaign, IL: Human Kinetics.

Hellweg, D. A. (1972). *An analysis of the perceptual and performance characteristics of the catching skill in 6-7 year old children*. Unpublished doctoral dissertation, University of Wisconsin, Madison.

Kay, H. (1970). Analyzing motor skill performance. In K. Connolly (Ed.), *Mechanisms of motor skill development*. New York: Academic Press.

Kelly, L., Dagger, J., & Walkley, J. (1989). The effects of an assessment based education program on motor skill development in preschool children. *Education and Treatment of Children,12*(2), 152-164.

Newell, K. (1984). Physical constraints to development of motor skills. In J. Thomas (Ed.), *Motor development during preschool and elementary years* (pp. 105-120). Minneapolis: Burgess.

Newell, K. (1986). Constraints on the development of coordination. In M. G. Wade & H. T. Whiting (Eds.), *Motor development in children: Aspects of coordination and control* (pp. 341-360). Dordrecht, The Netherlands: Nijhoff.

Office of Compensatory Programs. (1991a). *Student risk identification criteria.* (Available from Office of Compensatory Programs, Flint Community Schools, 923 East Kearsley St, Flint, MI. 48502).

Office of Compensatory Programs. (1991b). *Flint Community Schools: Objective-referenced prekindergarten screening test.* (Available from Office of Compensatory Programs, Flint Community Schools, 923 East Kearsley St, Flint, MI. 48502).

Payne, V. G. & Isaacs, L. D. (2001). *Human motor development: A lifespan approach* (5th ed.). Boston, McGraw Hill.

Roberton, M. A. (1977). Stability of stage categorizations across trials: Implications for the "stage theory" of overarm throw development. *Journal of Human Movement Studies, 3*, 49-59.

Roberton, M. A. (1978). Longitudinal evidence for developmental stages in the forceful overarm throw. *Journal of Human Movement Studies, 4*, 167-175.

Roberton, M. A., Williams, K., & Langendorfer, S. (1980). Prelongitudinal screening of motor development sequences. *Research Quarterly for Exercise and Sport, 51*, 224-231.

Seefeldt, V., & Haubenstricker, J. (1982). Patterns, phases, or stages: An analytic model for the study of development in movement. In J. A. S. Kelso & J. E. Clark (Eds.), *The development of movement control and coordination* (pp. 309-318). New York: Wiley.

Strohmeyer, H. S., Williams, K., & Schaub-George, D. (1991). Developmental sequences for catching a small ball: A prelongitudinal screening. *Research Quarterly for Exercise and Sport, 62*, 257-266.

Theeboom, M., Knop, P. D., & Weiss, M. R. (1995). Motivational climate, psychological responses, and motor skill development in children's sport: A field-based intervention study. *Journal of Sport Psychology, 17*, 294-311.

Ulrich, D. (1985). *Test of Gross Motor Development*. Austin, TX: Pro-ED.

Valentini, N. (1997). *The influence of two motor skill interventions on the motor skill performance, perceived physical competence, and intrinsic motivation of kindergarten children.* Unpublished masters thesis. Auburn University, Auburn, Alabama.

Valentini, N. (1999). *Mastery motivational climate motor skill intervention: replication and follow-up.* Unpublished doctoral dissertation. Auburn University, Auburn, Alabama.

Valentini, N., Rudisill, M. E., & Goodway, J. D. (1999). Incorporating a mastery climate into elementary physical education: It's developmentally appropriate! *Journal of Physical Education and Dance, 70(7)* 28-32.

Wickstrom, R. L. (1983). *Fundamental motor patterns* (3rd ed.). Philadelphia: Lea & Faber.

Williams, J. G. (1992). Effects of instruction and practice on ball catching skill: Single subject study of an 8-year-old. *Perceptual and Motor Skills, 75*, 392-394.

6

CHILDREN'S SENSITIVITY TO HAPTIC INFORMATION IN PERCEIVING AFFORDANCES OF TENNIS RACKETS FOR STRIKING A BALL

Sam Beak

Keith Davids

Simon Bennett

ABSTRACT

Recent ecological work has highlighted adults' sensitivity to haptic information for discriminating spatial characteristics of implements during wielding. However, there has been little work on children's perception of haptic information when assembling task-specific devices for actions. This study examined children's sensitivity to moment of inertia information in perceiving affordances of tennis rackets for striking a ball. Ten children wielded six rackets under visual and non-visual conditions in order to select optimal rackets for striking to a maximum distance. Racket preferences were collected initially and 12 months later in order to examine whether perceived affordances alter with a change in organismic constraints. Statistical analyses supported the notion that children were sensitive to moment of inertia information from the rackets during wielding. Changes in anthropometric data was observed over 12 months. This was consistent with a change in perceived affordances of the rackets. The findings imply that in order to facilitate the acquisition of ball skills in children, sports equipment needs to be more sensitive to changing physical dimensions of learners.

In ecological psychology, Gibsonian ideas of the cyclical relations between perception and action systems are predicated on two key concepts (Gibson, 1979). The first concept is that of affordances, where the environment consists of functional utilities taken with reference to a perceiver and his/her individual action capabilities. An affordance of an object is an invitation to act. It is a dynamic structure determined by the fit between properties of the environment and properties of the organism's action system (Gibson, 1979). The theoretical implication is that affordances change when the developmental status or motor capability of the actor alters (Gibson, Riccio, Schmuckler, Stoffregen, Rosenberg, & Taormina, 1987; Savelsbergh, Wimmers, van der Kamp, & Davids, 2000; Warren & Whang, 1987). It is apparent that changes to organismic constraints, either structural (i.e., alterations to limb length and muscle mass) or functional (i.e., changes in motor abilities, postural control, etc.) may influence perception of affordances for action (Konczak, 1990). The implication is that an affordance is not perceived by all individuals in the same way. A small aperture that invites a child to walk through may offer a different affordance to an adult, such as crawling through.

The second key idea in the Gibsonian approach to perception and action is that biological organisms are sensitive to (and with specific task experience become increasingly attuned to) certain invariant sources of information from surrounding energy flows (i.e., optic, haptic, auditory) as affordances for action. Identifying informational support for action remains, therefore, an important task for ecological psychologists (see Michaels & Beek, 1995; Williams, Davids, & Williams, 1999). Clearly these ideas have important implications for the organization of sport practice environments for the developing child, specifically in facilitating skill acquisition.

Previous ecological research on perceptual invariants has tended to focus on how optical invariants (e.g., tau) specify the affordances of objects for interception, for example during one-handed catching and striking with a bat (e.g., see Bootsma & van Wieringen, 1990; Lee, 1980; Michaels & Beek, 1995; Savelsbergh, Whiting & Bootsma, 1991). Recently, there has been a belated effort to identify other invariants, leading to a growing interest in the haptic information about object characteristics and affordances gained through dynamic touch (e.g., see Bingham, Schmidt & Rosenblum, 1989; Solomon & Turvey, 1988; Turvey, 1996; Turvey, Burton, Amazeen, Butwill & Carello, 1998). Haptic information emerges from receptors in the hand as it is compressed, and while its muscles, ligaments and tendons are stretched during manipulatory activities such as wielding, hefting (movement about the wrist whilst holding an object in the hand) and grasping of objects and implements (e.g., balls and rackets). The information provided by the muscular effort of exerting a force on an implement or object when wielding or hefting can be picked up by the nervous system and perceived in terms of affordances for specific actions such as striking or throwing.

Gibson (1966, 1979) believed that the significant perceptual contribution of the haptic system during manipulative skills was often overlooked because of the emphasis on information from movements of the body and body parts, rather than from what is felt. Furthermore, Bernstein (1996) believed that haptic proprioception was the primary perceptual system involved in the assembly of functional coordination patterns in movement systems. Following their lead, Turvey and colleagues have highlight how dynamic touch supports many common manipulative movements (for reviews see Turvey, 1996; Mitra, Riley, Schmidt & Turvey, 1998). The prevalence of manipulative movements in everyday life led Turvey et al. (1998) to argue that "the role of dynamic touch in the control of manipulatory activity may be both more continuous and fundamental than that of vision" (p.35). For this reason, the manipulation of visual information when manipulating a tennis racket was considered an important factor in our experiment. Following this viewpoint, we aimed to study the perception of affordances gained through haptic proprioception alone and during the integration of both visual and haptic information. In the absence of condition effects, it would be apparent that the results support the argument proposed by Turvey and colleagues (1998). That is, if visual information plays an important role during manipulative activities, one would expect to find evidence of difficulty in perceiving affordances when visual information is withdrawn. For example, a random selection across the entire range of rackets may suggest uncertainty within participants' choices.

So what source of haptic information could the sport performer be sensitive to when wielding an implement such as a racket? When simply holding a racket, information regarding its shape, size, texture, and structure may be obtained from the haptic system. Information about its resistance to being displaced (i.e., its mass) can also be acquired. However, typically rackets are not held still but are wielded. Wielding is a process where an implement is twisted and turned in alternate directions, not necessarily in a systematic manner. The impression a learner gets through wielding a racket is more accurately described as one of how easy or hard it is to rotate in different directions. A racket's resistance to rotation is defined by the term moment of inertia.

Work by Solomon and Turvey (1988) implies that it is the difference in the haptic invariant moment of inertia that actually provides the learner with key information regarding a racket's "feel." In a series of nine experiments, Solomon and Turvey (1988) examined how adults perceived the spatial characteristics of hand-held rods, which they could not see but could wield only by movements about the wrist. They found that perceived reaching distance was determined by the principal moments of inertia of the hand-rod system about the axis of rotation. Curiously, this and most other studies of dynamic touch (e.g., see also Pagano & Turvey, 1995) have only focused on the ability to perceive the spatial orientation of an occluded arm and/or implement. A further interesting question is whether these findings can generalize to natural settings where there is a need to perceive affordances for action rather than an implement's spatial characteristics. Ball games provide excellent natural contexts in which to study the perception of haptic invariants for action. Many ball games involve wielding of objects or implements for goal-directed actions such as throwing and striking. For example, when selecting implements for striking in baseball, field- and ice-hockey, lacrosse, tennis, squash, and badminton, wielding is an integral part of the decision-making process.

The affordances provided by haptic information in perceiving for action have been previously examined by Bingham et al. (1989). They argued that during goal-directed behavior, temporary flexible relationships between components of the movement system emerge as task-specific devices (TSDs) in attempts to satisfy movement goals such as striking a ball. Bingham et al. (1989) stressed the importance of good quality perceptual information in assembling TSDs because their dynamical organization is not stable and emerges under specific task constraints. They argued that when selecting an optimal object/implement for action its "properties must be scaled to the remaining components of this task-specific device according to its dynamical organization" (Bingham et al., 1989, p.507). An important point is that the assembly of TSDs is a dynamical process that is highly dependent on relevant sources of perceptual information "that are tied to properties of the environment and organism" (Fitzpatrick, 1998, p.40). For this reason, Bingham et al. (1989) were concerned with what they termed "the perceptual question." In their initial two experiments, they examined whether participants could optimally select an object that afforded throwing a maximal distance merely by hefting it to gain haptic information about it. The design of their initial studies required adults to perceive which object of a given size and preferred weight afforded throwing a maximum distance, in advance of actually performing the action. They found evidence to support the sensitivity of adults to haptic information, which was reinforced in later experiments when the participants threw a maximum distance with their most preferred object. However, in their studies, Bingham et al. (1989) did not manipulate visual information of the objects hefted. Therefore, the choice of object for throwing was dependent upon the information gained through both visual and haptic sources.

With respect to developing understanding of children's motor development, another relevant issue is that typically, previous research on ecological invariants has tended to focus on perception in adults (e.g., Bingham et al, 1989; Pagano & Turvey, 1995; Savelsbergh, Whiting, & Bootsma, 1991; Solomon and Turvey, 1988). Only a few studies have examined the sensitivity of infants and very young children to perceptual information during action. One example was a study by von Hofsten (1983) who examined visual timing in human infants. He found that infants (aged 34-36 weeks) could reach with a surprising level of accuracy and timing precision toward an object traveling in a circular path in front of them. Only 17 out of 144 trials resulted in the target being completely missed by the infants. Although von Hofsten's (1983) findings implied a fundamental role for optical information in infants' visual timing behavior, it is unclear whether children are similarly sensitive to haptic information such as moment of inertia.

For example, when children wield implements such as rackets in order to select the best one for striking a ball, are they sensitive to the differences in affordances from one racket to another? Some early evidence on infants' ability to perceive haptic information was observed by Gibson and Walker (1984). They found that one-month-old infants subsequently discriminated object softness from rigidity after having explored different objects with the hand or mouth. Rochat and Gibson (1985) also found similar results with neonates in a later study. These findings illustrated the early presence of a haptic exploratory system, which continues to develop as the infant matures and grows. As new action capabilities develop (i.e., the hands become more active and controlled), a whole new set of affordances become available for discovery. Through the process of active exploration the infant detects new sources of haptic information that facilitates the perception of new affordances. Such a theoretical idea obviously has implications for the assembly of TSDs in developing children, especially during skill acquisition.

The lack of previous work on sensitivity to haptic information in children raises developmental questions about changes in affordances over time and the design of striking implements for children's ball sports. Affordances of an object for action are determined by the information perceived by children with an intrinsic reference to their own action capabilities (Konczak, 1990). For example, although a racket affords an objective function to a child in sport (i.e., striking a ball), the invariant information gained from wielding a racket determines the perceived affordance for each particular individual. This perceptual judgment is shaped by the organismic constraints (e.g., structural or functional) of the perceiver. Thus, for a given child, two tennis rackets may not necessarily have the same perceived affordance for striking a ball over a long distance, although physically and mechanically they do. Through changes in structural organismic constraints (i.e., growth and development), it is predicted that the child's perception of the affordances of a striking implement can vary over time. The instability incurred by structural organismic constraints highlights the need for understanding the efficacy with which children can perceive haptic information for assembling TSDs for action.

Newell (1986) highlighted the strong influence that structural organismic constraints, incurred through prolific growth periods during infancy and early childhood, can have on processes of perception and action. For example, Jensen (1981) observed the effect of a 12-month growth period on the whole body moments of inertia of children ranging from 4-12 years old. He reported an average increase for whole body moment of inertia of 27.7% over the 12-month time span. Not only do growth spurts affect biomechanical constraints, but they also have a great effect on the perceptions of an individual interacting with the immediate environment (Newell, 1986). Newell's (1986) model of interacting constraints predicts that as organismic constraints change and interact with other constraints from the task and environment, the emergent behaviour will alter the perceptual judgment of the individual in each specific setting. Over an extended period of time, all children demonstrate some changes in structural organismic constraints through growth and development. How prolific these changes are could determine the size of the effect on a child's perceived affordances for action (Konczak, 1990; Newell, 1986).

The sample participating in our study included children aged 10 years. This particular age group was selected for their general motor ability (i.e., in postural control, coordination, and ball skills) but lack of specific wielding experience (as would be found in older children who played racket sports). Within the motor development literature, a vast majority of studies is concerned with perception and action in young infants (e.g., Adolph, Eppler & Gibson, 1993; Goldfield, Kay & Warren, 1993; Thelen, 1994; Ulrich, Thelen, & Niles, 1990). There is a lack of studies on the development of perception and action in school-aged children. At this age range, children begin to develop an interest in "organized sports" (i.e., tennis classes, athletic clinics, hockey teams, etc.). Knowledge of motor development at this age is relevant to sport practitioners and equipment design manufacturers in order that they understand how to enhance experience and facilitate the acquisition of different skills. It is particularly important to know how perceptions of affordances change during this period, what effect experience has on these perceptions, and perhaps more fundamentally, how development affects children's perception of information for affordances.

In this study, we conducted an experiment that examined the information sources children used in assembling a TSD for striking a ball with an implement. After Bingham et al. (1989), our aim was to examine "the perceptual question." That is, we were primarily interested in whether children could show reliable preferences for a tennis racket that optimally afforded the chosen task of striking a ball to a maximum distance in advance of actually performing the action. Specifically, we considered whether children could utilize visual and/or haptic sources of information for identifying the affordances of rackets for striking a ball. A further issue of interest was whether such affordances changed over time in developing children.

METHOD

Participants

Ten children (mean age = 10 years) participated in the study. Eight of the participants were female and two were male. All were right-handed except for one female. All participants were selected because they had had no previous coaching in any racket sports and had very limited experience in wielding a racket. A letter of consent explaining the detailed procedure and commitment over 12 months required by the children was sent to their parents and guardians. The letter highlighted that participants were free to withdraw from the study at any time if they so desired. Ten letters were sent to the parents of the children suitable to participate in the study and the consent rate was 100%.

Apparatus

The study required six identical rackets with equal moments of inertia.

These were donated by a well-known racket manufacturer (Prince, Inc., USA) whose junior tennis "Rad" range are marketed as purpose-designed racket" for use by 6-12 year-olds. To coincide with the age range of the participant group the racket used throughout our study was a Rad Ten. By using this same racket for all participants, it was possible to examine the effects of a universal-sized racket (i.e., marketed for all 10-year-olds) on the assembly of a TSD in children of similar age. Each racket was constructed of aluminum with length 63.5 cm and mass 0.252 kg.

Although initially having equal moments of inertia, each racket was altered to produce different overall moments of inertia. In order to precisely control this experimental manipulation, a mass of 0.05 kg [1] was added to the longitudinal axis of each of the six rackets at intervals of 10 cm.[2] The mass was covered in black tape to secure it to the racket and to prevent any biasing through knowledge of its value. The calculations for moment of inertia of the six racket systems (I_{RS}, where a racket system constitutes the racket and additional weight) were based upon the formula $I_{RS} = I_{butt} + mr^2$ where I_{butt} = moment of inertia of the racket about its butt end, m = mass of attached weight (kg) and r = position of weight from butt. The I_{butt} was calculated by Prince Inc. to be 0.0328 kgm^2 for each racket. With the addition of 0.05 kg at different positions along the longitudinal axis of the rackets, new moment of inertia values were calculated. Using the above formula values were I_{butt} = 0.0328 kgm^2, m = 0.05 kg and r = 0.106 m, 0.206 m, 0.306 m, 0.406 m, 0.506 m and 0.606 m respectively for rackets 1-6. Subsequently, the moment of inertia values for the six new racket systems were calculated to be 0.0334, 0.0349, 0.0375, 0.0410, 0.0456, and 0.0512

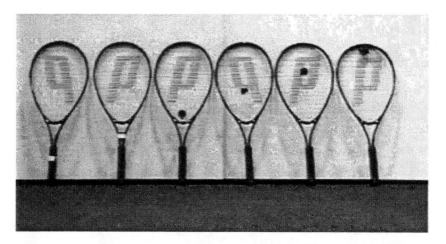

Fig. 1. The Rad 10 rackets provided by Prince Inc., in which moment of inertia was manipulated by adding a mass of 50 grams. The position of the individual weight increases with each racket by 10 cm. All the rackets were identical in weight, size and design but altered only in their moment of inertia values.

kgm^2 for rackets 1-6 respectively (see Figure 1). For the purposes of this experiment, the racket with the lowest moment of inertia (0.0334 kgm^2) was closest to the racket marketed as appropriate for 10-year-olds, and the highest value (0.0512 kgm^2) was closer to (inappropriate) rackets in the adult range. The values chosen for moments of inertia of the rackets in the present study were deliberately kept within this limited range. It is important to note that any evidence of clustering observed when children detected affordances of rackets for action could not be attributed to the use of an inordinately large selection range and would meaningfully support the notion of children's sensitivity to haptic information.

Experimental procedure

There were two different time intervals for data collection: initial and after 12 months. After the 12-month time manipulation, the children were asked if they had played any racket sports or received any coaching. No child had received additional specific wielding experience during this time. Each child was asked to wield the rackets at both points in time during an individual testing session lasting approximately 10 minutes on each occasion. There were two randomly ordered wielding conditions: visual and non-visual. The participants were required to wield each of the six rackets one at a time and were asked to judge each racket for its affordance for striking a tennis ball to a maximum distance. After wielding, participants indicated the preferred three rackets that optimally afforded such an action in a forced-choice paradigm. Participants were allowed to wield each racket as many times as they wished. The order of rackets presented was randomized so as to counterbalance sequence effects. Grip position was standardized throughout, with the participants holding the racket at the very end of its handle. Participants were not instructed how to wield, nor given a specific length of time in which to complete the procedure. The two conditions were separated by a five-minute rest period. In the visual condition, the participants were able to see the rackets. In the non-visual condition, vision of the rackets was occluded by the use of a large screen. The screen was designed with a hole in the middle to allow the participants unobtrusive wielding. A black sheet draped over the screen provided adequate deprivation of any visual information from the rackets (see Figures 2a and 2b).

In order to test the reliability of the children's perceived affordances for each racket, they were asked to return one week after the initial testing period and complete the procedures again. On this occasion all of the original participants were able to take part. The procedure was carried out in exactly the same manner as at the initial stage, one week previous.

Anthropometric Measures

To examine the possibility that a change in organismic constraints may be associated with the perceived affordances of the rackets, anthropometric measures were obtained from each participant at the initial and 12-month stages. These included height, body weight, segment lengths, and joint girths, as well as a strength grip test using a hand dynamometer. Three values were taken for each of the segment lengths and joint girths measured, and a mean value was then calculated.

RESULTS

An overall mean value for preferred moment of inertia was computed by weighting perceived judgments according to preference. Bingham et al. (1989) adopted a similar method, reporting that it provided a sensitive approach to analyzing the data on perceptual judgments for hefting objects. After Bingham et al. (1989), first preference racket was multiplied by three, second preference by two, and third preference by one. The sum of the weighted scores was then divided by six to obtain the mean weighted score. A two-way, 2 x 2 (Condition by Time) analysis of variance (ANOVA), with repeated measures on both factors, was used to analyze the mean weighted preference data. A significant main effect of Condition was found,

Fig. 2a: The visual condition where the participant was able to see the racket while wielding.

Fig. 2b: Wielding in non-visual condition. A screen was used to deprive the participants of visual information regarding the rackets.

$F(1,9) = 6.59$ ($p< 0.05$), but no effect of Time, nor Condition by Time interaction was reported. Because the main effect of Condition was clearly meaningful despite the lack of an interaction, and from observing the trend in Figure 3, it was decided that a simple effects analysis should be used as a clarification of the statistical outcomes (see Howell, 1993). Simple effects analysis indicated significant differences in mean weighted preferences across the 12-month time period for both the visual condition, $F(1,9) = 13.45$ ($p< 0.05$), and the non-visual condition, $F(1,9) = 7.88$ ($p< 0.05$). However, no simple effects were reported between conditions at either time phase.

To examine how the spread of variability changed over time and from one condition to another, the standard deviation (SD) scores were calculated from the 3 preferred rackets. These data were subjected to a two-way (Condition by Time) ANOVA with repeated measures on both factors. No significant main effects of Condition nor Time were found although an interaction in the data was observed, $F(1,9) = 20.80$ ($p< 0.01$). Simple effects analysis revealed significant differences between conditions at both the initial stage, $F(1,9) = 9.84$ ($p< 0.05$), and at 12 months, $F(1,9) = 10.98$ ($p< 0.05$). A significant difference was also found in the visual condition across the 12-month time period, $F(1,9) = 37.83$, but not for the non-visual condition.

In the visual condition children initially demonstrated high variability within their choice of rackets (mean standard deviation value $= 0.0072$). This finding significantly decreased to almost half the initial variability (mean SD $= 0.0038$) after the 12-month period. These results suggest that

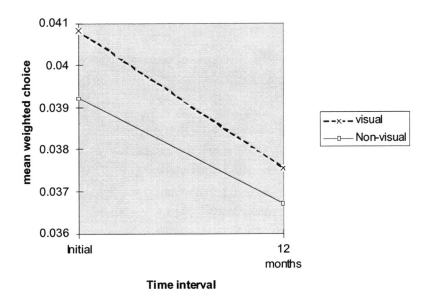

Fig. 3: The effects of Condition and Time across a period of 12 months showing a difference in mean weighted preference between the initial stage and at 12 months for both visual and non-visual conditions.

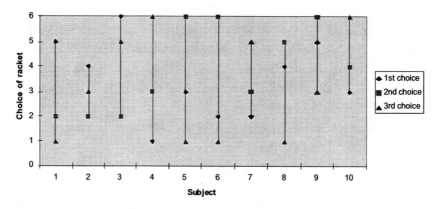

Fig. 4a: The data illustrate the variability in preferred choices in the visual condition at the initial stage. Note that racket 1 has a moment of inertia value of 0.0334 kgm^2 and is closest to the racket appropriate for a 10-year-old (as designed by Prince, Inc.). The rackets 1-6 all ascend in order of moment of inertia value so that racket 6 has a value of 0.0512 kgm^2 (i.e., the highest value).

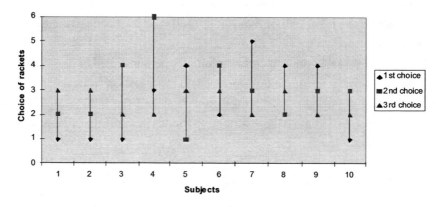

Fig. 4b: The data illustrate the clustering of preferred choices at the 12-month stage within the visual condition.

the children began to cluster their choices in the visual condition by selecting consecutive rackets yielding lower variability in moment of inertia values. Figures 4a & 4b illustrate the clustering effect within the visual condition across 12 months. Evidence of clustering and clear trends in preferred choice toward the lower end of the inertia scale (rackets 1-4) may be observed.

Although no effect of Time was found in the non-visual condition using the standard deviation scores, there was an effect using the mean-weighted preference scores. This outcome suggests that the children did alter their perceived choice of racket after 12 months but that the variability within those choices remained consistent with those chosen at the initial stage. Figures 5a & 5b illustrate the individual choice of rackets made under the non-visual condition across both time periods.

With the exception of five outliers in Figure 5b, the majority of participants selected rackets 1-4 with lower moment of inertia values. When introduced to the weighting system, these outliers produced a lower mean weighted value, which consist of higher moment of inertia values, than at the initial stage (see Figure 5a). For example, participant 10 chose rackets 3, 4, and 5 at the initial stage and then 1, 2, and 3, 12 months later. Although the variability was equal, the mean weighted preference was higher at the initial stage than that calculated for 12 months.

To analyze the reliability of the children's preferred choices, three separate analyses were performed on data collected across one week. These tests determined if children were randomly selecting rackets as preferred choices or whether they were in fact sensitive to moment of inertia information regarding the rackets' affordances. A two-way (Condition by Time) ANOVA with repeated measures on both factors was performed on the

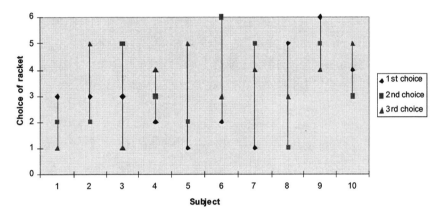

Fig. 5a: The data illustrate the individual choice of rackets selected under the non-visual condition at the initial stage.

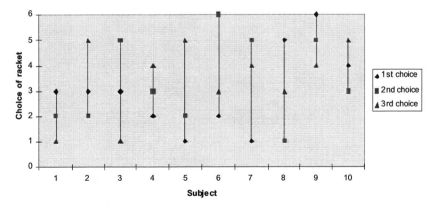

Fig. 5b: The data illustrate the individual choice of rackets selected under the non-visual condition at the 12-month stage. Although the variability within the choices does not significantly change, a difference in mean weighted scores can be observed. This is because of the higher number of rackets with increased moment of inertia values being selected at the initial stage compared to the lower moment of inertia rackets chosen after 12 months.

mean weighted preference data. Although a significant main effect of Condition was found, $F(1,9) = 16.24$ ($p < 0.05$), there was no main effect of Time, nor Condition by Time interaction. Simple effects analysis found significant differences between the visual and non-visual conditions at both the initial time period, $F(1,9) = 11.24$ ($p < 0.05$), and one week later, $F(1,9) = 11.01$ ($p < 0.05$). Because of the nature of ANOVA, these results could provide a false indication of reliability across the one-week time period, and an intra-class correlation coefficient was obtained to estimate the degree of reliability across one week. A significant correlation was found for the non-visual condition, $r = 0.74$ ($p < 0.05$) but not for the visual condition, $r = 0.094$ ($p > 0.05$). This finding indicated that the children in this study were able to make reliable choices of rackets under the non-visual condition but not when vision of the racket was available.

A second two-way (Condition by Time) ANOVA with repeated measures on both factors was performed on the standard deviation data obtained from the participants' first, second and third choices. Although a main effect of Time was reported, $F(1,9) = 17.09$ ($p < 0.05$), a simple effect analysis found no significant differences over Time for either Condition. However, a simple effect of Condition was obtained at the initial stage, $F(1,9) = 7.95$ ($p < 0.05$). These results suggested a high level of consistency in the spread of variability yielded from the three rackets children selected initially, compared to the three selected one week later.

The anthropometric data collected before and after 12 months (see Tables 1 & 2) suggested that a change in structural organismic constraints had occurred. Furthermore, these results demonstrated the large degree of variability between the participants in the overall moment of inertia for each striking system. For example, consider the values of Participants 1 and 3 in Table 1. Participant 3 wielded with a moment of inertia value almost double that of Participant 1. The same differences can also be observed for Participants 4 and 5.

DISCUSSION

The aim of this experiment was to examine whether children could demonstrate reliable preferences for a tennis racket that optimally afforded striking a ball to a maximum distance, in advance of performing the action. Further, the experiment was designed to observe the effect of a 12-month time period upon the perception of affordances. The results demonstrated a clear difference between the visual and non-visual conditions in the way that the children perceived the affordances of each racket. Although the range of variability in choices remained consistent over one week, the children's choice of rackets was only found to be reliable in the non-visual wielding conditions. These results support claims that haptic information

Table 1

Anthropometric data from initial stage illustrating the variability, between subjects, in the overall moment of inertia for each striking system.

	1	2	3	4	5	6	7	8	9	10
Height (cm)	128.7	138.9	145.9	148.6	130.2	136.9	148.5	140.8	146.0	135.3
Body weight (kg)	25.10	33.00	40.70	39.00	24.00	33.00	35.8	31.3	30.6	26.6
Upper arm length (cm)	24.60	29.35	29.50	30.75	26.30	28.7	29.7	27.6	30.35	26.2
Lower arm length (cm)	18.90	21.25	21.50	23.75	18.30	20.85	22.1	22.15	23.1	19.75
Hand length (cm)	13.90	15.15	15.95	16.40	13.80	16.05	15.9	15.6	16.3	14.4
Grip test (kgW)	10	11.75	13.25	15.5	8.5	12.5	15.5	15	12.25	12
Striking system 1 inertia (kgm^2)	1648.403	2700.680	3208.742	3501.885	1703.87	2605.254	2994.053	2493.623	2838.322	1913.722
Striking system 2 inertia (kgm^2)	1648.404	2700.681	3208.744	3501.886	1703.872	2605.256	2994.055	2493.624	2838.324	1913.724
Striking system 3 inertia (kgm^2)	1648.407	2700.684	3208.746	3501.889	1703.875	2605.258	2994.057	2493.627	2838.326	1913.726
Striking system 4 inertia (kgm^2)	1648.410	2700.687	3208.750	3501.892	1703.878	2605.262	2994.061	2493.630	2838.330	1913.730
Striking system 5 inertia (kgm^2)	1648.415	2700.692	3208.755	3501.897	1703.883	2605.267	2994.065	2493.635	2838.335	1913.735
Striking system 6 inertia (kgm^2)	1648.421	2700.697	3208.760	3501.903	1703.888	2605.272	2994.071	2493.640	2838.340	1913.740

Note: Striking system 1-6 represents the upper and lower arm, hand and rackets 1-6 respectively.
Body segment moment of inertia for each subject, was calculated through adapting Jensen's model (1978).

Table 2

Anthropometric data collected after 12 months, illustrating the variability, between subjects, in the overall moment of inertia for each striking system.

	1	2	3	4	5	6	7	8	9	10
Height (cm)	130.0	143.4	153.2	156.2	130.2	138.5	155.5	144.9	150.8	143.1
Body weight (kg)	27.5	35.8	48	48.2	28	35.5	42.4	34.9	35	31.5
Upper arm length (cm)	25.6	30.7	30.9	33.4	27.2	30.5	31.6	29.9	30.9	28
Lower arm length (cm)	18.9	23.6	23.8	26.2	19.2	23	24.4	23.6	24.3	21.5
Hand length (cm)	14.1	16.1	17.5	17.2	14.7	17.1	17.6	17.1	17.1	16.1
Grip test (kgW)	6.0	10.5	19.0	16.5	5.0	8.0	17.0	11.0	8.0	9.5
striking system 1 inertia (kgm^2)	1842.890	3262.707	4158.482	4891.059	2042.388	3178.178	3952.365	3115.346	3316.403	2493.991
striking system 2 inertia (kgm^2)	1842.892	3262.708	4158.483	4891.061	2042.389	3178.179	3952.366	3115.348	3316.404	2493.992
striking system 3 inertia (kgm^2)	1842.894	3262.711	4158.486	4891.063	2042.392	3178.182	3952.369	3115.350	3316.407	2493.995
striking system 4 inertia (kgm^2)	1842.898	3262.714	4158.489	4891.067	2042.396	3178.185	3952.372	3115.354	3316.410	2493.999
striking system 5 inertia (kgm^2)	1842.902	3262.719	4158.494	4891.071	2042.400	3178.190	3952.377	3115.358	3316.415	2494.003
striking system 6 inertia (kgm^2)	1842.908	3262.725	4158.499	4891.077	2042.406	3178.195	3952.382	3115.364	3316.421	2494.009

may be more important during dynamic touch than vision (e.g., Michaels and Beek, 1995; Mitra et al., 1998; Turvey et al., 1998). Without the presence of visual information the children could only have based their judgments on the haptic information gained through wielding the rackets. As each racket only differed through the moment of inertia, the findings suggested that the children were sensitive to these changes and were able to perceive the differences in moment of inertia values from one racket to the next.

The results also suggested that as time progresses, there was a trend for children's perceived affordances to change (see Figure 3). The data on perceptual judgments from this study support the earlier findings of Bingham et al. (1989) and Solomon and Turvey (1988), and have extended them to show that children, as well as adults, are sensitive to haptic information sources such as moment of inertia. It appears that haptic information supported the choices that children make about implements for use in action. Taken together, the current findings and those of Solomon and Turvey (1988) suggest that moment of inertia is a very important haptic invariant that is present in many different performance settings throughout life in which objects and implements have to be wielded. The evidence suggests that children's early sensitivity to moment of inertia information can be exploited for attunement in different performance domains.

A qualitative observation in this experiment across both time phases was that participants spent a longer time wielding in the non-visual condition, often asking for specific rackets to be returned for further wielding. The returned rackets were frequently chosen as one of the three preferred choices. This observation supported a similar finding reported by Bingham et al. (1989) in a visual condition. Their participants repeatedly asked to reheft those objects they later identified as optimal for throwing. However, during the visual condition in the current experiment, the children rarely asked if they could wield a particular racket again. This specific outcome may have been because of the children based their perceptual judgments predominantly on visual information rather than haptic information gained from wielding the rackets. This observation contradicts previous suggestions from Rock and Harris (1967) that the sense of touch does not educate vision and that vision dominates touch. It is possible that in the visual condition, instead of focusing on the action capabilities of each racket, the children's attention may have been drawn toward the aesthetic appearance of the racket (as is well understood by manufacturers) or the positions of individual weights. Similar observations have been made in the psychophysical literature on human perception. Klatzky and Lederman (1992) found that when both visual and haptic information were present, the participants in their study indicated through their judgments that geometric properties (particularly shape and size) were more cognitively salient than material properties (e.g., texture, hardness, and weight). However, when visual information was absent the participants tended to base their judgments on material properties.

When relying solely on the haptic information available for pick up from the rackets, it is arguable that the children found it difficult to perceive the changes in moment of inertia between each racket, therefore requiring an extended wielding period. This extended perceptual exploration behavior is to be expected as children seek to optimize TSDs for action (Fitzpatrick, 1998). In the non-visual conditions, the children relied upon their haptic-perceptual system to gain information about the rackets. Although they had all gained general wielding experience during daily routines, these children did not have any specific experience in wielding tennis rackets. Therefore, their haptic-perceptual system may have been lacking specific attunement at that time. Without a prior understanding of what type of racket would afford striking a ball to a maximum distance, the children may have found the information difficult to pick up, which was reflected in extended wielding time.

Another influential factor may have been the use of relatively minute manipulations in moments of inertia of the rackets causing the children difficulty in perceiving the affordances for action. However, despite the small range of moment of inertia values chosen for this study, there was evidence of a clustering of preferred choices especially after 12 months (see Figures 4 and 5). These observations provided support for the notion that children are sensitive to small changes in moment of inertia. From an originally narrow range of six rackets (0.0334 - 0.0512 kgm^2), the majority of participants selected rackets that demonstrated an even tighter range after 12 months (0.0334 - 0.0410 kgm^2).

Although the participants were the same chronological age and the rackets used remained constant across individuals, the moment of inertia values calculated for the overall striking subsystem (i.e., the upper arm, lower arm, hand, and racket) for each child indicated a large degree of inter-individual variability (see Tables 1 and 2). These findings have important implications for skill acquisition, particularly in relation to the design of sports equipment. At present, there is a tendency to use universally scaled equipment during the skill acquisition process for young children in many ball games practices. Because there is obviously no "universal 10-year-old", it follows that there is no "universal 10-year-old racket or bat." As already illustrated in Table 1, a snapshot view of the anthropometric measures for each participant resulted in vast differences within the overall moment of inertia values for the six striking systems. This in turn will arguably have had an effect upon the perceived affordances of each racket. But how do these action capabilities, as perceived by each individual, change over time?

Newell's (1986) model predicts that organismic constraints change over time and interact with task and environmental constraints, altering the perceived affordances of the individual in each specific setting. Within the boundaries of this experiment, and in association with a change in structural organismic constraints (see Newell's model, 1986), one had expected to see differences in preferred choice of rackets after the 12-month time period. Clearly, Figure 3 depicts such a change in perceived affordances, but can they be attributed to a change in structural organismic constraints? The difference in participants' anthropometric data reported in Table 2 provided some support for the notion that perceived affordances may have altered with respect to a change in structural constraints.

When compared to Table 1, it was apparent that all the participants in Table 2 had grown over a 12-month period. The effect this period of growth had on the overall inertia values for each striking system can be observed clearly. In all cases, the inertia values increased, some considerably more than others, therefore altering structural organismic constraints. Following Newell's model (1986), the interaction of these organismic constraints with those of the task and environment should allow new movement behaviors to emerge, leading to a change in action capabilities and perceived affordances (Konczak, 1990). As a dynamic, self-organizing, complex movement system, an individual passes through periods of stability and instability where certain functional subsystems are perturbed by changes in structural organismic constraints. During periods of growth, children's movement systems are often subjected to perturbations and transition stages that can be identified by changes in behavior (Newell, 1986; Thelen, 1995). The data from the current study supported Bingham's (1988b) argument that as the functional subsystems of the developing movement system change, altering overall organismic constraints, the learner needs to re-atune some of the components of TSDs in order to achieve movement goals.

In this study, there were huge differences noted in the moment of inertia of each individual child's body segments. The result was individually different perceived affordances for each particular implement. Sports rackets marketed for juniors are often based upon the mythical average child and their putative action capabilities at certain chronological ages. This marketing approach makes no consideration of nonlinearities in the development of organismic constraints such as moment of inertia of limb segments. Some children experience sudden growth in limb length, whereas others are late developers who remain a similar size across different chronological ages. During normal physical education lessons or coaching sessions in tennis, the use of a universal-sized racket is extremely common. Yet the similarities in organismic constraints between young learners are not quite so evident! Although it is quite easy to understand how these constraints affect the perception of affordances, the specific role that structural and functional organismic constraints play is harder to define. The reason for such confusion is the intertwined nature of these constraints within the performer. A change in structural constraints (e.g., muscle to fat ratio) may influence a change in functional constraints (e.g., postural control), which may then influence the perception of affordances. Future research needs to consider both structural and functional organismic constraints, their roles as separate influences in the perception of affordances, as well as their influence upon each other.

Finally, an important question to emerge from the work on haptic invariants for action concerns whether children are able to judge for themselves, in advance, those implements that afford optimal performance. Currently, work is ongoing to map the "perceptual function" obtained in this study to the kinematics of action when children actually strike a ball for maximum distance (see Bingham et al., 1989). The findings from the current experiment supported the view that if children are to acquire ball skills efficiently, the utilization of implements body-scaled in relation to intra-individual organismic constraints appears theoretically sound. Further research is needed to examine whether the ecological concept of body-scaling can inform equipment design as a pre-requisite for ball skill acquisition (see Konczak, 1990).

Acknowledgments

The authors are grateful to Prince, Inc., USA for the provision of the Rad 10 tennis rackets employed throughout the experiments. We also thank the children and staff of Cranberry Primary School, Cheshire, UK, for their participation and assistance in carrying out this study.

REFERENCES

Adolph, K.E., Eppler, M.A., & Gibson, E.J. (1993). Crawling versus walking infants' perception of affordances for locomotion over sloping surfaces. *Child Development. 64*, 1158-74.

Bernstein, N. A. (1996). "On dexterity and its development". In M.Latash & M.T. Turvey (Eds.), *Dexterity and its development* (pp. 2-244). Mahwah, N.J.: Lawrence Erlbaum Associates.

Bingham, G. (1988b). Task specific devices and the perceptual bottleneck. *Human Movement Science, 7*, 225-264.

Bingham, G., Schmidt, R.C., & Rosenblum, L. (1989). Hefting for a maximum distance throw: A smart perceptual mechanism. *Journal of Experimental Psychology: Human Perception and Performance, 15*, 507-528.

Bootsma, R.J., & van Wieringen, P.C.W. (1990). Timing and attacking forehand drive in table-tennis. *Journal of Experimental Psychology:*

Human Perception and Performance, 18, 507-528.

Fitzpatrick, P. (1998). Modeling coordination dynamics in development. In K.M. Newell & P.C.M. Molenaar (Eds.), *Applications of nonlinear dynamics to developmental process modeling*, (pp. 39-62). Mahwah, New Jersey: Lawrence Erlbaum Associates.

Gibson, J.J. (1966). *The senses considered as perceptual systems*. Boston: Houghton Mifflin.

Gibson, J.J. (1979). *The ecological approach to visual perception*. Boston: Houghton Mifflin.

Gibson, E.J., Riccio, G., Schmuckler, M., Stoffregen, T.A., Rosenberg, D., & Taormina, J. (1987). Detection of traversability of surfaces by crawling and walking infants. *Journal of Experimental Psychology: Human Perception and Performance, 13*, 533-545.

Gibson, E.J., & Walker, A.S. (1984). Development of knowledge of visual-tactual affordances of substance. *Child Development*, 55, 453-460.

Goldfield, E.C. (1995). *Emergent Forms Origins and Early Development of Human Action and Perception*. New York: Oxford University Press.

Goldfield, E.C., Kay, B.A., & Warren, W.H., Jr. (1993). Infant bouncing: The assembly and tuning of action systems. *Child Development, 64*, 1128-1142.

Howell, D.C. (1993). *Fundamental statistics for the behavioral sciences* (3rd Ed). Belmont, CA.: Duxbury Press.

Jensen, R.K. (1978). Estimation of the biomechanical properties of three body types using a photogrammetric method. *Journal of Biomechanics, 11*, 349-358.

Jensen, R.K. (1981). The effect of a 12-month growth period on the body moments of inertia of children. *Medicine and Science in Sports and Exercise, 13*, 238-242.

Klatzky, R.L. & Lederman, S.J. (1992). Stages of exploration in haptic object identification. *Perception & Psychophysics, 52*, 661-670.

Konczak, J. (1990). Toward an ecological theory of motor development: The relevance of the Gibsonian Approach to vision for motor development research. In J.E. Clark and J.H. Humphrey (Eds.) *Advances in motor development research* (Vol. 3, pp.201-224). New York: AMS Press.

Lee, D.N. (1980). Visuo-motor coordination in space-time. In G.E. Stelmach, & J. Requin (Eds.), *Tutorials in motor behaviour* (pp.281-293). Amsterdam: North Holland.

Michaels, C., & Beek, P. (1995). The state of ecological psychology. *Ecological Psychology, 74*, 259-278.

Mitra, S., Riley, M.A., Schmidt, R.C. & Turvey, M.T. (1998). Vision and the level of synergies. In L.R. Harris and M.Jenkin (Eds.), *Vision and action* (pp.314-331). New York: Cambridge University Press.

Newell, K.M. (1986). Constraints on the development of coordination. In M.G. Wade & H.T.A. Whiting (Eds.), *Motor development in children: Aspects of coordination and control* (pp. 341-359). Dordrecht: Nijhoff.

Pagano, C.C., & Turvey, M.T. (1995). The inertia tensor as a basis for the perception of limb orientation. *Journal of Experimental Psychology: Human Perception and Performance, 21*, 1070-1087.

Rochat, P., & Gibson, E.J. (1985). Early mouthing and grasping: development and crossmodal responsiveness to soft and rigid objects in young infants. *Canadian Psychologist.* 26(2), 452.

Rock, I., & Harris, C.S. (1967). Vision and touch. *Scientific American, 216*, 96-104.

Savelsbergh, G.J.P., Whiting, H.T.A., & Bootsma, R.J. (1991). Grasping Tau. *Journal of Experimental Psychology: Human Perception and Performance* 17, 315-322.

Savelsbergh, G., Wimmers, R., van der Kamp, J., & Davids, K. (2001). The development of movement control and coordination. In M.L. Genta, B. Hopkins, and A.F. Kalverboer (Eds.), *Basic issues in Developmental Biopsychology.* Dordrecht: Kluwer Academic Publishers.

Solomon, H.Y. & Turvey, M.T. (1988). Haptically perceiving the distances reachable with hand-held objects. *Journal of Experimental Psychology: Human Perception and Performance, 14*, 404-427.

Thelen, E. (1994). Three-month-old infants can learn task-specific patterns of interlimb coordination. *Psychological Science, 5*, 280-285

Thelen, E. (1995). Motor development: A new synthesis. *American Psychologist, 50*, 79-95.

Turvey, M.T. (1996). Dynamic touch. *American Psychologist, 51*, 1134-1152.

Turvey, M.T., Burton, G., Amazeen, E.L., Butwill, M. & Carello, C. (1998). Perceiving the width and height of a hand-held object by dynamic touch. *Journal of Experimental Psychology: Human Perception and Performance, 24*, 35-48.

Ulrich, B.D., Thelen, E., & Niles, D. (1990). Perceptual determinants of action: Stair-climbing choices of infants and toddlers. In J.E. Clark & J.H. Humphrey (Eds.), *Advances in Motor Development Research* (Vol. 3, pp. 1-15). New York: AMS Press.

Von Hofsten, C. (1983). Catching skills in infancy. *Journal of Experimental Psychology: Human Perception and Performance, 9*, 75-85.

Warren, W., & Whang, S. (1987). Visual guidance of walking through apertures: Body-scaled information for affordances. *Journal of experimental psychology: Human perception and performance. 13*, 371-383.

Williams, A.M., Davids, K. & Williams, J.G. (1999). *Visual perception and action in sport.* Routledge: London.

Footnotes

[1] In order to keep the physical dimensions of each racket equal, moment of inertia was manipulated by the addition of an external 0.05 kg mass. This value was calculated so that the overall mass of each racket (0.302 kg) was similar to the Rad 12 (0.307 kg) i.e., the racket designed and marketed for a 12-year-old. By keeping the racket dimensions within Prince's junior range the children would not be forced to choose rackets they would normally discard due to perceived heaviness (i.e., as with an adult racket)

[2] The decision to manipulate the distance instead of mass was primarily due to the effect it would have in changing the overall moment of inertia (I) of the racket. From the formula $I = mr^2$, distance, r, has a larger effect on I because its value is squared.

DEVELOPMENTAL TRENDS IN PERCEIVING AFFORDANCES: A PRELIMINARY INVESTIGATION OF JUMPING DISTANCES

Martin E. Block

ABSTRACT

The purpose of this study was to determine if a dimensionless pi value could be calculated to capture the affordance for jumping distances across children of different ages and biodynamic capabilities. Male subjects ages three, seven, and 11 years old, and college age adults judged (yes/no response) whether or not various lengths of plastic could be jumped across using a two-footed take-off and landing. After judging each distance a total of three times, several anthropometric measurements were taken along with each person's maximum standing long jump. Three pi values were calculated using the two traditional measures of leg length and eye height as body-scalers, as well as actual maximum jumping distance to represent a biodynamic scaler that encompasses all of the biodynamic factors that go into jumping. Results showed that all four groups of subjects, including the youngest age group, could judge if a distance could or could not be jumped across. Furthermore, it was determined that only the biodynamic scaler was effective in capturing the affordance for jumping distances across subjects of varying ages, heights, and maximum jumping distances.

Many people have been faced with the dilemma of how to cross over a puddle that blocks their path. If the puddle is very small, all one has to do is to take a slightly longer step than normal to cross over it. If the puddle is larger, one may have to jump over the puddle. And if the puddle is still larger, one may choose to avoid the puddle altogether and walk around. While we all have miscalculated this task at one time or another (and no doubt gotten wet in the process!), it is remarkable that so often we choose and execute the correct movement for the task. Perhaps even more remarkable is that children of varying ages, body types, and levels of skillfulness also are extremely accurate in matching movements to a task. How is it that a mover, particularly a child, comes to judge accurately whether a puddle is "jumpable"?

One of the fundamental questions of interest to those studying the development of motor skills is how the developing child comes to recognize, organize, and then execute a specific action that matches a specific environment. Utilizing an ecological approach to perception, the purpose of this preliminary investigation was to determine if young children who have just acquired the ability to perform the standing long jump were as accurate as older children and adults in determining if a distance could be jumped across? Specifically, are movers with greater skill more accurate at judging their movement capabilities in a particular environment compared to less skilled movers?

Jumping within the Ecological Approach to Perception

Warren (1983) suggested that environmental properties can be usefully scaled relative to actor's own action systems. That is, a critical characteristic of a mover is used as a standard to measure the functional utility of the environment (e.g., jumpability of a puddle) (Carello, Grosofsky, Reichel, Solomon, & Turvey, 1989; Heft, 1989; Mark & Vogele, 1987; Warren, 1984, 1988). When properties of the mover and the environment are defined using the same dimensions (e.g., mass, length, time), the result is a "dimensionless ratio" or "pi" number that uniquely characterizes a mover-environment fit (Carello et al., 1989; Warren, 1984, 1988). In terms of affordance, dimensionless, body-scaled pi numbers can indicate *critical action boundaries* in which limits of one action are reached and a transition to another action is required (Carello et al., 1989; Mark & Vogele, 1987; Turvey & Carello, 1986; Warren, 1984, 1988). A value below a critical pi number indicates that a movement can be successfully accomplished (a puddle can be jumped), and a value above the critical pi number indicates that a movement cannot be accomplished (a puddle cannot be jumped).

Whereas body-scaled information is no doubt important in helping a mover match a movement to its environment, exactly which body-scalers actually describe an affordance for action for an organism is still unknown. The majority of studies that have examined body-scaled information for affordances have used body dimensions such as eye-height (Mark, 1987; Mark & Vogele, 1987), leg length (Warren 1984; Burton, 1990), shoulder width (Warren & Wang, 1987) and arm length (Carello et al., 1989). In fact, most of these studies found that such simple scalers could be used to calculate a dimensionless ratio of the mover-environment fit. However, other studies found that simple scalers could not be used to calculate such a dimensionless ratio. For example, Carello et al. (1989) found that differences in reaching by long- and short-arm subjects could not be completely accounted for by arm length alone. They noted that arm length alone could not account for the tremendous biomechanical complexity in the shoulder joint. The authors suggested that perceived reach could be scaled to actual reach because "actual reach is the true effective arm, because it necessarily reflects the biomechanical intricacies that a model of the effective arm should incorporate" (1989, p. 42). Similarly, Konczak, Meuwssen, & Kress (1992) found that differences between younger and older women's perception of climbable riser heights could not completely be accounted for by leg length but could be accounted for by a more biodynamic scaler–flexibility. Finally, Ulrich, Thelen, and Niles (1990) found that children who recently acquired the skill to climb stairs chose riser heights that were based on their locomotor abilities and experiences as opposed to anthropometric measurements such as eye-height and leg length.

Therefore, it appears then that whereas body metrics are important in describing affordances, additional sources of information in the form of biodynamic factors can influence the mover-environment fit and must be accurately accounted for by the mover when perceiving affordances (Heft, 1989; Mark & Dainoff, 1988; Warren, 1984). As noted by Warren (1984), movers must scale their world in terms of biodynamical limits of systems of action. If movements such as reaching and stair climbing (which outwardly appear to be related to body dimensions such as arm and leg length, respectively) cannot be accounted for through simple body-scalers, then it is unlikely that more complex actions that utilize more degrees of freedom, as well as moving a mass such as jumping, can be captured through the use of simple body dimensions. That is, it is unlikely that a body-scaler such as leg length alone provides enough information about the mover-environment fit to enable a mover to accurately detect the affordance for jumping distances given that jumping involves the complex interrelationship between muscular strength, balance, flexibility, technique or form, intra- and inter-limb coordination, including coordination between the arms and legs, and "the nebulous qualities of courage and confidence that can have an impact on the development of jumping skill" (Wickstrom, 1983, p. 65). A mover must have information about all of these factors, essentially knowledge of how these factors interrelate and define jumping capabilities, if she or he is expected to determine if a particular environment affords jumping.

Developing the Ability to Perceive Affordances

Whereas the vast majority of affordance research has focused on adults, recently there has been research concerning children. For example, Burton (1990) found that children could detect when an obstacle afforded going over or under, Gibson and Schmuckler (1989) found that children could detect when a surface afforded walking across, Pufall and Dunbar (1992) found that children could detect when a height afforded sitting upon or stepping over, and Newell, Scully, Tenenbaum, and Hardiman (1989) found that children could detect when they needed to change their grasping pattern to pick up varying size blocks. Apparently, young movers are as capable as older movers in detecting what the environment affords for action, and these young movers make these judgments based on information that is scaled to their own body dimensions and biodynamic capabilities.

In addition, children seem to be able to perceive affordances soon after they acquire a particular motor skill. For example, Gibson and Schmuckler (1989) noted that children who could only crawl did not perceive differences in surfaces (supported walking vs. did not support walking) whereas children who could walk, including relatively new walkers, did detect the difference (either did not try to go on surface or changed pattern to a crawl).

While it appears that children are able to perceive affordances, what has yet to be determined is if children can continually perceive changes in what the environment affords as their body dimensions and biodynamic capabilities change. It is apparent that developmental changes in the "action system" in childhood brings changes in the affordances of the environment (Gibson, 1987). That is, changes in body dimensions such as height or biodynamic capabilities such as strength allow developing movers the ability to perform new actions in the environment that were not previously possible (Heft, 1989; Konczak, 1990). As noted by Konczak (1990), "Perception does not only determine the action patterns of the observer, but the observer's motor development has in turn an impact on his/her perception." (p. 219).

In terms of jumping, can a child who accurately perceived that a puddle did not afford jumping over at age three given his or her biodynamic capabilities accurately perceive that puddle now affords jumping at age seven given his or her new capabilities? Unfortunately, developmental studies previously mentioned did not focus on this particular issue but focused on (a) changes in abilities that leads to the acquisition of a completely different skill (e.g., Gibson & Schmuckler—changes leading from crawling to walking), or (b) differences between subjects of different ages but who have all acquired the most skillful level of the skill (e.g., Pufall and Dunbar—sitting and stepping over for six- and 10-year-olds, all of whom were skillful in these tasks).

Thus, the purpose of this investigation is twofold. First, this study is designed to determine if movers of different ages, heights, and jumping abilities (the latter determined by maximal jumping distance) can accurately judge whether a skilled movement can or cannot be successfully performed. This will be examined by asking adults and children ages three, seven, and 11 years of age to judge whether various distances can or cannot be jumped. Each person's **perceived** maximum jumping distance will then be compared to his **actual** maximum jumping distance. One might speculate that older movers and more skilled movers would be more "in tune" with their bodies and would be more accurate at detecting the affordance for jumping distances compared to younger and less skilled jumpers. However, from an ecological approach, one would predict that even younger and less skilled jumpers would be able to detect affordances for action. Therefore, it is hypothesized that all jumpers, regardless of their age or abilities, will be able to match what distances they perceive can be jumped compared to what distances they actually can jump.

The second purpose of this investigation is to determine if a dimensionless pi value can be found that captures the unique affordance for jumping distances for all movers regardless of age and jumping abilities. This question will be examined by scaling a person's perceived critical action boundary for jumping distance to some key body dimension and calculating a dimensionless pi value. Most studies have used eye-height or leg length as body-scalers to calculate pi values. Because such factors probably have some role in describing jumping distances, these body dimensions were used in an effort to describe the affordance for jumping distances. However, studies by Konczak, Meeuwsen, and Cress (1990) and Carello et al. (1989) suggest that such simple body-proportion measures may not adequately capture the affordance for jumping across movers of varying body proportions and skill levels and that a more dynamic measure will be needed. As noted earlier, jumping is a complex movement involving the interaction of many factors (e.g., strength of many muscle groups, balance, flexibility, coordination, technique, courage, etc.). Therefore, it is virtually impossible to select one or two biodynamic factors that relate to a mover's jumping abilities. For example, leg strength in the extensor muscle group would not be a good indicator of jumping ability if a person had limited balance or technique (Wickstrom, 1983). Therefore, similar to Carello et al. (1989), actual jumping distance also will be used as a biodynamic-scaler to represent the delicate interrelationship between the varying biodynamic factors that describe a mover's jumping capabilities.

METHODS

Participants

Subjects included a total of 199 male children and adults divided into the following four groups: 35 adults 18-26 years of age; 43 children 2.5-4.5 years of age (3-year-olds); 53 children 6-8 years of age (7-year-olds); 68 children 10-12 years of age (11-year-olds). The adult group was sampled from physical education activity classes at the University of Maryland, and the children were sampled from a daycare center in Tucson, Arizona, and private daycare centers and primary schools in the metropolitan Washington, D.C. area. Group descriptive data of the 199 subjects who participated in the study are presented in Table 1. A frequency analysis was conducted to determine if each group was relatively normally distributed in terms of actual maximum jumping distance and height. This analysis revealed that the frequencies for each group were indeed normally distributed for height and for maximum jumping distances so that there were low standard errors and representation at both extremes of the distribution (a minimum of +/- two standard deviations).

The ages for the children's groups were selected based on the empirical evidence that children can first demonstrate a two-footed jump for distance around the age of three years (Clark & Phillips, 1985). Since one of the purposes of this study was to determine if children can accurately detect affordances at the onset of a new skill, the inclusion of the three-year-old group was appropriate for the study of distance jumping. Once a child acquires the ability to jump distances, there is a gradual improvement

Table 1
Descriptive Data for all Groups of Subjects

3 yr	Age(mths/yrs)	HT(in)	MJ(in)	Wt(lb)	LL(in)	EH(in)	PJ(in)
mean	44.0/3.7	39.9	24.1	34.2	21.8	35.4	27.6
min	34.0/2.8	35.0	10.3	25.5	18.0	30.0	10.5
max	54.0/4.5	43.0	40.7	42.0	25.0	39.0	46.5
SD	5.3/0.4 2.1	7.2	4.1	1.6	2.2	8.7	
SE	0.81	0.32	1.09	0.62	0.25	0.33	1.33
7 yr							
mean	90.8/7.6	50.1	46.9	57.0	29.5	45.5	46.9
min	79.0/6.6	43.0	28.3	39.5	24.0	38.5	25.5
max	102./8.5	54.5	61.0	95.5	33.0	50.5	67.0
SD	6.2/0.5 2.4	6.9	10.6	1.9	2.4	7.7	
SE	0.85	0.34	0.94	1.46	0.26	0.32	1.06
11 yr							
mean	130.4/10.9	58.2	56.0	87.8	35.2	53.4	54.9
min	114.0/9.5	53.0	32.7	57.5	30.5	48.0	34.5
max	144.0/12.0	67.0	75.7	140.0	40.0	63.0	76.5
SD	7.2/0.6 3.0	8.7	21.1	2.2	2.9	10.0	
SE	0.88	0.36	1.05	2.56	0.26	0.35	01.2
Adults							
mean	256.6/21.3	71.5	85.7	170.3	42.6	66.7	81.7
min	233.0/19.4	63.5	66.0	115.0	37.5	59.5	64.0
max	316.0/26.3	77.0	106.7	283.0	50.0	74.5	103.5
SD	18.74/ 1.5	3.45	9.27	33.1	2.7	3.6	10.3
SE	3.17	0.58	1.57	5.60	.46	.60	1.7

Key:
HT = Height
MJ = Actual Maximum Standing Long Jump
WT = Weight
LL = Leg Length (hip to floor)
EH = Eye Height
PJ = Perceived Maximum Standing Long Jump

in the absolute distance a child can jump throughout childhood and into adolescence (Espenschade & Eckert, 1980). It also has been reported that the arm and leg action of the jumping pattern changes during the childhood years with significant differences between three and seven years of age (Clark & Phillips, 1985; Wickstrom, 1983) (see Table 2 for the developmental sequence for jumping distances). However, the majority of seven-year-olds still cannot demonstrate the most skillful jumping pattern (Clark & Phillips, 1985). Therefore, the seven-year-olds represented children whose jumping pattern and absolute distances jumped were different from the three-year-olds, yet not at the most skillful level of jumping. Finally, the 11-year-olds represented children who may have acquired the most skillful jumping pattern as defined by Clark & Phillips (1985).

Thus, the three age groups selected provided a sample of children who represented the spectrum of jumping development from the onset of

Table 2
Developmental Sequences for the Standing Long Jump[1]

Level I

Arm Action - no arm action, arms remain immobile throughout propulsive phase, may exhibit shoulder retraction ("winging") close to take-off.

Leg Action - Stepping out; one-footed take-off.

Level II

Arm Action - shoulder flexion only; arms remain immobile during lower extremity flexion. Shoulder flexion occurs with lower extremity extension; some shoulder abduction may be seen.

Leg Action - Knee extension precedes heels up.

Level III

Arm Action - incomplete biphasis arm action; shoulder hyperextension occurs during lower extremity flexion; shoulder flexion occurs with lower extremity extension; shoulder flexion incomplete (less than 160^0)

Leg Action - Knee extension and heels up simultaneously

Level IV

Arm Action - Complete biphasis arm action; same as level III except should flexion is complete (greater than 160^0) at take-off.

Leg Action - Knee extension follows heels up.

[1] From Clark, J.E., & Phillips, S.J. (1985). A developmental sequence of the standing long jump. In J.E. Clark & J.H. Humphrey (Eds.), *Motor development: Current selected research* (Vol. 1, pp. 73-85). Princeton, NJ: Princeton Press.

jumping to an age that might show the most skillful jumping pattern. This age range will help answer the question: Can children with different levels of skillfulness and who use qualitatively different jumping patterns perceive the affordance for jumping distances?

Procedures

All subjects were dressed in loose fitting clothing and soft-soled shoes that did not hinder their ability to demonstrate a maximum standing long jump. Each subject was tested individually in a quiet but large play area inside or outside his school. Because testing took place in a variety of settings, care was taken to have adequate lighting and a relatively consistent background at each setting.

After the subject was given time to get acquainted with the environment, the examiner explained the procedures. Verbal explanations and demonstrations were provided to the two older age groups and the adults. Children in the two youngest age groups were given extra training on the task with pieces of plastic that were not within the ranges actually used during testing. Training consisted of having the child stand at one edge of an extremely short and extremely long piece of plastic and, with prompting as needed, judge correctly that the distance could or could not be jumped using a two-footed take-off and landing. In some instances, subjects in the youngest age group were allowed to jump over a piece of plastic to ensure that he fully understood the task. Training continued until the child demonstrated an ability to independently make yes/no judgments.

During the actual collection of data, subjects stood at one end of a piece of blue plastic (measuring 1/8th-inch thick by 12 inches wide and ranging from three inches to nine feet in length in three-inch increments) and judged (verbal yes/no response) whether the distance across a piece of plastic could be jumped across using a two-footed take-off and landing. After the first perceived jump, the plastic piece was taken away and a different length piece was placed in front of the subject. This new piece of plastic and all subsequent pieces were presented randomly, and the subject was not able to see the plastic piece until it was placed in front of him. The subject then judged the jumpability of the new plastic piece following the procedure above. Each subject made a total of three such judgments for each distance presented. Based on pilot work and work reported by Espenschade (1960), the examiner estimated what range of lengths to present each subject. What occasionally resulted in the initial set of presentations was the inclusion of lengths that were excessively long or short for a particular subject (i.e., the subject had already responded "yes" or "no" to several other, longer or shorter lengths). After this first set of presentations, these extraneous pieces were excluded for the last two sets of presentations so that each subject was presented only those lengths that would elicit a minimum of three "yes" and three "no" responses. Thus, subjects actually viewed and made a judgment on anywhere from 19 to 25 pieces of plastic. depending on how quickly the examiner could determine the point at which three yes and three no responses could be elicited. The range of lengths presented for each group varied based on actual jumping abilities (i.e., how far subjects could jump). As it turned out, there was a greater range in jumping abilities in older subjects compared to younger subjects. The actual range of distances were as follows:

3-year-old	1/4 feet	to	4 1/2 feet
7-year-old	2 feet	to	6 feet
11-year-old	3 feet	to	7 1/2 feet
adults	3 feet	to	9 feet

If necessary during testing, some of the three-year-olds (approximately half) were allowed to demonstrate an understanding of yes/no by jumping over the distances they perceived as jumpable and not jumping (shaking their heads no) over distances they perceived as not jumpable. Such an accommodation is not uncommon in affordances research with young children (e.g., Gibson et al., 1987; Ulrich et al., 1990). No feedback was given during the experiment other than reinforcement for good attitude for the younger subjects.

After all the judgments had been made, each person's actual maximum jumping distance (best of three jumps) was measured along with total height (floor to top of head), eye height (floor to center of eyeball), leg height (floor to ischial prominence), and weight (in pounds). The following dependent measures were then calculated (means for each subject and means for each of the groups).

1. *Perceived maximum jumping distance (i.e., critical action boundary):* The distance that a subject perceived to be his maximum jumping distance (i.e., the critical action boundary for jumping) was used as the dependent measure. This critical action boundary was defined as the point at which a person judged a distance to be jumpable 50% of the time and not jumpable 50% of the time (Warren, 1983). This was determined by taking the three judgments (yes/no responses) at each distance and calculating a percentage of "yes" responses. For example, a person who judged "yes" two out of three times at a given distance received a score of 66% yes response at that distance. The critical action boundary of 50% was interpolated from the data.

2. *Pil: Ratio of critical action boundary to actual maximal jump* (biodynamic measure): This was calculated by dividing the distance that was defined as the critical action boundary by each person's actual maximum jumping distance. For example, if a critical action boundary was 36 inches and a persons maximum jumping distance was 42 inches, then 36 divided by 42 = .857.

3. *Pi2: Ratio of critical action boundary to leg-length*: This was calculated by dividing the distance that was defined as the critical action boundary (as determined above) by a person's leg-length. For example, if a critical action boundary was 36 inches and a person's leg length was 24 inches, then 36 divided by 24 = 1.50.

4. *Pi3: Ratio of critical action boundary to eye-height*: This was calculated by dividing the distance that was defined as the critical action boundary by a person's eye-height. For example, if a critical action boundary was 36 inches and a person's eye-height was 54 inches, then 36 divided by 54 = .667.

Data Analysis

A Pearson product-moment correlation was calculated between (1) perceived maximum jumping distance as defined by that distance at which the subject responds with 50% "yes" judgments, and (2) a person's actual maximum jumping distance to determine if males of different ages, heights, and skill levels were accurate at judging if a distance was jumpable or not jumpable (alpha was set at .01). Also, absolute and algebraic differences were calculated to determine how accurate subjects were at detecting the affordance for jumping distances. Absolute differences were calculated by taking the difference (without regard to direction of difference, i.e., positive or negative) between perceived and actual maximal jumping for each subject. Algebraic difference between perceived and actual maximal jumping were determined for each subject by subtracting actual maximum jump distance from perceived maximum jump distance (taking into account the direction of the difference). A subject who **overestimated** how far he could jump would have a perceived maximal jump value that was greater than his actual maximal jump value (positive value). On the other hand, a subject who **underestimated** how far he could jump would have a perceived maximal jump value that was less than his actual maximal jump value (negative value). Mean absolute and algebraic differences were then calculated for each subgroup (to determine if there was any developmental trend) as well as for all groups together.

Four multiple regression analyses were used to determine if a dimensionless pi value could be calculated to describe this affordance independent of age, body dimensions, and performance level. The first multiple regression used *perceived maximum jumping distance* as the criterion and a person's age, actual maximum jumping distance, height, weight, leg length, and eye height as the predictors. The next three multiple regressions used *pi values* as the criterion (pi values were calculated using actual maximum jumping distance, eye-height, and leg length as body-scaled references) and age, height, eye-height, leg length, weight, and actual maximum jumping distance as the predictors to determine if one pi value could be used to capture the affordance for jumping for all subjects independent of the predictors. If a calculated pi value was independent of these factors, then the amount of variance that could be accounted for by the regression equation (the R^2 value) would be low when pi was the criterion. On the other hand, if the pi value was not independent of age, body dimensions, and/or performance level, then the R^2 value would be high. The Statistical Package for the Social Sciences (SPSS-PC) was used for all analyses.

RESULTS

Pearson-product moment correlation between perceived maximum jumping distance (i.e., critical action boundary) and actual maximum jumping distance was significant (0.932, $p<.001$). Figure 1 graphically depicts the correlation between perceived and actual maximum jumping distances for the four groups of subjects combined.

The average absolute and algebraic difference between perceived and actual maximum jumping for the four groups of subjects are contained in Table 3. Also, mean "effect-size" (E- size) differences were calculated for each group by dividing a group's mean absolute difference by their standard deviation for either actual maximum jump (E-size[jump]) or height (E-size[height]). The E-size measure, described in standard deviation units, eliminated variations across groups because of different jumping distances or heights. For example, an E-size[jump] difference of .96 for the adult group indicated that the difference between how far an adult actually could jump compared to how far he perceived he could jump differed on average

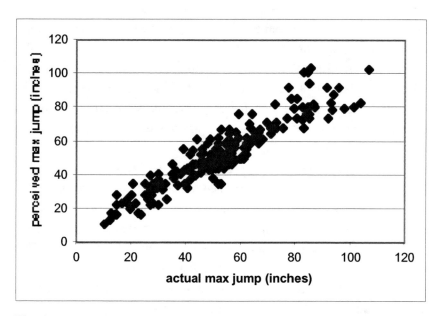

Fig. 1. Correlation between perceived maximum jump and actual maximum jump—all subjects.

Table 3

**Mean, Absolute, Algebraic, and Effect-size (E-size)Ddifferences
Between Perceived and Actual Maximum Jump Distances**

Group	MJ	PJ	Absolute	Algebraic	E-size [jump]	E-size [height]
3-yr-olds	24.1"	27.6"	4.97 in	+ 3.5 in	0.69	2.37
7-yr-olds	46.9"	46.9"	4.92 in	+ 0.0 in	0.71	2.05
11-yr-olds	56.0"	54.9"	5.66 in	- 1.1 in	0.65	1.89
adults	85.7"	81.7"	8.9 in	- 4.0 in	0.96	2.58

by nearly one standard deviation unit. Mean E-size differences also can be found in Table 3.

In terms of mean absolute error and algebraic error, it appears that the adults are the least accurate at judging how far they can jump. It is interesting to note that even with the scaled E-size measurements, the adults still appear to be the least accurate at judging how far they can jump.

The calculation of mean algerbaic differences for each group showed that adults and 11-year-olds tend to **understimate** how far they can jump while the three-year-olds tend to **overestimate** how far they can jump. The 7-year-olds appear to be in transition between over and underestimating. Calculating each person's algebraic error separately indicated that 71% of the adults (25/35) and 63% of the 11-year-olds (43/68) underestimated how far they could actually jump while 83% of the three-year-olds (36/43) and 52% of the seven-year-olds (28/53) overestimated how far they could jump.

As expected, adult jumpers and older children judged farther distances to be jumpable compared to younger children. Similarly, jumpers within each group who had greater actual maximum jumping distances (i.e., more skilled jumpers) judged farther distances to be jumpable compared to other jumpers in their group who had shorter actual maximum jumping distances.

The second question was whether a dimensionless pi value could be calculated to describe the mover-environment fit for jumpability for all subjects regardless of age, maximum jumping performance, and height. Four multiple regression analyses were conducted. The first multiple regression used perceived maximum jumping distance as the criterion and age, actual maximum jumping distance, height, leg length, eye height, and weight as the predictors. This multiple regression was conducted to establish the relationship between the predictors and perceived maximum jumping distance (although this was somewhat established with the simple correlations). The succeeding three multiple regressions used pi values calculated with the

following body-scalers as the criterion: pi1–**actual maximum jump**, pi2–
leg-length, and pi3–**eye-height**. The same predictors used in the first regression analysis were used in the later three analyses. Because the interest of this analysis (and all subsequent regression analyses) was in the
overall regression results and not the incremental regression results,
all of the predictor variables were assigned the same level of entry
(Pedhazur, 1982, p. 88).

The multiple R for the first regression equation using perceived maximum jumping distance as the criterion was 0.937. Thus, the predictors
accounted for approximately 88% (R^2 = 0.878) of the variance in perceived maximum jumping distance. Given the strong association between
each of the predictors and perceived maximum jumping (see Table 4), it
was not surprising that so much of perceived maximum jumping distance
could be accounted for in this equation.

Table 4
Correlations Between Perceived Max Jump and Selected Variables

max jump:	$r = .932$*leg-length:*	$r = .851$
height:	$r = .874$*eye-height:*	$r = .876$
age:	$r = .868$*weight:*	$r = .780$

In the next three regression analyses, perceived maximum jump distance was substituted with the pi values discussed above. Recall that for a
dimensionless pi value to be effective as a unique descriptor of the mover-
environment fit, it should not be associated with any specific variable or
group of variables. That is, the R value in the regression analysis would
have to be low as would the R^2 value (the "accounted variance"). The
results of the three multiple regressions with pi as the criterion are presented in Table 5.

As can be seen in Table 5, the amount of variance that could be accounted for in the equation (i.e., the R^2 value) was very high when an ex-

Table 5
Results from Multiple Regressions

Criterion	Multiple R	R^2
perceived max jump	0.937	0.878
pi1 percjump/maxjump	0.482	0.232
pi2 percjump/leglength	0.791	0.626
pi3 percjump/eyeheight	0.793	0.628

trinsic measure of jumping was used (nearly 88% when perceived maximal jumping was the criterion). However, when pi1 (an intrinsic measure) was used as the criterion, the amount of variance that could be accounted for by the predictors was substantially reduced (less than 24%). This was not the case when pi2 or pi3 were used as the criterion. In these latter two cases, the variance accounted for was still very high, approximately 63% in both equations. It appears then that the pi value that comes closest to capturing the mover-environment fit for jumping distances is the one that used actual maximum jumping distance (pi1) as the body-scaler.

DISCUSSION

The purpose of this study was to determine if children and adults of varying ages, body dimensions, and physical abilities could accurately judge if a distance could be jumped across using a two-footed take-off and landing. That is, could children and adults detect the **affordance** for jumping distances. It was a further purpose of this study to determine if a dimensionless pi value could be calculated using some body-scaled metric that captured the unique mover-environment fit (affordance) for jumping distances for all subjects independent of age, height, weight, and maximum jumping distance. These questions were examined from an ecological perspective of perception in which the mover and the environment are described in concert with each other (Gibson, 1979,1986; Turvey & Carello, 1988; Warren, 1988).

Results support the notion that children can accurately judge if a distance could or could not be jumped across (the affordance for jumping distances). The correlation between perceived and actual maximum jumping distance was significant (0.932, $p<.001$), and the absolute difference between these two values was relatively low (less than one standard deviation). Even the youngest children in this study, those with presumably the least amount of experience in jumping forward, were able to accurately detect the affordance for jumping distances. That is, their perceptions of how far they could jump were closely related to how far they actually could jump. Such findings are consistent with an ecological view of perception, which suggests that a mover can perceive the limits of an action very soon after that mover acquires the capability to perform that action (Gibson, 1987; Palmer, 1989; Ulrich et al., 1990).

Interestingly, the absolute difference as well as the effect size difference was greater in the adult group compared to that found in the children's groups. Thus, it appeared that children were more accurate than adults in detecting the affordance for jumping. There are two possible explanations for these findings. The most obvious explanation for the differences found between the adult's perception compared to the children's is the fact that the adults were judging much greater distances. The average actual maximum jumping distance for the adults was 85.7 inches compared to 24.1, 46.9, and 56.0, for the three-year-olds, seven-year-olds, 11-year-olds, respectively. While calculating the differences as an effect size did take differences in actual maximal jumping into consideration, it still can be argued that the farther the distance to be judged, the greater likelihood of error. For example, many of the adults were making judgments on distances of six feet or more (an average of 120%of their standing height) whereas many of the three-year-olds were making judgements of less than two and a half feet (an average of 60% of their standing height). There certainly is more room for error when greater distances are involved.

Secondly, the adults had the least amount of *current* experience with the standing long jump. Many of the adults reported that they had not performed a standing long jump since junior high school while many of the seven- and 11-year-olds reported that they had performed a standing long jump within the past year in their physical education classes. It also can be argued that many of the three-year-olds who have just acquired the ability to jump forward spend a good portion of their young lives playing and experimenting (albeit practicing) with their newfound ability to jump forward. As noted by Heft (1989), exploration and experience helps movers learn more about their motor skills, while at the same time learning about critical environmental features. In essence, experience helps the mover fine tune his or her ability to extract critical information from the environment as it relates to affordances for action (Gibson, 1987; Heft, 1989; Mark et al., 1990; Ulrich et al., 1990). Thus, lack of experience in jumping by adults in this study may have diminished their accuracy in perceiving the particular affordance for the standing long jump. These results are similar to the result of Mark et al. (1990) in which practice improved accuracy of perceiving the affordance for sitting.

Another interesting finding was that most of the adults underestimated how far they could jump (25 out of 35) as opposed to the three- and seven-year-olds who tended to overestimate how far they could acually jump. These results are similar to Mark (1987), Mark and Vogele (1988), and Carello et al. (1989) in which their adult subjects tended to underestimate their cabililities. But why would there be a developmental trend in which younger children overestimate and older children and adults underestimate? One possible explanation is that adults were more cautious of their estimations in an effort not to make an error. Adults in general have had more opportunity to judge their capabilities in a variety of movement activities and settings, and no doubt they have lived with the consequences of overestimating their abilities. Overestimation, unlike underestimation, can lead to failure of a task and even injury. As suggested by Carello et al. (1989), underestimating in reaching can be considered pragmatic and conservative in that underestimating provides a safety cushion for the reacher (will not reach so far as to displace the center of support). Adults in this study, and to some extent the 11-year-olds, may have consciously (or unconsciously) underestimated their skills to provide a safety/success cushion in their judgments. This safety/success cushion may not have been utilized by younger children who may have been less cautious in their estimations of what they could or could not do.

These results are not surprising given previous data on perception of academic abilities in children (e.g., Parsons & Ruble, 1977; Stipek, 1981; Stipek & Hoffman, 1980). Whereas subjects in the current study were not under the same social pressure regarding success and failure as children in an academic setting, results from academic research is interesting to note. For example, Parsons and Ruble (1977) found that previous success/failure experiences had a greater and more systematic influence on older school-aged children's (nine and a half- to 11-year-olds) expectancies than on the expectancies of preschoolers (three and a half- to five-year-olds). That is, there was a general decline in expectancies with age. The authors presented two hypotheses for these results. First, they suggested that older children may be more responsive to failure and less responsive to success compared to younger children. Alternatively, they proposed that older children may have learned that it is "more ego protective and/or more socially acceptable to express less rather than more certainty of success" (1977, p. 1079). Similarly, Stipek (1981) found that second and third graders made more realistic, performance-related judgments of their own abilities compared to kindergarteners, and Stipek and Hoffman (1980) found that three- and four-year-old children tended to make higher judgments of their future performance compared to seven- and eight-year-olds.

In the case of judging if a distance can or cannot be jumped, it was clear that the three groups of children each responded differently in terms of their judgements. The three-year-olds overestimated how far they could jump, the 11-year-olds underestimated how far they could jump, and the seven-year-olds were in transition between these two states. This is not to say that an individual child or group of children intentionally approached the task in a certain way. All of the children were told to make as accurate a judgment as possible, and it appeared that the vast majority of the subjects made every effort to comply with this directive. It may be that the younger children in this study were less affected by past successes or failures as suggested above by Stipek (1981) and Stipek and Hoffman (1980). On the other hand, as Parson and Ruble (1970) suggested, the younger children may not have used the protective strategy of underestimating their abilities like the 11-year-olds and adults. Certainly, much more research is needed to determine why such a developmental trend may occur in perceiving affordances for action.

Regarding the second question, pi1 (which used actual maximum jumping distance as a biodynamic-scaler) came closest to capturing the unique mover-environment fit (i.e., the affordance) for jumping distances. A true dimensionless pi value would have been the same for all subjects independent of their age, maximum jumping distance, and height (including leg length and eye height). The pi values that used leg length and eye height as body-scalers (pi2 and pi3, respectively) were clearly not the same across subjects. That is, as maximum jumping distance increased, the corresponding pi value increased proportionately. Pi2 and pi3 were not effective in capturing the affordance for jumping distances across subjects with varying ages, heights, and maximum jumping distances. These results contrast findings from previous studies in which leg length and/or eye height were effective body-scalers (e.g., Mark, 1987; Warren, 1984). However, these findings are consistent with Ulrich et al., (1990) in which variations in body proportions did not explain why new walkers and toddlers selected certain riser heights over others when presented with several different stair sets, Konczak et al. (1990) in which leg length did not explain differences in the affordance for stair climbing, and Carello et al. (1989) in which arm length did not explain differences in the affordance for reaching. Why would a biodynamic-scaler be more effective than body-metric scalers in capturing the affordance for jumping distances for subjects of such varying body proportions and abilities? Actual maximum jumping distance captures the true dynamics of jumping and thus reflects the action potential of the mover (Carello et al., 1989; Ulrich, Thelen, & Niles, 1990). That is, the calculation of actual maximum jumping distance includes the impact of such biomechanical factors as leg strength, speed, flexibility, coordination (e.g., take-off angle, timing, arm action), and control, as well as body proportions. Because it is virtually impossible to measure all of these elements separately, they are all included in the measurement of **actual maximum jumping distance**. Thus, the use of such a measure more accurately reflects individual differences between movers and thus captures the unique mover-environment fit (affordance) for jumping distances. Pi2 and pi3 (scaled only to body proportions) fails to consider these other dynamic factors.

Thus, it appear that biodynamic-scalers should be used in conjunction with body metric scalers as a referent for the mover. Biodynamic scalers takes into account a mover's capacity for movement (action potential), as well as his or her body dimensions. Such a measure is more in line with Gibson's notion of an affordance. Recall that Gibson defined an affordance as the functional utility of the environment in terms of what actions it can support given the **unique movement capabilities of the mover** (Gibson, 1977; Warren, 1983, 1988). Body dimensions alone do not capture the movement capabilities of the mover, whereas biodynamic scalers take into account the action potential of the mover as well as body dimensions.

Ideally, researchers could partition out various biodynamic factors that are related to skilled movement and use these as scalers. Such partitioning was successfully done by Konczak et al. (1990) when they found that leg strength and flexibility were effective biodynamic scalers for stair climbing in older vs. younger women. Unfortunately, most movements do not lend themselves to such partitioning. As noted by Carello et al. (1989) in their study of reaching, the complexity of the shoulder joint precluded the use of body metrics or other biodynamic measures to truly capture the affordance for reaching. In the case of jumping in which leg action and arm action must be coordinated, in which jumping skill is defined by a delicate interrelationship between balance, strength, flexibility, courage, and confidence, it is virtually impossible to partition biodynamic factors into scalers. Thus, a more global measure may be needed when analyzing such motor behaviors.

REFERENCES

Bingham, G.P., Schmidt, R.C., & Rosenblum, L.D. (1989). Hefting for a maximum distance throw: A smart perceptual system. *Journal of Experimental Psychology: Human Perception and Performance, 15,* 507-528.

Burton, A.W. (1990). Assessing the perceptual-motor interaction in developmentally disabled and nonhandicapped children. *Adapted Physical Activity Quarterly, 7,* 325—337.

Carello, C., Grosofsky, A., Reichel, F., Solomon, H.Y., & Turvey, M.T. (1989). Visually perceiving what is reachable. *Ecological Psychology, 1,* 27-54.

Clark, J.E., & Phillips, S.J. (1985). A developmental sequence of the standing long jump. In J.E. Clark & J.H. Humphrey (Eds.). *Motor development: Current selected research* (pp. 73-85). New York: Princeton Press.

Espenschade, A.S. (1960). Motor development. In W.R. Johnson (Ed.), *Science and medicine of exercise and sports* (pp. 419-439). New York: Harper & Row.

Espenschade, A.S., & Eckert, H.M. (1980). *Motor development* (2nd ed.). Columbus, OH: Charles E. Merrill.

Gibson, E.J. (1987). Introductory Essay: What does infant perception tell us about theories of perception? *Journal of Experimental Psychology: Human Perception and Performance, 13,* 515-523.

Gibson, E.J., Riccio, G., Schmuckler, M.A., Stoffregen, T.A., Rosenberg, D., & Taormina, J. (1987). Detection of the traversability of surfaces by crawling and walking infants. *Journal of Experimental Psychology: Human Perception and Performance., 13,* 533-544.

Gibson, E.J., & Schmuckler, M.A. (1989). Going somewhere: An ecological and experimental approach to development of mobility. *Ecological Psychology, 1*, 3-25.

Gibson, E.J., & Walk, R.D. (1960). The visual cliff. *Scientific American,
202*, 64-71.

Gibson, J.J. (1977a). The theory of affordances. In R. Shaw & J. Bradford
(Eds.), *Perceiving, acting, and knowing: Toward an ecological
psychology*. Hillsdale, NJ: Erlbaum.

Gibson, J.J. (1986). *The ecological approach to visual perception*. Hillsdale,
NJ: Lawrence Erlbaum (original work published 1979).

Heft, H. (1989). Affordances and the body: An intentional analysis of
Gibson's ecological approach to visual perception. *Journal for the
Theory of Social Behavior, 19*, 1-30.

Konczak, J. (1990). Toward an ecological theory of motor development:
The relevance of the Gibsonian approach to vision for motor development research. In J.E. Clark & J.H. Humphrey (Eds.), *Advances in motor development research* (Vol. 3, pp. 201-223). New
York: AMS Press.

Konczak, J., Meeuwsen, H.J., & Cress, E.M. (1992). Changing affordances
in stair climbing: The perception of maximum climbability in young
adult and older women. *Journal of Experimental Psychology:
Human Perception and Peformance, 18*, 691-697.

Mark, L.S., (1987). Eyeheight-scaled information about affordances: A study
of sitting and stair climbing. *Journal of Experimental Psychology:
Human Perception and Performance, 13*, 361-370.

Mark, L.S., Balliett, J.A., Craver, K.D., Douglas, S.D., & Fox, T. (1990).
What an actor must do in order to perceive the affordance for sitting. *Ecological Psychology, 2*, 325-366.

Mark, L.S., & Dainoff, M.J. (1988). An ecological framework for ergo-
nomic research. *Innovations, 7*, 8-11.

Mark, L.S., & Vogele, D. (1987). A biodynamic basis for perceived categories of action: A study of sitting and stair climbing. *Journal of Motor
Behavior, 19*, 367-384.

Michaels, C.F., & Carello, C. (1981). *Direct perception*. Englewood Cliffs,
NJ: Prentice Hall.

Newell, K.M., Scully, D.M., Tenebaum, F., & Hardiman, S. (1989). Body-
scaled and the development of prehension. *Developmental psycho-
biology, 22*, 1-13.

Palmer, C.F. (1989). The discriminating nature of infants' exploratory actions. *Developmental Psychology, 25*, 885-893.

Parsons, J.E., and Ruble, D.N. (1977). The development of achievement-
related expectancies. *Child Development, 48*, 1075-1079.

Pedhazur, E.J. (1982). *Multiple regression in behavioral research* (2nd ed.).
Fort Worth, TX: Holt, Rinehart and Winston, Inc.

Phillips. S.J., Clark. J.E., & Petersen, R.D. (1985). Developmental differences in standing long jump take-off parameters. *Journal of Human Movement Studies, 11*, 75-87.

Pufall, P.B., & Dunbar, C. (1992). Perceiving whether or not the world affords stepping onto and over: A developmental study. *Ecological Psychology, 4*, 17-38.

Stipek, D.J. (1981). Children's perceptions of their own and their classmates ability. *Journal of Educational Psychology, 73*, 404-410.

Stipek, D.J., & Hoffman, J.M. (1980). Development of children's performance-related judgements. *Child Development, 51*, 912-914.

Turvey, M.T. & Carello, C. (1986). The ecological approach to perceiving-acting: A pictorial essay. *Acta Psychologica, 63*, 133-155.

Turvey, M.T., & Carello, C. (1988). Exploring a law-based, ecological approach to skilled action. In A.M. Colley & J.R. Beech (Eds.), *Cognition and action in skilled behavior*. North-Holland: Elsevier Sciences Publishers.

Turvey, M.T., Shaw, R.E., Reed, E.S., & Mace, W.M. (1981). Ecological laws of perceiving and acting: In reply to Fodor and Pylyshyn (1981). *Cognition, 9*, 237-404.

Ulrich, B.D., Thelen, E., & Niles, D. (1990). Perceptual determinants of action: Stair climbing choices of infants and toddlers. In J.E. Clark & J.H. Humphrey (Eds.). *Advances in motor development research* (Vol. 3, pp. 1-15). New York: AMS Press.

Warren, W.H. (1983). *A biodynamic basis for perception and action in bipedal stair climbing* (Doctoral dissertation, University of Connecticut, 1982). *Dissertation Abstracts International, 43*, 4183-B.

Warren, W.H. (1984). Perceiving affordances: Visual guidance of stair climbing. *Journal of Experimental Psychology: Human Perception and Performance, 10*, 683-703.

Warren, W.H. (1988). Action modes and laws of control for the visual guidance of action. In O.G. Meijer & K. Roth (Eds.), *Complex Movement Behaviour: The motor action controversy* (pp. 339-380). North-Holland: Elsevier Science Publishers.

Warren, W.H., & Whang, S. (1987). Visually guidance of walking through apertures: Body-scaled information for affordances. *Journal of Experimental Psychology: Human Perception and Performance, 13*, 371-383.

Warren, W.H., Young, D.S., & Lee, D.N. (1986). Visual control of step length during running over irregular terrain. *Journal of Experimental Psychology: Human Perception and Performance. 12*, 259-266.

Wickstrom, R.L. (1983). *Fundamental motor patterns* (3rd ed.). Philadelphia: Lea & Febiger.

REVIEWS

8

THE MOUNTAIN OF MOTOR DEVELOPMENT:
A METAPHOR

Jane E. Clark
Jason S. Metcalfe

ABSTRACT

Throughout history, the field of motor development has employed a number of metaphors to explain how motor skills develop. These metaphors have typically described either the products or the processes of development, but few metaphors have provided an integrated framework to facilitate our understanding of both. Using Clark's characterization of six periods in motor skill development and concepts from the dynamic systems perspective, we present the metaphor of "the mountain" as an integrated framework to characterize both the products and processes of motor development. The metaphor of the mountain emphasizes the cumulative, sequential, and interactive nature of motor skill development as an emergent product of lifelong changes in multiple sources of constraint on behavior. Implications of selecting a developmental metaphor are discussed with regard to the utility of such descriptions for generating new insights and ultimately leading to formalized theories and models for a deeper understanding of the fundamental questions in motor skill development.

As infants, we all were once challenged to reach out for a toy we wanted or to walk independently across the living room carpet. Later in our lives, some of us may have become skilled basketball players, cellists, or dancers, while others were pleased to drive our cars safely or walk across the kitchen without spilling our coffee. Whether we become Olympians or not, across our lives, our motor skills will be dramatically transformed. Understanding how these transformations occur and what results from these transformations is the focus of motor development. That is, motor development has been defined as the changes in motor behavior over the lifespan *and* the processes that underlie these changes (Clark & Whitall, 1989, p. 194).

To understand motor development is no small challenge. Over the last century, researchers have discovered a vast catalog of facts and relationships about when and in what order motor skills appear as well as the factors that influence these behaviors. But, how can we put all this information together to make sense of it? What is the relationship between the appearance of one motor skill and the disappearance of another? Why do some individuals develop skills and others do not? In science, we use several approaches for organizing what we know and what we might expect in the future. In general, these approaches come under the heading of "theory building." Theories take the facts we have discovered and provide a framework within which these facts can be systematically related.

Theories represent formal systems within which facts are connected and predictions are made about future events. Part of theory construction is the use of models and metaphors. Models too are formal systems. A model gives us a way of visualizing or representing concepts that are often difficult to grasp. For example, an inverted pendulum has been employed as a physical model of upright standing. We can "see" a pendulum (basically a ball atop a stick) standing on a surface. What forces, applied where, will push it over? Models can also be symbolic. Such symbolic representations usually take the form of mathematical equations depicting the phenomenon. In our upright standing example, an equation could be derived that would represent the behavior of the pendulum. If we changed parameters of the equation, for example, increasing the stiffness of the pendulum, we would predict specific outcomes such as increasing sway frequency. Would these predictions hold true for the behavior of a person standing quietly? By having a model of the behavior, we can generate and test formal hypotheses to help us understand the phenomenon better.

Another heuristic device that is used in science is the metaphor. As Snow writes, "Models are scientific metaphors..." (1973, p. 82). A metaphor, like a model, is when one object or idea stands for another, indicating a similarity or analogy between the two. Though the distinction between the two may be blurred, we will distinguish them on their level of formality. A model is a formal system that is usually connected to a set of empirical data, whereas a metaphor is often the first approximation of a representation and is therefore less formal and more speculative. Both are judged on their utility in conceptualizing difficult phenomena as well as their capacity to generate new and insightful ideas.

As we try to understand motor development, theories, models, and metaphors are important tools that we use. In this chapter, we focus on metaphors that have been used for representing the "big picture" of how motor skills change across the lifespan. From conception to the end of life, how do our *purposeful, goal-directed* movements change? Our quest is to understand how individuals become skillful in their movement. Skillful movement is characterized by its efficiency, its adaptability, and its certainty of outcome (Clark, 1994, 1995). To be skillful, a performer must move with biomechanical, psychological, and physiological efficiency. While being consistent, the skilled performer must also maintain the adaptability to adjust when conditions change. As we examine metaphors of motor development, we seek those that focus on representing the changing nature of motor behavior across the lifespan with a view to those behaviors that lead to motor skill.

SELECTING AN APPROPRIATE METAPHOR
FOR MOTOR DEVELOPMENT

Although it is not within the scope of this chapter to thoroughly discuss the use of metaphors in theory construction, it is important to address some dimensions for assessing the quality of a metaphor for conceptualizing the development of motor skills. In this section, we highlight key elements of a suitable metaphor and later follow with a brief critique of some metaphors that have previously been employed in our field. In the final section, we review a metaphor that we have used as a framework for teaching motor development and one that may help us better understand the relationship between the products and processes of lifespan motor development.

Two Levels for Assessing Metaphors

The quality of a scientific metaphor should be considered on two levels. The first is at the level of the metaphor itself, or what we will call the level of *local application*. Local application refers to aspects of the metaphor that influence its quality and suitability with respect to the phenomena that the scientist wants to represent. Such factors include how well the chosen representation fits with knowledge about the nature of the phenomena, simplicity, and the extent to which the metaphor aids in deployment and extension of knowledge of the phenomena. Evaluation of the metaphor at this level is based on the criteria of *usefulness*. As Reese and Overton (1970) discussed, theoretic characterizations in the form of metaphors "cannot be assessed as true or false" rather, they can only be "more or less useful" (p.120). In other words, the metaphor does not need to directly correspond to the phenomena; rather, the metaphor should provide a framework for the development of adequate characterizations to assist in understanding the phenomena. An example of a question one would ask with respect to motor development, is "How similar is the metaphor to the process of change in skill development?" Does the metaphor accurately *represent* what is known about how motor skills change?

Whereas the local application of the metaphor is critical to its usefulness, a metaphor must also fit with a broad view of how nature is organized. This level, the level of *global assumptions*, considers the metaphor with respect to fundamental assumptions regarding the *nature* of the process the scientist wishes to represent. When considering the global assumptions of a metaphor, we want to know whether it adequately reflects the organization of relations between elements of the metaphor as well as how it can be situated within the larger organization of nature. In developmental theory, global assumptions often appear at the level of the individual-

environment relationship. The classic example of this is the dualist thinking that has led to the nature-nurture debate (Overton, 1998).

Assessing a Developmental Metaphor

At both levels, there are important issues to consider when selecting
a metaphor that will help us understand developmental change. At the *global* level rests the issue of nature-nurture relations. Whereas current thinking has moved away from questions of an either-or viewpoint and toward
an adoption of the so-called interactionist position, many still address nature-nurture relations tacitly assuming that they are independent and distinct (Overton, 1998). Our position is that a metaphor is inadequate if it
merely allots places for nature and nurture to separately exert influences on
development in an additive fashion. An informed metaphor will recognize
that heredity and environment are ends of the same continuum and the critical
influence on development is their mutual, *inter*dependent interaction.

At the *local* level, developmental issues may be organized as *product* and *process* issues. Product issues are those that relate the metaphoric
object to the observations of developmental change. Does the metaphoric
object "look like" a developing organism? Process issues, on the other hand,
are those that relate the metaphor to theoretical characterizations regarding
the underlying nature of developmental change and its mechanisms. What
does the metaphor suggest about *how* development occurs?

From our perspective, there are a number of particularly important
issues regarding the characterization of the products of motor development.
A metaphor should consider developmental change as *age related but not
age determined*. That is, when constructing a developmental metaphor,
one must consider developmental progress itself as the most appropriate
means of demarcating change rather than age. It is not that "Maria had her
first birthday, so now she will be able to walk", rather "Maria was standing
on her own last week, which means walking is on its way." Secondly, an
appropriate metaphor will not represent the lifespan as an "inverted-U"
such that birth to adulthood is an increase in development followed by a
decline from adulthood to death. Rather, development is always progressive and is characterized by lifelong adaptation of what is learned to changes
in the structure (or function) of the body as well as the environment (Smith
& Baltes, 1999).

Last, we come to an assessment of what a metaphor connotes about
the underlying process of developmental change. Development is *sequential* and *cumulative*. Previous accomplishments are the foundations on which
later accomplishments are built. At the same time, owing to this progressive
and cumulative process, individual differences become greater as development progresses. Previous experiences never disappear, but form the basis of
the individual's *motor repertoire*. The process connoted by a metaphor must

capture both the regularities and the individual differences seen in development.

From the preceding discussion it is clear that choosing an appropriate metaphor is not a task that should be taken lightly. Here we have provided a minimal set of considerations to assist in deciding on an appropriate analogy or metaphor for the developing human. In what follows, we assess a few of the metaphors that have been used throughout the study of motor development.

METAPHORS FOR MOTOR DEVELOPMENT

Watching children grow and change from infancy to adulthood is striking in the similarities and differences observed. Trying to understand what appears to be universal and yet individual, simple and yet exceedingly complex, has provoked scientists to employ a variety of metaphors in theorizing about development.

In motor development, like development in general, metaphors are abundant. These metaphors fall into three categories: those that focus on the developmental *product*, i.e., the descriptions of motor behaviors that are observed; those that focus mostly on the *process*, i.e., the explanations of change, and *integrated* metaphors that focus on both product and process. It is the latter that would be most useful as a heuristic because it would not only seek to explain what behaviors occur when and in what order but would also offer an explanation about why these changes occur and would be most consistent with our definition of motor development.

Metaphors as Descriptions of Behavior

Biology has provided a rich source for metaphors in development and indirectly for motor development. The use of biological metaphors dates back to Aristotle who compared the stages of the human fetus to steps in evolution (Gould, 1984). These ideas were introduced again in Haeckel's "biogenetic principle" (i.e., recapitulation) in which the embryonic stages repeat, in proper sequence, the evolutionary history of the species (Haeckel, 1866). Empirically, the early embryologists saw unfolding, stage-like changes driven primarily by genetic codes. These ideas influenced many of the developmentalists of the first half of the 20th century. In fact, the concept of "stages" as a metaphor has been one of the most enduring legacies of biology. Consider the butterfly that goes through dramatically different life stages. Life begins in the egg and proceeds to a caterpillar (larva) stage, which is followed by the dormant chrysalis stage (pupa) that precedes the adult (imago) stage.

In humans, stages are less radical, but nonetheless, developmentalists have found the stage metaphor compelling. For example, the human lifespan is often characterized by the stages of infancy, childhood, adolescence, middle age, and old age. Basically, the stage is a synonym or descriptor for behaviors in a particular age range. Thus, saying an individual is in the adolescent stage indicates which behaviors we expect to see in an individual in that stage but says nothing about how the individual got to that stage. It is possible that the stage metaphor could become explanatory, i.e., address the issue of process, but according to Brainerd (1978), this would require that the metaphor include explanations of *how* an individual progresses from one stage to another. That is, to say that an infant walks because she is in stage *x* of motor development is merely descriptive. To be explanatory requires a process by which the infant got to stage *x* from a previous stage.

In cognitive development, the major stage metaphor comes from the work of Piaget (cf. 1952). In developmental psychology, stages, it is argued, follow lawful properties (Pinard & Laurendeau, 1969). First, all individuals pass through the stages, referred to as universality. Second, they pass through the stages in an invariant order—the property of intransitivity. Finally, an individual in a stage will exhibit predominantly behaviors characteristic of that stage—demonstrating stability.

In motor development, many seem to accept the notion of stages, but only Roberton (1977a, 1977b, 1978, 1982) explicitly wrote of "stages" and how they could be tested. It was Roberton's notion that the sequential changes observed in the development of forceful overarm throwing could be characterized into stages. However, Wohlwill (1973) argued that stages are not about intratask development (such as development within throwing) but rather should characterize the individual at some stage of development across many tasks (i.e., intertask development). Indeed, in 1980 Roberton agreed with Wohlwill and characterized the changes in throwing as "developmental steps" (Roberton & Langendorfer, 1980). Since then, no one in motor development has explicitly argued for a stage model or metaphor. Yet, several textbooks in the field continue to adopt "stage-like" depictions of the changes in motor behavior across the lifespan. Payne and Isaacs (1999) use the "age stages" of prenatal, infancy, early, middle, and late childhood, adolescence, early, middle, and late adulthood. Gabbard (2000) describes the changes in motor behavior as a "developmental continuum." Using similar age-stage descriptions, Gabbard adds "phases" of motor development along side the stages to depict the overlap and complementary nature between motor behavior and the traditional age-stages.

Cratty (1970) offered a somewhat different descriptive metaphor. His metaphor, although not explicitly stated to be "tree-like", is pictorially similar to a tree. The trunk of the tree is comprised of four channels or attributes (cognitive, perceptual, motor, and verbal). Each channel (or limb) grows out from the trunk toward more mature behavior. Limbs bifurcate and create more limbs. For example, in the motor channel "manipulating objects" splits into throwing, stacking and scribbling. Cratty suggested his model was not a "layer cake" (presumably of the age-stage variety) but rather a "latticework" whereby the tree limbs would "connect" with each other.

Metaphors as Developmental Process

Some metaphors in development never address what behaviors might be seen or in what order they might appear. Instead, these metaphors attempt to capture the *process* by which change occurs. One of the oldest metaphors to address the process of development was proposed by Gesell (1946). He suggested the "loom" was a natural metaphor as it captured the interweaving of the threads to form designs or patterns. Processes of development, wrote Gesell, were like the intricate cross-stitching or interlacing that organizes the system into a pattern of behavior.

In the late 20th century, the principal metaphor of developmental psychology was the "mind-as-computer." Simon (1962) offered this metaphor as he detailed an information processing theory of intellectual development. To Simon, computer programs governed performance at a particular level of development and change occurred when a computer program took an earlier ("younger") program and transformed it into an "older" program. One might see this transformation program as the "grower program." As computers became part of everyone's daily life, the metaphor became all the more compelling. Today such common expressions as "I need your input", "I can't retrieve that" or "I'm not a multi-tasker" are direct derivatives of the computer metaphor. Although this is a powerful metaphor, it is not without its problems. A machine metaphor views development as static and dependent on outside agents to build and program the system (Thelen & Smith, 1998). However, development is dynamic, non-linear, and self-organizing (Thelen & Smith, 1994, 1998). Thus, Thelen and Smith (1998) argue that a better metaphor would be a "mountain stream" —ever changing, dynamic, and influenced by many factors (constraints). In this same vein, picking up on the ecological metaphor used by Gibson (1966, 1979), van Geert (1991, 1993, 1994) sees an individual's growth and development much like an ecosystem that changes and develops as competing animals and plants change.

Although these metaphors may tell us *how* change occurs, they are mute as to when, in what order, or what types of behaviors we might expect to see across the individual's lifespan.

Metaphors for both Developmental Process and Product

Metaphors that describe the product of development such as the behaviors of a child during the preschool years, give us an important framework for characterizing or describing motor behavior across the lifespan. Metaphors that represent the process by which development occurs, such as "growing programs," represent notions about *how*, if not *why*, the developmental change occurs. Whereas each of these types of metaphors is important, ideally we seek an *integrated* metaphor that characterizes both product and process.

Gallahue and Ozmun (1995) proposed an "hour glass" metaphor to represent both the process and product of development. As the sand falls through the hourglass (the *process*), layers build up creating the phases and stages of motor development (the *product*). The sand gets into the hourglass through two funnels, one from the "hereditary" container and the other from the "environment" container. The hereditary container has a lid on it, signifying that this sand is fixed in its contribution. The environmental container, on the other hand, is open and sand can be added across the lifespan. Although the flowing sand represents how the various phases and stages are "built", how the amount and timing of sand from each container is determined is never explained. Like the computer metaphor, the hourglass requires a "builder"—an outside agent that would determine the amount of sand to flow, from which container sand would come, and when sand would flow. At some point, according to Gallahue and Ozmun, the hourglass turns over—around the late teens to early 20s. Again, an agent or "builder" is required for such an action. Why and how does this transformation occur? The inversion of the hourglass results in the top sand creating the periods of adulthood and old age. Interestingly, the metaphor includes heredity and lifestyle filters between the sand at the top and the empty glass below. These filters control the speed at which the sand passes.

No other metaphors could be found in the motor development literature that represent motor behaviors across the lifespan as well as the processes that account for these changing motor behaviors. The metaphor we propose in the following section, the "Mountain of Motor Development" is an attempt to provide such a metaphor.

THE MOUNTAIN OF MOTOR DEVELOPMENT

In this final section, we revisit Clark's (1994) characterization of six periods in lifespan motor development through the metaphor of learning to climb a mountain. Climbing the mountain of motor development (Figure 1) is an apt metaphor in that it takes years to learn, embodies an inherently sequential and cumulative process, and is influenced by individual skills and abilities as well as individual differences in context and practice. It is also representative of the ultimate accomplishment of motor development (the peak of the mountain), that is, the attainment of skilled motor action! Additionally, we expand Clark's developmental framework by extending

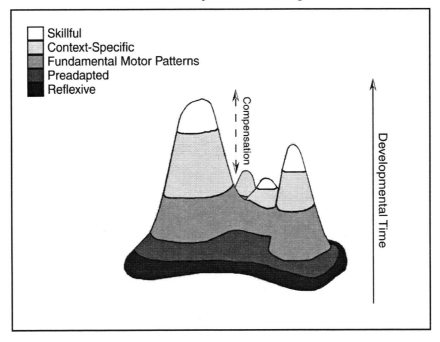

Fig. 1. One possible representation of the mountain of motor development. Developmental periods are demarcated by shading indicated in the legend at the top left. See text for details.

the metaphor to characterize *both* the products and the process of motor skill development. Because our purpose is to discuss the metaphor we leave detailed discussion of the periods to Clark's earlier presentation (Clark, 1994).

Global assumptions

In our discussion of the mountain, we hope to demonstrate that our chosen metaphor is consistent with our theoretical perspective namely, dynamical systems (c.f. Clark, 1995, 1997; Kelso, 1995; Thelen & Smith, 1994, 1998). In the language of dynamic systems, development is seen as an emergent product of a self-organizing process wherein changing constraints define the potentialities and behavioral options at each point in the lifespan. Such constraints, as well as their influence on development, have been identified as deriving from the organism, the environment, and the task at hand (Newell, 1986). Thus, as we will discuss at the end of this chapter, we view learning to climb the mountain as a nonlinear, self-organizing process that is driven by the goal of becoming an adaptive, autonomous actor in the world.

Importantly, it is the goals of the task that specify the *interaction* between the organism and the environment, and this interaction is revealed as the behavioral products of developmental change. We see this as fitting in that the path up the mountain, as well as the level of success attained, are products of the characteristics of the mountain, environmental conditions on the mountain, and the individual skills and abilities of the mountaineer. In other words, in both cases (metaphoric and literal), the results emerge from the interaction among many changing constraints and are not pre-determined by either the mountaineer or the mountain alone.

The Mountain as a Description of Product

What are the products of motor development? Certainly, this seems to be a trivial question that would typically be met with an extensive list of motor milestones, fundamental behaviors, and specific skills that humans achieve throughout their lives. But for our purpose of understanding motor development, such catalog listings would be too extensive and unproductive. Humans are remarkably adaptive and exhibit a tremendous capacity to "solve" an almost infinite number of motor problems. With development, our motor repertoires become highly differentiated within and across individuals. The problem in a metaphor is that to describe such complexity based on particular skills would either require (a) a metaphor that fails to meet the requirement of simplicity and thus be useless as a heuristic device, or (b) a general categorization of behaviors that would fail to illustrate the richness and versatility of human motor behavior.

Instead, we consider the products of motor development in a slightly more abstract sense. That is, becoming an adaptive, skilled and autonomous actor in the environment is the product of development. Once in the world, the infant's task, quite simply, is to adapt to and function in the new, complex, and ever-changing environment. Thus, the mountain of motor development demarcates developmental periods, and the products associated with those periods, in terms of *adaptive developmental goals and the movements employed to meet those goals*.

Based on these developmental goals, Clark (1994) identified six major periods in motor skill development. Beginning around the third gestational month, these periods are (1) reflexive, (2) preadapted, (3) fundamental patterns, (4) context-specific, (5) skillful, and (6) compensation. Progression up the mountain is highly individualized while at the same time follows a cumulative, sequential process that characterizes most typically developing individuals. Skills and experiences from each period provide the basis for the extensions and refinements of the motor repertoire in subsequent periods. Importantly, age is not directly represented in the mountain. As with two climbers of different experience and skill levels, progress is determined by the specific constraints for each individual and not merely time spent on the mountain. In the following presentation of the mountain, some specific behaviors will be discussed, as will associated age ranges; however, these are not to be seen as the primary concepts that define the mountain. They are presented more to illustrate the principles underlying the metaphor as well as to connect the metaphor to what is known about the typically developing child.

Prenatal development. When does the journey up the mountain of motor development begin? A likely "beginning" is when we have a body to move and muscles that are functional. Though this may be truthful, it is also relatively incomplete. What is important to remember is that all development is an emergent product of changing constraints. The mountain itself is a source of constraints and the developing individual is another source. We thus begin the climb as the constraints begin to interact.

A mountain's structure exists before the climber arrives at its foot, and so too are the constraints particular to an individual present long before the first cell divides. Before a child is conceived, his or her parents have been traveling their own individual journeys up the mountain. Their health and dietary habits (i.e., smoking, alcohol, caffeine use), the environmental conditions they experience (i.e., exposure to radiation or lead), and many other factors about their individual development will influence their physiological state and may be passed on to their child through the reproductive cells they contribute (Berk, 1994). This is not to say that the child's future is determined prior to birth. Rather, we consider the influence of genetics as the point at the base of the mountain that a climber chooses to begin. It could be a gentle and gradually rising foothill or a steep and rocky cliff. Either of the two is surmountable, but some starting points are more difficult than others. Further, it is not always the case that the starting point is indicative of future difficulties that may be encountered. The slowly rising foothill, after all, might lead to a deep gorge while the sheer cliff might give way to a well-traveled path. The point is that changing constraints drive development and lifelong motor development results from the interaction among many sources of constraint, some of which are interacting even before conception.

Reflexive period. Being delivered from the cramped, muffled, and warm environment of the womb into a cold, noisy, and bright external environment is a traumatic introduction to the world. The first period on the mountain, the reflexive period, helps the neonate adapt to this major transition. Lasting from approximately the third gestational month until two weeks after birth, the primary goals of this period are to (1) facilitate survival and (2) "open a dialogue with the environment." Previously described as beginning at birth (Clark, 1994), the current notion of the reflexive period is that it can be subdivided into two similar yet distinct portions defined as pre- and post-natal reflexive periods.

The subdivision of the reflexive period comes from the fact that the infants experience a major transition upon entrance into the external world. Environmental constraints are dramatically different in the world as compared to the infants' intrauterine experience. In addition to environmental changes are transformations within the infant's body. During birth, for example, infants produce large amount of stress hormones, causing increases in alertness, assisting in oxygenating blood to the brain and heart to compensate for constrictions and reductions in air flow during labor and helping to absorb excess fluid in the lungs to prepare the newborn for his first gasps of air (Berk, 1994). Without a doubt, such tremendous changes produce what is likely to be one of the most difficult transitions in an individual's life. Whereas prenatal movements could be considered a simple "turning on" of the neuromotor apparatus, it also seems that these movements serve a preparatory function in anticipation of the difficult first weeks of life during which the infant recovers from the birthing process.

During the reflexive period, actions fall into two general categories: spontaneous and reflexive movements. *Spontaneous movements* are movements such as kicking, mouthing, or arm flailing, that do not appear to be elicited by a particular stimulus or environmental context. *Reflexive movements*, on the other hand, are relatively stereotyped motor responses to specific stimuli. Reflexive behaviors can be categorized into two broad types: primitive and postural. Primitive reflexes subserve basic functions necessary for survival such as feeding (e.g., rooting and sucking) and protection from potentially harmful stimuli (e.g., moro and tongue protrusion). Postural reflexes are those that involve responses to changes in orientation relative to the environment. Whereas both types of reflexes are present in some form both pre- and post-natally, because of the dramatically different environments, the repertoire of actions seen in prenatal life is much more limited than those observed after birth.

Though reflexes are advantageous for facilitating survival, a more subtle value of reflexes, as well as spontaneous movements, is that they "open a dialogue" with the external world. Indeed, all adaptive behaviors occur in response to sensory stimulation, as well as produce sensory consequences. At birth, the infant is bombarded with a complex array of continuously changing sensory stimuli. How does the infant learn to make sense of such sensations? Many have argued that infants must exploit their actions to assign adaptive meaning to their sensory environment (E.J. Gibson, 1987, 1997; J.J. Gibson, 1979). As behaviors in the reflexive period result from and produce sensory stimuli, it seems reasonable to assume that the body has evolved to "teach" the system what sensations are coupled with which actions. This may be seen in reflexes that have no necessary survival value, yet have remained with our species through thousands of years of evolution. Take, for example, the asymmetric tonic neck reflex. This reflex occurs in response to a lateral turning of the head and is characterized by an extension of the arm in the direction of the turn as well as a flexion of the arm on the contralateral side. It is possible that this coupling of gaze direction with arm extension will serve less as a means for survival and more as a rudiment of visually-guided reaching (Fukuda, 1961).

The reflexive period is necessary to acquaint the infant with the mountain, but would be counter-productive if it lasted too long. For movement to be *adaptive* it needs to be flexibly tailored to task and context. Once the infant has recovered from the traumatic transition from pre- to postnatal life and begins to voluntarily initiate movements, we see the first major passage up the mountain of motor development. Metaphorically, the reflexive period marks the beginning of the journey, but to successfully proceed requires caregivers who will "carry" the infant along the first part of the path up the mountain.

Preadapted period. The passage to the preadapted period, while marked by the onset of voluntary movement, is not simply because of a disappearance or inhibition of reflexive behaviors. The beginning of the preadapted period is marked by the infant applying the rudimentary sensory-motor patterns from the reflexive period toward the goal of becoming an independent and adaptive actor in the world. The concept of preadaptation (Bruner, 1973) is chosen to represent the fact that movements in this period exhibit a *species-typical sequence* that characterize a progressive mastery of the body in a gravitational environment (Clark, 1994). Evolution has provided a set of genetic constraints that ensure a body structure as well as an arrangement of musculature that enables a functional motor repertoire. Although there is a nearly infinite range of possibilities for organizing the body's degrees of freedom (Bernstein, 1967), the reflexes help to define some of the fundamental sensory-motor relationships (Easton, 1972) that allow the infant to explore how her body works within our gravitational environment.

The primary goal of the preadapted period is the achievement of independent function. Two basic requirements of independent function are the ability to feed oneself and to move through the environment and seek out sources of nourishment. At birth, the pull of gravity proves to be too much for the infant to lift her head, much less support her body and move about. At the same time as gravity limits her movement, the objects and sounds of the world, as well as her own internal drives to find nourishment, motivate the initiation of her struggle against gravity. First with the head on the trunk, followed later by the head and trunk on the hips, and eventually with the whole body balanced over the small base provided by the feet, the infant progressively builds a sequence of behaviors that ultimately lead to independent stance and locomotion.

The emergence of manipulative skills also follows a sequence of pre-adapted movement patterns (Bushnell, 1985). Initial attempts at reaching, called pre-reaching, are characterized as "flinging" the arm toward a visually fixated object. With little coordination and driven largely by muscles around the shoulder, these early movements are rarely effective and never result in grasping the object. As improvements in posture continue, the infant stabilizes the trunk so as to increase control over prehensile movements. Over time, the primitive relationship between the eye and hand that was partially formed in the reflexive period (e.g., asymmetric tonic neck reflex) is exploited by the infant in the first visually guided and successful reaches. These reaches, however, are far from the quality of the skilled and somewhat automatic reaches observed towards the end of the preadapted period (around 9-12 months). Yet, with the onset of the successful reach comes refined hand-mouth coordination. Indeed, the infant does not eat every object that comes to his mouth, but when the coordination has developed to the point where an object can be efficiently obtained and placed in the mouth, the infant is clearly capable of self-feeding.

The passage out of the preadapted period, then, is marked by the joint accomplishment of self-feeding and walking behaviors. The preadapted period typically lasts from two weeks until the end of the first year of life and is rate-limited by the onset of independent walking. Importantly, the preadapted period is a time when infants learn how to work within the constraints defined by their body and the surrounding environment. Behaviors observed during this time are generalized actions aimed at one primary, adaptively necessary goal—to get off of the ground and find food. Nature and evolution have provided the general constraints for accomplishing this goal, but no detailed map has been included in the genes. The details of the path up the mountain are left up to a dynamic interaction between the constraints defined by the organism, environment, and the developmental goal.

Fundamental patterns period. Equipped with the basic patterns of coordination for manipulation and locomotion, the infant climbs to a period during which these patterns are further elaborated into the "building blocks" of later context-specific motor skills. The overall goal of this period is to build a sufficiently diverse motor repertoire that will allow for later learning of adaptive, skilled actions that can be flexibly tailored to different and specific movement contexts. While the fundamental patterns period is entered during the child's infancy, it will last for most children until about seven years where their fundamental patterns are applied to a specific context. From this "base camp", if you will, progress up the mountain becomes increasingly specific to the domain or context (e.g., throwing will become pitching). As seen in Figure 1, this is a time where individual constraints will lead to differentiation in the developmental trajectory (separate peaks of the mountain range). Though most typically developing children eventually achieve the fundamental patterns, considerable differences begin to emerge between those who have enriched and varied movement experiences as compared to those who do not.

There are three domains of motor behavior that emerge during this period on the mountain. First are the fundamental *locomotor* patterns. While the infant's first steps mark the passage into the fundamental patterns period, continued progress occurs *during* the fundamental patterns period.

Three months after an infant takes her first steps, she demonstrates the leg movement patterns that have the adaptability and regularity of the mature adult. After about six months of walking experience, the infant will run. Perhaps the more remarkable achievement occurs as infants and toddlers explore the various modes of locomotion, eventually producing asymmetric patterns such as galloping, sliding, and hopping. These later emerging locomotor patterns provide an exquisite example of how meager beginnings such as the symmetric pattern of walking can be built upon and diversified to yield a range of coordination patterns that may flexibly be applied to a variety of task and environmental contexts.

Although adaptive locomotion is critical to an individual's ability to move through an environment, humans also need to develop a basic set of coordination patterns for interacting with the environment. Two categories of such interactive coordination patterns include *object projection* and *object interception*. For object projection patterns such as throwing, the individual initially has control of the object and projects it into the environment. Development of object projection skills involves changes in force-production, as well as learning efficient whole-body coordination for appropriately applying force to the projected object. Object interception patterns, on the other hand, are those behaviors in which the object is moving within the environment and the individual wishes to intercept it. There are two forms of object interception including *object reception* and *object deflection*. For object reception such as catching, the goal is to control the object, taking it from its movement path. Object deflection, on the other hand, requires an interception, but rather than capturing the object, it is sent away (deflected). Striking and kicking are examples of object deflection. Important constraints for object interception are those involving perceptual judgments about the timing necessary to initiate the appropriate pattern of coordination. Further, object interception patterns require an ability to continuously update the movement pattern using a coupled visual-proprioceptive feedback system to judge whether the trajectory of the movement is destined for success or failure. Again, we see how an earlier accomplishment, visually guided reaching in infancy, provides a basis for elaborating the motor repertoire to include catching tossed balls.

To complete the repertoire of fundamental movement patterns, the human needs not only gross motor capabilities but also must be able to manipulate objects in the environment. The fundamental *fine-motor manipulative patterns* are those which involve the use of the small muscles of the hands for a variety of behaviors ranging from communication to tool use. In the preadapted period, the infant struggles with the ability to accurately and efficiently get the arm to an object and take hold of it. For example, grasping starts out as primarily whole-hand, undifferentiated movements (e.g., the power grip for writing) that through the fundamental patterns period, become differentiated to the extent that the five-year-old learns to write his name and draw pictures of his family (e.g., the adult, dynamic tripod grasp).

Importantly, the motor patterns developed during this period will provide the basis for later *motor skillfulness*. Games and sport, such as baseball, soccer, and basketball involve running, jumping, catching, and throwing skills. Artistic endeavors such as painting and playing the piano are context-specific applications of fine-motor manipulative skills such as writing and utensil use. Even everyday behaviors such as typing, eating, or crossing a busy intersection will require competence in the fundamental motor patterns from these three domains. Indeed, these fundamental motor patterns form a base camp to which the individual may always return as he attempts to climb the various peaks (skills) on the mountain of motor development.

Context-specific period. As the child establishes his basic motor repertoire, he eventually begins to apply the fundamental patterns toward a variety of task and environmental contexts. The passage into the context-specific period occurs when the child no longer runs for the sake of running but instead begins to impose additional task constraints on how, where, and why he is running. Keeping in mind that the goal of motor development is to become an adaptive, skilled, and autonomous actor in the environment, the goal of the context-specific period is to learn how to adaptively apply fundamental movement patterns to a variety of constrained situations. Certainly, humans require a protracted period of development as compared to other members of the animal kingdom. In the context-specific period, we begin to see the advantage of this long-term process. That is, this is a time when the human learns the range and versatility of his motor repertoire and how his actions can be adapted to a number of specific situations. In the metaphor of the mountain (Figure 1), context-specific development is shown as multiple and specific peaks of varying heights. In some cases, the context-specific peak is seen as an end in itself, meaning that the ability to adapt a movement to an environment, as opposed to skilled movement, is the only goal the actor may have.

Generally speaking, with sufficient experience within a particular context, a child may pass into the context-specific period as early as four or five years of age. Take for example Tiger Woods, the professional golfer, who was clearly beyond the fundamental patterns period at a very early age. One can think of many similar examples in which early experience has accelerated the progress towards a specific peak on the mountain. Yet, a more typically developing child would be expected to make the passage into the context-specific period around the age of seven.

Because humans encounter new movement contexts throughout their lives, they will continuously return to the base camp of the fundamental patterns period, followed by a new passage onto another peak (context-specific period) of the mountain. Consider, for example, the adult attempting to learn the guitar when having no previous experience with stringed instruments. In order to climb this new peak on the mountain, he will have to return, however briefly, to the fundamental fine-motor manipulative patterns before being able to adaptively make the appropriate finger placements for chords, or flexibly differentiate the fingers to sound a melodic arpeggio. This is an important reminder that lifelong development, while being age-related, is not determined by the time spent on the mountain (getting older). Individual experience is certainly a large influence over the developmental changes that occur during the context-specific period.

Related to this is the fact that from the context-specific period onward, development of motor skills becomes increasingly individualized. The preadapted and fundamental patterns periods are the primary times when species-typical behaviors develop that are common to all humans. After the fundamental motor repertoire has been established, however, motor skill development becomes influenced more by cultural, familial, and social constraints. A boy who is raised in the town that holds the state-championship for football will likely be encouraged to apply his fundamental patterns to the task constraints of football. Yet, if that boy comes from a family of carpenters, he will likely be raised in an environment where tool use and craftsmanship are considered more important than being a sports hero. Further, if that boy were raised in South America or Europe, cultural influences might result in his becoming a soccer player rather than a quarterback. These and other environmental factors will provide strong influences on the specific applications of fundamental patterns during the context-specific period.

Because development in the context-specific period is driven by particular tasks and experiences, another important rate-limiter is the development of perceptual-cognitive capabilities. If fundamental patterns are to conform to a particular task such as a sport or game, the child needs to perceive and understand the *rules* and *context-specific knowledges* associated with those tasks. For example, while the child may know how to throw a ball, in a baseball game knowing when, where, and to whom she should throw the ball becomes a critical aspect of being successful. Because of the specificity of knowledge required for context-specific adaptation, *experience* with the particular task and environment also takes on a critical role in this period on the mountain.

The context-specific period is an important time in the life of the developing child. It is a time that can either stifle or facilitate progress towards becoming an adaptive, autonomous actor in our complex world. Although all typically developing humans enter the context-specific period, it is again important to recognize that experience and environmental influences are major determinants of how fast and how far the individual will ascend the mountain of motor development. As with climbing a mountain, progress becomes more difficult the further one climbs. In addition to a well-developed fundamental motor repertoire, dedicated practice and experience become major factors in the level of skillfulness that an individual will reach. Thus, the passage between the context-specific and the skillful period is driven primarily by the individual's motivation to excel as well as the opportunities they have to devote to sharpening their particular skill.

Skillful period. With enough dedicated practice and experience, the individual soon will pass from context-specific competence to skill. The goal of this period is the achievement of skillful behavior. Motor skill is characterized as being voluntary, efficient, and adaptive (Clark, 1994, 1995). Once true skill is achieved, the performer can apply his or her behavior with maximum certainty in a variety of contexts and situations. Psychological efficiency is demonstrated by the performer's ability to focus on strategy, rather than maintaining attention on the performance of the skill (Hatfield & Hillman, 2001). Physiological and mechanical efficiency are seen in the ability of the individual to maximize work output, while at the same time keeping physical effort to a minimum. Take a skilled basketball player, for example, who can gracefully weave her way through three opponents while at the same time feigning a shot at the goal and executing a "no-look" pass to her teammate.

Certainly, no individual becomes skillful across a wide range of behaviors and contexts. Rather, attainment of skill is largely specific to a particular sub-domain of motor behavior. The first passage into the skillful period generally coincides with two general achievements. First and foremost, the individual must have significant context-specific experience with the particular behavior. The importance of dedicated practice and experience cannot be stressed enough. Without the proper opportunities and support, as well as explicit guidance from other experienced individuals (such as parents, peers, or coaches), achievement of skill would likely not occur. Secondly, the passage into skillfulness tends to coincide with the onset of puberty and the adolescent growth spurt, at approximately 11-13 years of age. The dramatic increases in body size, strength, and cognitive-emotional capabilities that coincide with adolescence are important constraints that allow differentiation between competent and skilled movers.

Of course, many examples may be discussed in which skill is evident at young ages. One has only to watch Olympic gymnasts to realize that the young can demonstrate very high-level performances. Yet, as no two mountain peaks are the same, skill in one sub-domain does not necessarily imply skill in any other. An individual's skills are dependent upon their own particular constraints and are specific to those behaviors with which she or he has had significant practice and experience. Of course, certain competencies that are common between skills may influence the rate at which the individual may achieve skillfulness in a new behavior. For example, a skilled wrestler may decide to study judo. Whereas the specific postures and techniques may be different between the two sports, certain abilities such as balance control, timing, and knowledge of how to upset the opponents balance may provide the wrestler an advantage over the complete novice.

Finally, it is important to acknowledge that skillfulness occurs on its own continuum. Different individuals may be climbing different peaks of the mountain. Not everyone becomes an Olympic athlete or a world-renown musician. However, for some individuals, skill eventually becomes *expertise*. Expertise is exceptionally skilled motor performance that occurs because of an optimal interaction of biological and environmental constraints, as well as years of dedicated practice and experience (Ericsson, Krampe, & Tesch-Romer, 1993; Ericsson & Lehmann, 1996). Certainly no one becomes an expert performer overnight. Those who become experts often began the context-specific application of their skill very early in life, but professional athletes, Olympians, and concert-musicians alike do not generally achieve the rewards for their years of practice until well into their 20s.

To enter the skillful period on the mountain may take years of practice and experience with specific motor skills. Nearly all typically developing people will obtain some motor competence within their lifetime. Consider the average person navigating through their home to get a glass of water in the dark of night. Clearly, such ability represents skillful locomotor control in that in an impoverished visual environment, the task is easily accomplished. At the same time, such ability also comes from years of walking through a vast range of environments from dry, well-lit pavement to an uneven, slippery lawn at dusk. The skillful period, as with all other periods on the mountain, comes from a progressive building and refinement of the motor repertoire. From the meager beginnings of the infant who cannot lift his head at birth, comes the ability to drive a manual transmission car, dance a polka at a wedding, or even perform a triple axle on ice skates in the Olympics. Although skillfulness is metaphorically at the peaks of the mountain, it is not the end of the process of motor development.

Compensation period. Throughout the discussion of the mountain of motor development, two major themes have been discussed. First, the mountain presents a story of development as lifelong, cumulative, and progressive adaptation. Second, the changes seen across the lifespan are because of changing constraints from the organism, environment, and task. As these constraints change, so do the behaviors that we observe. From the newborn to the skilled adult, motor development represents an emergent process of progressive adaptation. As with all of the previous periods on the mountain, this holds true for the final period of motor development, the compensation period.

The word "compensate" is defined as "to make up for" or "to counterbalance." Compensation implies that a part of a system is not performing up to standard and the rest of the system must adapt in order to accomplish the goal. In the case of motor development, this can be thought of as a change in the constraints that produce a behavior and a subsequent behavioral re-organization to afford continued function. Clark (1994) defined the compensation period as a time when the system adapts, or compensates, for detrimental changes in organism constraints. There are two ways in which the compensation period can be brought about, including *injury-induced*: a change in organism constraints associated with an injury and *aging-associated*: the typical changes in organism constraints that are associated with the process of aging.

The difference between the two types of compensation has to do with the typical developmental directionality associated with each. Injury-induced compensations are generally considered bi-directional in that throughout life, all individuals have setbacks in their progress up the mountain. Occasionally, these are permanent changes such as in the case of a traumatic accident leading to changes in the structural or functional features of the body. However, most often these are discrete injuries that lead to a temporary need to return to a previous fundamental base camp in order to adapt the behavior for continued function in everyday life. In some cases, because of this discrete return to the fundamental patterns period, the injury-induced compensation may lead to an expansion of the motor repertoire. An example of this is in the case where an individual is forced to learn how to write with the non-dominant hand while the dominant arm is recovering from a broken bone. Aging-associated compensation, on the other hand, is generally considered to have a progressive developmental direction. This is because despite the fact that the system remains adaptive during aging, there are certain organism constraints that will progressively undergo reduced function with continued development.

The important commonality between the two types of compensation, however, has to do with the fact that compensation implies a fundamental capability of the system to adaptively reorganize to maintain function within the external world. Indeed, many theories exist regarding the aging body. Unfortunately, most of these theories focus on aging as a regressive state in which the body deteriorates. To consider aging as an adaptive process, rather than as a regressive one seems a more powerful and optimistic means of characterizing the nature of change across the lifespan. Aging is not merely an overturning of the process of development. Rather, we consider aging as a compensatory state in which the body may maintain most of its function throughout the end of the lifespan.

Depending on the physiological system, as well as the individual's life history and level of activity, different developmental courses can be seen within the aging-associated compensation period. For example, it is relatively well established that normal, healthy, older adults can maintain cardiac and muscular function through routine exercise (Spirduso, 1995). At the same time, other systems such as skeletal bone density and macular degeneration in the visual system seem to be influenced very little by maintaining an active, healthy lifestyle. Clearly, there are declines associated with old age. However, increases in pathology and decreased activity or disuse also seem to be major contributing factors to these changes. Yet, the aging body retains its capacity to respond to activity across many physiological systems and thus, aging is not simply process of progressive decline.

From infant to older adult, development is driven by progressive adaptation. The primary goal of a mover in the world is to be an adaptive and autonomous actor in the environment. Whether learning motor behaviors for the first time or compensating for detrimental changes in organism constraints, development continues through the process of adaptation. While through the majority of the lifespan, motor abilities improve with experience in the external world, it is important to remember that adaptive function is the goal of motor development. Though one may or may not return to a previous level of skillfulness following a compensation period, one can typically manage to meet the goal of maintaining adaptive function.

Atypical development and the mountain. Although our presentation of the mountain has primarily discussed the typically developing human, it is important to note that this framework can be used with those who follow a different path. The process embodied by the mountain applies to all humans. Whereas some may have to climb a different mountain than most, their path up that mountain will be the result of the same process. That is, the constraints may differ and the limitations may be harder to circumvent, but the developmental products will result from interaction between the individual, environment, and the task.

Further, in the language of the mountain, the products (developmental goals) will also be similar. For the child who is developing atypically, the passage up the mountain will still include the reflexive, preadapted, fundamental, and context-specific periods. Yet, these periods will be tailored to their own organismic constraints. For example, the child born with cerebral palsy will have a preadapted period in which they learn to walk. According to Holt, however, the child with cerebral palsy has to learn to manage a system with a fundamentally different functional architecture and thus different organismic constraints that will shape their gait patterns (Holt & Jeng, 1992). Therefore, instead of walking with the energy-efficient gait pattern of the typically developing individual, the pattern of locomotion used by the child with cerebral palsy is one that emphasizes postural stability. What this suggests is that when attempting to understand atypical development as well as design developmental interventions for climbing the mountain, it is critical to consider all sources of constraint.

The Mountain as Description of Developmental Process

Throughout this presentation of the mountain of motor development, our focus has been primarily on relating the products of development metaphorically through the various periods on the mountain. However, a close read of this presentation also reveals a few themes that are indicative of how the mountain may relate to the process of development. These themes are important enough that they merit a more explicit discussion. Specifically, these themes involve the goal of development, the importance of development as a cumulative and history-dependent process, and the consequences of the interactional nature of development.

Autonomy as a Goal of Development

Perhaps one of the most critical questions for developmental theory is the question of *why*. That is, why climb the mountain of motor development? Is there a goal toward which development progresses? The field of developmental psychology has been characterized as divided at the level of the root metaphor by the question of whether or not development is goal directed (Reese & Overton, 1970). Even the current conception of development adopted by those working from the dynamic systems perspective is that there is no necessary teleology, or goal-directed nature, to development. As stated by Thelen and Smith (1998), "The mountain stream metaphor depicts behavioral development as an *epigenetic process*, that is, truly constructed by its own history and systemwide activity" (p. 569). Although we find this metaphor agreeable at one level, it does not provide an intuitive means of understanding the species-typical regularities seen in human development.

Rather than adopting a split, either-or position, we choose to consider development as a process that has a non-specific goal, which organizes the epigenetic process in such a way as to produce species-typical behaviors. This non-specific goal is to become an adaptive, skilled, and autonomous actor in the environment. In order to achieve this goal, the developing organism must seek out adaptive solutions by *actively* interacting with the environment. The motor repertoire is formed as the actions of the system are exploited to select the most adaptive solutions from the array of possible choices given by the current constraints. A particular solution becomes adaptive when it facilitates progress toward the goal of autonomous function given the current set of constraints. Thus, as with the mountain stream metaphor, developmental products "fall out" of the systemwide, active interactions with the environment. Concisely, development is inherent in the system and, therefore, the process itself becomes the goal of development. Indeed, if the mountaineer's goal was merely to "get to the top", a helicopter would suffice. The reason for climbing the mountain is *to climb the mountain*. That is, learning to climb the mountain is inherently rewarding because it provides the climber with an increased array of choices for adaptive and skilled behavior.

History Dependence and Developmental Process

Given that the process of selectively seeking adaptive solutions is the goal of motor development, we must also recognize the importance of history as a major factor. Development is not a stage-like process in which previous states are disconnected from current and future states. Development is cumulative. When climbing a mountain, the choices made at a lower elevation will influence the nature and range of choices that may be made higher up. The path up the mountain builds upon itself, forming a foundation for continued progress toward the peak. Likewise, in motor development, both physiological maturity and experience are parts of the history of the developing system that provide a functional basis for later elaboration of the motor repertoire.

Of course, motor development is not necessarily a one-way path to the top of the mountain. As Lerner (1998) discusses, human development is characterized by *relative plasticity* that exists over the lifespan. What this means is that a certain amount of flexibility exists that affords the *potential* to learn motor skills throughout the lifespan. One may always move up and down the mountain range within reasonable limits. Yet, this plasticity is relative in the sense that it interacts with the individual's current developmental level. Because development is history-dependent and cumulative, the available motor repertoire changes along with development. Again, analogous to climbing a mountain, once a certain point is reached it may not be possible to "start over." Rather, depending on where on the mountain the individual is, it might be more efficient to select the most adaptive behavior from the current motor repertoire instead of attempting to re-learn at the level of the fundamental patterns. Alternatively, at some point the climber may have to "retrace" her steps, returning to a fundamental base camp in order to attempt an alternate route toward other peaks (context-specific and skillful behaviors), particularly if the current path is not passable.

The Interactive Nature of Development

The final theme represents a return to the global assumption that underlies our conception of motor development. That is, fundamentally, the metaphor of the mountain assumes that the most important influence on development is the interaction between nature and nurture. Further, we do not consider nature as fundamentally distinct from nurture. Indeed, the structure of a mountain is not static. Environmental conditions such as precipitation and wind lead to erosion and rock falls, which over millions of years alter the structure of the mountain. Similarly, genetic constitution both within a species as well as within a family is an emergent property of the experiences and constraints of each individual in the lineage. Current evidence suggests that even within an organism, genetic materials are not static "on-off" entities that determine an individual's fate. Rather, genetic expression, observed as a phenotype, is determined by the interaction between the DNA code, biophysical laws, and the environmental milieu within which that code is to be expressed (Elman et al., 1996).

More explicitly, the development of motor skills results from the *interaction between the constraints* (organismic, environmental, and task) that are specific to each individual. To the extent that the constraints are similar across individuals such as in the reflexive and preadapted periods, regularity and stereotypy will be observed. However, the further up the mountain an individual climbs, because of the cumulative nature of development, the more specific the constraints will become to that individual.

Finally, development is a nonlinear process. Throughout the lifespan and across different time-scales, the rate of development can appear linear, nonlinear (i.e., exponential), discontinuous, at a plateau, or even regressive. Certainly, for development to show such a diverse range of trajectories, it must result from a dynamically interactive rather than a linearly additive process. As seen in Figure 1, the process of development occurs over a range of "peaks" in the mountain. The level of skill attained is known to vary across individuals, as well as across behaviors within an individual. Indeed, development cannot be described as the result of a stage-like process in which *all* skills progress at the same rate. Considering behavior as an emergent property because of the interaction between constraints that are specific to individuals, as well as to particular skills, allows for a ubiquitous description and characterization of the *how* and *why* of motor development.

BEYOND THE METAPHOR: SUMMARY AND CONCLUSIONS

In this chapter, we have discussed the utility of the metaphor as a tool to provide a framework for understanding complex phenomena such as the development of motor skills. After discussion of metaphors as process, product, and integrated (process-product) descriptions, we forwarded our own integrated metaphor in an attempt to provide a simple, yet relatively complete picture of critical features and principles of the developing motor system. In this metaphor, which we call "the mountain of motor development", developmental progress is seen as the result of a process in which changing constraints interact and self-organize, yielding a cumulative and sequential pattern of developing motor skills.

Although this metaphor is useful as a heuristic device to facilitate an understanding of motor development, it is important to remember that metaphors are not to be ends unto themselves. Metaphors are first steps in building toward more formalized models and theoretical frameworks. In the first section of this chapter, we argued that metaphors are to be assessed on the criteria of usefulness. Certainly, if the mountain provides an intuitive and accurate means to communicate knowledge about motor development and thus, facilitates teaching and learning, then on one level we have been successful in our intent. At the same time, we present the mountain to inspire new ways of understanding for both the researcher and the teacher of motor development. The challenge for the future, then, is to go beyond the metaphor.

REFERENCES

Berk, L.E. (1994). *Child development* (3rd ed.). Needham Heights, MA: Allyn & Bacon.

Bernstein, N.A. (1967). *The co-ordination and regulation of movements.* Oxford: Pergamon Press.

Brainerd, C.J. (1978). The stage question in cognitive-developmental theory. *The Behavioral and Brain Sciences, 2,* 173-213.

Bruner, J.S. (1973). Organization of early skilled action. *Child Development, 44,* 1-11.

Bushnell, E.W. (1985). The decline of visually guided reaching during infancy. *Infant Behavior and Development, 8,* 139-155.

Clark, J.E. (1994). Motor development. In V.S. Ramachandran (Ed.), *Encyclopedia of human behavior* (Vol. 3, pp. 245-255). New York: Academic Press.

Clark, J.E. (1995). On becoming skillful: Patterns and constraints. *Research Quarterly for Exercise and Sport, 56,* 173-183.

Clark, J.E. (1997). A dynamical systems prespective on the development of complex adaptive skill. In C. Dent-Read & P. Goldring-Zukow (Eds.), *Evolving explanations of development* (pp. 383-406). Washington, D.C.: APA.

Clark, J.E. & Whitall, J. (1989). What is motor development? The lessons of history. *Quest, 41,* 183-202.

Cratty, B.J. (1970). *Perceptual and motor development in infants and children.* New York: Macmillan.

Easton, T.A. (1972). On the normal use of reflexes. *American Scientist, 60,* 591-599.

Elman, J.L., Bates, E.A., Johnson, M.H., Karmiloff-Smith, A., Parisi, D., & Plunkett, K. (1996). *Rethinking innateness: A connectionist perspective on development.* Cambridge, MA: The MIT Press.

Ericsson, K.A., Krampe, R.T., & Tesch-Romer, C. (1993). The role of deliberate practice in the acquisition of expert performance. *Psychological Review, 100,* 363-406.

Ericsson, K.A. & Lehman, A.C. (1996). Expert and exceptional performance: Evidence of maximal adaptation to task constraints. *Annual Review of Psychology, 47,* 273-317.

Fukuda, T. (1961). Studies on human dynamic postures from the viewpoint of postural reflexes. *Acta Oto-Laryngologica, 161,* 1-52.

Gabbard, C. (2000). *Lifelong motor development* (3rd ed.). Needham Heights, MA: Allyn & Bacon.

Gallahue, D.L., & Ozmun, J.C. (1995). *Understanding motor development.* (3rd ed.). Madison, WI: Brown & Benchmark.

Gesell, A. (1946). The ontogenesis of infant behavior. In L. Carmichael (Ed.), *Manual of child psychology* (pp. 295-331). New York: John Wiley & Sons.

Gibson, E.J. (1987). Introductory essay: What does infant perception tell us about theories of perception? *Journal of Experimental Psychology: Human Perception and Performance, 13,* 515-523.

Gibson, E.J. (1997). An ecological psychologist's prolegomena for perceptual development: A functional approach. In C. Dent-Read & P. Zukow-Goldring (Eds.), *Evolving explanations of development: Ecologial approaches to organism-environment systems* (pp. 23-45). Washington, DC: American Psychological Association.

Gibson, J.J. (1966). *The senses considered as perceptual systems.* Boston: Houghton-Mifflin.

Gibson, J.J. (1979). *The ecological approach to visual perception.* Boston: Houghton-Mifflin.

Gould, S.J. (1984). Relationship of individual and group change. *Human Development, 27,* 233-239.

Haeckel, E. (1866). *Generelle Morphologie der Organismen* (2 vols.). Berlin: Georg Reimer.

Hatfield,B.D. & Hillman,C.H. (2001). The psychophysiology of sport: a mechanistic understanding of the psychology of superior performance. In R.N. Singer, H.A. Hausenblas, & C.M. Janelle (Eds.), *Handbook of sport psychology* (pp. 362-388). New York: John Wiley.

Holt, K.G., & Jeng, S.F. (1992). Advances in the biomechanical analysis of the physically challenged child: Cerebral palsy. *Pediatric Exercise Science, 4,* 213-235.

Kelso, J.A.S. (1995). *Dynamic patterns. The self-organization of brain & behavior.* Cambridge, MA: MIT Press.

Lerner, R.M. (1998). Theories of human development: Contemporary perspectives. In R.M. Lerner (Ed.), *Handbook of child psychology, Vol. 1: Theoretical models of human development* (5th ed., pp. 1-24). New York: John Wiley.

Newell, K.M. (1986). Constraints on the development of coordination. In M.G. Wade and H.T.A. Whiting (Eds.), *Motor development in children: Aspects of coordination and control* (pp. 341-360). Boston: Martinus Nijhoff.

Overton,W.F. (1998). Developmental psychology: Philosophy, concepts &

methodology. In R.M. Lerner (Ed.), *Handbook of child psychology. Vol 1: Theoretical models of human development* (5th ed., pp. 107-188). New York; John Wiley.

Payne, V. G., & Isaacs, L.D. (1999). *Human motor development: A lifespan approach.* (4th ed.). Mountain View, CA: Mayfield.

Piaget, J. (1952). *The origins of intelligence in children.* New York: International Universities Press.

Pinard, A. & Laurendeau, M. (1969). "Stage" in Piaget's cognitive-developmental theory: Exegesis of a concept. In D. Elkind & J. Flavell (Eds.), *Studies in cognitive development* (pp. 121-170). New York: Oxford University Press.

Reese, H. W., & Overton, W. F. (1970). Models of development and theories of development. In L. R. Goulet and P. B. Baltes (Eds.), *Lifespan developmental psychology* (pp. 115-145). New York: Academic Press.

Roberton, M.A. (1977a). Stability of stage categorizations across trials: Implications for the 'stage theory' of overarm throw development. *Journal of Human Movement Studies, 3,* 49-59.

Roberton, M.A. (1977b). Motor stage: Heuristic model for research and teaching. *Proceedings of the NAPECW/NCPEAM National Conference* (pp. 173-180). Orlando, FL.

Roberton, M.A. (1978). Longitudinal evidence for developmental stages in the forceful overarm throw. *Journal of Human Movement Studies, 4,* 167-175.

Roberton, M.A. (1982). Describing 'stages' within and across motor tasks. In J.A.S. Kelso & J.E. Clark (Eds.), *The development of movement control and coordination* (pp. 293-307). New York: John Wiley & Sons.

Roberton, M.A. & Langendorfer, S. (1980). Testing motor development sequences across 9-14 years. In K. Newell, G. Roberts, W. Halliwell, & C.H. Nadeau (Eds.), *Psychology of motor behavior and sport – 1979* (pp. 269-279). Champaign, IL: Human Kinetics.

Spirduso, W.W. (1995). *Physical dimensions of aging.* Champaign, IL: Huamn Kinetics.

Simon, H.A. (1962). An information processing theory of intellectual development. *Monographs of the Society for Research in Child Development, 27.*

Smith, J., & Baltes, P. B. (1999). Life-span perspectives on development. In M. H. Bornstein & M. E. Lamb (Eds), *Developmental psychology: An advanced textbook* (4th ed., pp. 47-72). Mahwah, NJ; Erlbaum.

Snow, R.E. (1973). Theory construction for research on teaching. In RMW Travers (Ed.), *Second handbook of research on teaching.* Chicago: Rand McNally.

Thelen, E. (1986). Development of coordinated movement: Implications for human development. In M.G. Wade & H.T.A. Whiting (Eds.), *Motor development in children: Aspects of coordination and control* (pp. 106-119). Boston, MA: Martin Nijhoff.

Thelen, E. & Smith, L.B. (1994). *A dynamic systems approach to the development of cognition and action.* Cambridge, MA: MIT Press.

Thelen, E., & Smith, L.B. (1998). Dynamic systems theories. In R.M. Lerner (Ed.), *Handbook of child psychology. Vol. I. Theoretical models of human development* (5th ed., pp. 563-634). New York: John Wiley & Sons.

van Geert, P. (1991). A dynamic system model of cognitive and language growth. *Psychological Review, 98,* 3-53.

van Geert, P. (1993). A dynamic systems model of cognitive growth: Competition and support under limited resource conditions. In L.B. Smith & E. Thelen (Eds.), *A dynamic systems approach to development: Applications.* Cambridge, MA: MIT Press.

van Geert, P. (1994). *Dynamic systems of development.* London: Harvester Wheatsheaf.

Wohlwill, J. (1973). *The study of behavioral development.* New York: Academic Press.

Acknowledgments

We wish to thank the following individuals for their insightful comments, critiques, and suggestions regarding this chapter: Jill Whitall, Kaleb McDowell, Kathy Levit, Li-Chiou Chen, and Stephen Kim. We also thank the Kinesiology undergraduate students at the University of Maryland whose insightful questions (and challenges) over the years have led to sharpening our thinking about the concepts underlying "the mountain."

Funding for the preparation of this chapter was provided in part by National Science Foundation Grant #9905315.

9

HOW CHILDREN AND SENIORS DIFFER FROM ADULTS IN CONTROLLING RAPID AIMING ARM MOVEMENTS

Jin H. Yan

Jerry R. Thomas

V. Gregory Payne

ABSTRACT

This article focuses on characteristics of arm movements involving speed and accuracy (speed and accuracy trade-off, Fitts' Law, 1954). Specifically, this article reviews selected research with an emphasis on kinematic differences in rapid and goal-directed arm movements from a lifespan developmental perspective. Meyer's optimal sub-movement model (OSM) (Meyer et al, 1988) is used to explain how and why children and the elderly differ from young adults in controlling arm movements. Research findings clearly have suggested that children and seniors use different control mecha-nisms to produce fast and accurate movements when they are com-pared with young adults. We believe that adopting OSM may result in a better understanding of human motor behavior that requires speed and accuracy.

Two general approaches are often taken in the study of human motor behavior (Stelmach & Diggles, 1982). The first, which has a longer history than the second one, is the so called top-down or information processing approach. The primary focus of this framework is on the cognitive processes, events, or decisions prior to and during the production of movements. Adams' (1971) "closed-loop" model, Henry and Rogers' (1960) "memory drum" theory, Keele's (1968) notion of motor programs, and Schmidt's (1975) theories of schema and generalized motor programs are representative of the "top-down" approach. The second approach, which has played an important role in motor behavior research for the last 15-20 years, is the "bottom-up" or dynamical systems approach. The major concerns of this viewpoint are the individuals and the network structure (Abernethy & Sparrow, 1992), and the influence of physical properties such as gravitational force, muscle spring force, and body/segmental weight on movements (e.g., Kelso, Putnam, & Goodman, 1983; Turvey, Shaw, & Mace, 1978). These two approaches are dichotomized as central vs. peripheral. Both approaches have their advantages and disadvantages in explaining human motor behavior (Abernethy & Sparrow, 1992).

For the past three and half decades, it has been widely accepted and well documented in the literature of motor behavior that cognitive and motor functions are closely associated with human movement control, learning, and development (e.g., Henry & Rogers, 1960; Schneider & Schmidt, 1995; Shapiro, 1978; Shapiro, Zernicke, Gregor, & Diestel, 1981). A central or cognitive representation of the movement (e.g., a motor program) is assumed to control or guide the execution of a class of motor tasks (Keele, 1968; Schmidt, 1975, 1991). Even though the notion of motor programs has been challenged by the newer dynamical systems approaches, theoretically and practically the cognitive approach remains an important explanation for movement control and learning. In fact, the resources of cognitive constructs such as central representations, memory, experience, or knowledge are necessary in human motor behavior (Abernethy & Sparrow, 1992).

Using a cognitive perspective, we discuss characteristics of human arm movements that require speed and accuracy. The goal is to highlight important developmental differences in children, young adults, and senior citizens, and attempt to shed light on movement control mechanisms. To accomplish this objective, Fitts' law (speed and accuracy trade-off, Fitts, 1954) and a number of explanations for the speed/accuracy trade-off (Plamondon & Alimi, 1997) will be discussed first. Then, a brief account of the theories and methodological concerns related to the control of rapid movements will be summarized. Second, a body of literature emphasizing kinematic differences in rapid and goal-directed arm movements will be discussed. In addition, taking a lifespan developmental approach, studies related to the age differences in arm movement control will be reviewed. Third, Meyer's optimal sub-movement model (OSM, Meyer, Abrams, Kornblum, Wright, & Smith 1988) will be used as a framework to discuss how and why children and the elderly differ from young adults in controlling ballistic aiming arm movements. Finally, topics for future research in this area are presented.

THE MODELS OF "SPEED-ACCURACY TRADE-OFF"

"Speed/accuracy trade-off" is a common movement feature observed in many daily activities or motor performance: while movement speed increases, movement accuracy decreases, or vice versa (Fitts, 1954). For example, driving a car fast can reduce driving accuracy such as staying within the lane or avoiding obstacles, reaching too fast may result in knocking over a cup, or a fast typing speed can yield more typing errors. Many computer games require rapid and accurate responses with the mouse or a joystick. In many sports, striking a fast moving ball is more difficult than hitting a still or slow ball, throwing at a small target may require the performer to slow down the throwing velocity more than throwing at a large target, or in the long jump, a fast approach is more challenging than in running slower for hitting the take-off board. All these examples highlight an inverse relationship between movement speed and accuracy. Because movement velocity and accuracy are two of the most important requirements in many motor activities, the speed/accuracy trade-off has attracted a great deal of research in both field- and laboratory-settings (Plamondon & Alimi, 1997).

According to Fitts' law (Fitts, 1954), the trade-off function between movement speed and accuracy can be expressed by the "index of difficulty" *(ID)*, which is determined or affected by the movement amplitude (*A*) and the target size (*W*). On one hand, as *A* increases, so does the *ID*; consequently, the movement speed decreases (accuracy also declines to a certain degree). On the other hand, as *W* decreases, the movement *ID* increases, resulting in a reduction in both movement speed and accuracy (see Schmidt & Lee, 1998, for details). Although the *A* and *W* might not have an equivalent effect on the *ID* (Sheridam, 1979), manipulating either the *A* or *W* (or both the *A* and *W*) within a given motor task and observing the movement provides important insights into movement control. For instance, using this experimental paradigm, researchers can investigate and understand the complex relationship among movement factors that may influence the sensory-motor systems (e.g., perception, movement preparation, and execution). In addition, by reducing movement difficulty or complexity for the novices, movement instruction or practice can be used to maintain a relatively high movement speed or accuracy (see Christina, 1992, for details).

Using a variety of measurement devices (e.g., high speed video, digital tablets, three-dimensional tracking systems, computer mouse/keyboard), researchers are able to examine the kinematic characteristics of the speed and accuracy trade-off. In a fast, single segment and goal-directed arm movement, a bell-shaped curve with two stages of movement has been noted in terms of movement speed (e.g., Warabi, Noda, & Kato, 1986). As indicated in Figure 1, the first stage is an acceleration phase, in which the movement is fast and covers most of the movement distance. The second is a deceleration phase or "homing" phase in which the performer may slow down and correct the movement for accuracy (e.g., Haaland, Harrington, & Grice, 1993; Heuer, 1984; Welford, Norris, & Shock, 1969; Wing & Miller, 1984). Whereas a motor program may control the entire part of a rapid aiming arm movement, to some extent, sensory feedback seems to contribute to movement accuracy within the second stage of movement as the arm "homes" in on the target ("on-line" control, Burton, 1987; von Donkelaar & Frank, 1991).

The question, however, is that in addition to using the traditional variables of movement time (MT) and/or movement timing (the portion of the time to reach peak velocity relative to the segmental MT) to probe the motor control mechanisms, what are the other significant characteristics of

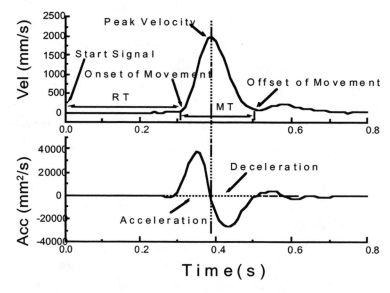

Fig 1. Velocity and acceleration curve for a rapid and goal-directed movement. Used by permission of the authors. Yan, J.H., Thomas, J.R., Stelmach, G.E. & Thomas, K.T. (2000). Developmental features of rapid aiming arm movements across the lifespan. *Journal of Motor Behavior, 32*, 121-140.

these two stages (acceleration and deceleration)? Additionally, in terms of movement quality (e.g., speed, accuracy, smoothness, and consistency), does the second phase have more movement jerk (less smooth), more "on-line" corrections, or less movement consistency and linearity than the first stage as arm movement slows and performers use visual information to control movements? Little information is available regarding the motor characteristics within the phases of acceleration and deceleration. Examining the differences between these two phases would enhance the understanding of the control systems in fast and target-directed arm movements and yield useful information relative to the kinematic characteristics of the speed and accuracy trade-off.

Furthermore, Plamondon and Alimi (1997) reviewed a number of theories related to the speed/accuracy trade-off and offered a comprehensive account for each theory. Based on their review, Plamondon and Alimi argued that their newly proposed interpretations of the speed/accuracy trade-off (e.g., delta-lognormal, neuromuscular synergy, and quadratic laws) can simplify the relationships of human physical components or biological systems in the movements that require speed and accuracy. Central to this notion is that neuromuscular networks or commands coordinate all movement-related elements and determine the spatial and/or temporal individualities of the movement that requires speed and accuracy (Plamondon, 1995). Despite the fact that a number of explanations or theories have been projected for the speed/accuracy trade-off, none of the models consider differences in children or the elderly (Stelmach & Thomas, 1997). A life-long developmental perspective ought to be taken into the consideration when addressing the observation from movements involving a speed/accuracy trade-off.

THEORETICAL AND METHODOLOGICAL CONCERNS

Because of the fact that human body is a complex system and human movements involve many processes (e.g., physical, mental, and cognitive), typically the study of motor behavior occurs in the laboratory settings and uses simple movement tasks. To capture and examine the characteristics of human motor and cognitive performance, a diversity of motor tasks has been utilized. Some examples include curvilinear repositioning tasks or horizontal linear tracking tasks (e.g., Gerson & Thomas, 1977; Kelso & Norman, 1978; Klapp & Rodriguez, 1982; Pease & Pupnow, 1983; Shapiro, 1977), tapping tasks (e.g., McCracken, 1983; Salmoni, 1983; Sugden, 1980), holding a stylus to hit targets (e.g., Fischman, 1984; Kerr, 1977; Wallace, Newell, & Wade, 1978; Yan, Thomas, & Stelmach, 1998; Yan, Thomas, Stelmach, & Thomas, 2000), and various timing tasks (e.g., moving hand in different directions or knocking down barriers in a specific order with goal-time intervals, or pressing telegraphic keys or micro-switches; Burton, 1986, 1987; Glencross, 1972; Langley & Zelaznik, 1984; Moxley, 1979). Additionally, throwing/tossing a beanbag or rolling/kicking a ball at a target (Carson & Wiegand, 1979; Kerr & Booth, 1977; Porretta, 1982) and coincidence-anticipation tasks have been commonly used to examine sensory-motor performance of children and adults (Wade, 1980; Wrisberg & Mead, 1981). The majority of the tasks mentioned here deal with movement speed, accuracy, and other important movement demands (e.g., complexity and difficulty).

Regarding the control mechanisms for diverse motor tasks, Magill (1998) and Schmidt and Lee (1998) indicate that different control procedures are used to regulate the specific tasks based upon the nature of the motor tasks (e.g., long and slow movement vs. short and fast movements) and requirements for the tasks (e.g., movement speed and accuracy demands or the number of movement segments). For a long duration, slow, or self-paced movement (e.g., positioning or tracking tasks), movements are thought to be primarily controlled by augmented feedback (Adams, 1971; Magill, 1998). In contrast, for a ballistic and goal-oriented movement or in a situation that the performer has certainty about the movement outcomes (e.g., baseball pitching or striking), the actions are fundamentally navigated by a pre-planned or constructed central representation (e.g., a motor program; Christina, 1992; Henry & Rogers, 1960; Keele, 1968; Schmidt, 1975). However, there has been a controversy regarding the functions of different control mechanisms. Several reports seem to show a de-

creasing role of central control and an increasing role of peripheral control
(e.g., Kelso & Schoner, 1988; Kelso, Southard, & Goodman, 1979).
Beaubaton and Hay (1982) and Bard, Hay, and Fleury (1985) suggested
that even in a rapid arm movement, feedback might contribute to accuracy.
The integration of central control and on-line monitoring may result in
rapid and accurate movements.

In terms of response and movement measurement, "simple reaction
time" (SRT) is one of the most conventional paradigms in analyzing the
cognitive processes in movement control and learning (e.g., Annett & Annett,
1979; Klapp & Rodriguez, 1982; Sheridan, 1981; Simon & Slariero, 1975).
The basic assumption for the SRT method is that the processes of motor
programming need time (Klapp, 1975; Zelanik, Shapiro, & Carter, 1982).
Accordingly, by manipulating the experimental conditions (and/or subjects'
characteristics) and measuring RT, one can examine the cognitive functions in response and movement preparation. Based on the RT assumption,
there are two major lines of research. The first is to discover movement
variables or factors that affect programming time (e.g., the effect of the
number of movement parts and/or movement accuracy requirement on RT;
Christina, 1992; Henry & Rogers, 1960). The other investigates how these
variables or factors are prepared or specified during the processes of motor
programming. Rosenbaum (1980) has developed a pre-cuing method for
this line of research (Larish & Stelmach, 1982; Zelanik, Shapiro, & Carter,
1982).

In addition to RT, MT, force, and EMG measures, numerous dependent variables have been used to examine the control of aimed arm movements over the last two decades. When examining movement "products"
or "outcomes", movements can be assessed for end-point accuracy (constant error, variable error, absolute error, or absolute constant error, e.g.,
Gerson & Thomas, 1977; Klapp & Rodriguez, 1982) or speed (e.g., Yan et
al., 1998). On the other hand, movements can be quantified during the
processes of execution. For example, "pauses" or "intervals" between suc-
cessive movement segments in the sequence of a ballistic arm movement
can be used to indicate the consistency of movements (e.g., Burton, 1987;
Povel & Collard, 1982; Yan et al., 1998). If motor programs are well developed, we assume that the "inter-segment-interval" or "pauses" should
be minimal and consistent across different target locations (e.g., the notion
of unitary movement control; Keele, 1968).

Furthermore, the straightness of movement path (movement linearity) reflects the movement coordination of related body joints in a given
movement. Therefore, it has been employed to investigate the processes of
arm movement control (Abend, Bizzi, & Morasso, 1982; Buchanan, Kelso,
& Fuchs, 1996; Yan, Thomas, Stelmach, & Thomas, in progress). Statistically, the correlations of MT within and between movement segments can
serve as an indicator for movement consistency. The theoretical assump-

tion for this statistical approach is that the execution of one motor program produces coherent or consistent movement speed, resulting in high and stable "inter-segment" correlations (Wulf & Schmidt, 1988; Yan *et al.*, 1998).

More importantly, movement jerk, a third derivative of movement displacement (Flash & Hogan, 1985; Hogan, 1984; Hogan & Flash, 1987), can capture the feature of movement smoothness, and consequently it has been commonly used in handwriting studies (e.g., Wann, 1987), arm movement tasks (e.g., Flash & Hogan, 1985; Schneider & Zernicke, 1989, Yan *et al.*, 2000; Yan, Hinrich, Payne, & Thomas, 2000), and gait research (e.g., Hreliac & Martin, 1993). Smooth movements are also related to better joint coordination (Hogan & Flash, 1987; Uno, Kawato, & Suzuki, 1989). The study by Yan, Thomas *et al.* (2000) suggested that the development of movement planning resulted in less movement jerk while using "on-line" corrections led to higher jerk. In addition, children produce less movement jerk in handwriting as the results of writing experience (Wann, 1987). These studies clearly suggest that movement jerk is a useful motor output measure to examine the execution of arm movement. In the following sections, to emphasize lifespan changes, we will discuss the kinematic differences in children and the elderly in rapid/goal-directed arm movements.

HOW DO CHILDREN AND SENIORS DIFFER FROM ADULTS IN SPEED ACCURACY TRADE-OFF?

Children's Developmental Characteristics

Children's motor performance has been studied extensively from a cognitive or psychomotor perspective. Numerous studies (e.g., Chi & Gallagher, 1982; Gallagher & Thomas, 1980; Kail, 1986, 1988; Thomas, 1980) have reported significant age-related differences in children's information processing speed and quality, where processing speed refers to the functional rapidity of information processing (Thomas, 1980), and processing quality refers to how much information can be processed in a certain period of time and how accurately the information is processed (Chi & Gallagher, 1982). Research has suggested that as children get older, they process information faster, or process more information in the same length of time, or process information with fewer errors (e.g., Chi, 1976; Chi & Gallagher, 1982; Kail, 1986, 1988; Wickens, 1974). A general and central mechanism changing with age may be responsible for the differences in the speed and quality of processing (Chi, 1976; Kail, 1986, 1988; Thomas, 1980).

Developmental work with children and adults suggests that in performing motor tasks that require speed and accuracy, children react more slowly to the stimuli (longer reaction time, RT) and move slower (increasing movement time, MT) than young adults (Dunham & Reid, 1987; Hay, 1981; Salmoni & McIlmain, 1979; Sugden, 1980; Thomas, Gallagher, & Purvis, 1981). Task conditions such as movement difficulty, amplitude, or accuracy change the means of movement preparation and implementation (Burton, 1987; Hay, 1981; Wallace, Newell, & Wade, 1978). Specifically, as the number of movement segments increases, seven- and nine-year-olds demonstrate arm movements that are slower and more variable than those of the 11-year-olds and college-age adults. One of the possible reasons is that young children primarily rely on feedback or on-line corrections, whereas older children or young adults plan the response prior to the onset of the movement, resulting in fast and consistent movements (Burton, 1986).

Thus, several important questions have arisen for developmental motor control (Hay, 1990). For instance, why do children show age-related characteristics in planning and executing ballistic aiming arm movements? Also, are young children capable of integrating motor programming and feedback information within a given movement task? (Hay, 1979) In addition, a further inquiry is necessary relative to children's use of strategies for rapid and accurate movements, a characteristic that may be age-associated: without much preparation, young children may start the movement as quickly as possible and correct the movements during the execution. In contrast, older children or young adults may plan the task in advance and be less dependent on feedback information for movement speed and accuracy (Stelmach & Thomas, 1997). Because MT or movement speed is simply the "product" of movements, utilizing additional movement parameter measures that capture movement "processes" may offer insight into a number of issues. Examples include programming vs. on-line control for children, the possibilities of integrating feed-forward (planning) and feedback control (on-line), and the use of strategies by children in managing rapid and accurate motor tasks.

In studying children's developmental motor control, the notion of motor programs (a central and abstract representation of the action, Keele, 1968; Schmidt, 1975) has led to several experiments (Yan, Thomas et al., 2000), in which children performed rapid aiming arm movements under different movement conditions (various movement complexities, response uncertainty, and use of advanced cues) on the surface of a digitizer. A group of movement parameters was employed to capture the "processes" of movement execution (movement velocity, jerk, linearity, timing, and inter-segment-intervals). In comparison with older children (nine years of age) and young adults (24 years of age), young children (six years of age) demonstrated slower, more variant and jerky, and less linear arm movements. Increasing movement complexity (e.g., a greater number of movement segments) resulted in poorer response qualities for all age groups, especially for younger ones. Movement accuracy demands, response uncertainty, and lack of advanced cues affected the performance of the nine-

and 24-year-olds more than that of the six-year-olds. The reduced impact of these manipulations on the younger children could be due to their use of on-line monitoring rather than programming. This is not the case for older children and young adults who used programming instead of feedback control and had performance disrupted by the manipulations.

Recently, Yan, Thomas, Stelmach, and Thomas (in progress) examined movements in terms of the invariant features and the attentional and cognitive processes. The task was to move the hand as rapidly as possible between the home position and the target. The pre-school children (about 5 years of age) were significantly more variable than the school-age children (eight- and 10-year-olds) in the variables of pause time ("inter-segment-intervals" at home and target positions) and MT between/within segments. The five-year-olds demonstrated deficits that were not seen in the eight- and 10-year-olds. First, the MTs were less consistent (the correlations were lower among movement segments). Second, the five-year-olds paused at home and target positions longer than the eight- and 10-year-olds. The results supported the proposal that younger children might rely on on-line corrections to control the movement (Burton, 1987) or re-load one motor program multiple times to complete the task (Wood & Ging, 1991; Wulf & Schmidt, 1988). As a result, young children may require a higher level of cognitive effort (attention) for their movement control.

A speculation for young children's use of on-line control is that they may be constrained by the duration of motor programming. In other words, a motor program for young children may run for a shorter time than in older children. The literature suggests that with practice motor programs increase in duration and complexity (Schmidt, 1991; Schmidt & Lee, 1998). This may also apply to children's motor control. When children become older and gain more movement experience, motor programs may become more complex and have a longer duration, leading to improvements in motor performance. Because age-related but not age-dependent changes in motor behavior are the focus for developmental investigations, age and experience ought to be taken into the consideration of motor performance (Shapiro, 1977). Thus, this topic seems to be an important one in the study of developmental control and learning and further study of the formation of motor programs for young children is warranted.

Despite the fact that young children primarily depend on feedback information to control their movements, they could use preprogramming if advanced information was provided. In the second experiment of the same study (Yan et al., in progress), the motor task was identical to the one used in the first experiment—alternating the hand between the home position and the target several times. Information about the number of movement segments was provided to the preschoolers prior to the movement response and execution (a pre-cue was not provided in the first experiment). The results suggest that these pre-school children were able to preplan the tasks and produce precise and consistent movement outputs. Alternatively, their "on-line" control could be reduced or changed to preprogramming control when they were provided appropriate information about the nature of the movement before the action. The message or implication from this experiment is that pre-cues facilitate planning and ultimately results in a better motor performance. Practically, child learners should be given important information regarding a particular motor task before the trials so they may be able to prepare for practice and performance.

To examine developmental kinematics of arm movements in a real-world motor task, Yan, Payne, and Thomas (2000) and Yan, Hinrichs, Payne, and Thomas (2000) instructed three groups of young females (three-, four-, and six-year-olds) to throw tennis balls as hard (fast) as possible toward a target on the wall. A three-dimenssional video system recorded the performance from the front/right-side views. The analyses revealed that age-associated differences in the measures of velocity and jerk (for the hand and ball) and other kinematic variables (e.g., timing of hand peak velocity relative to ball release, joint angles, and angular velocities). The three- and four-year-olds not only moved their hands slower and with higher jerk than their older counterparts, but also demonstrated an underdeveloped velocity profile for arm movement. Under speed and accuracy demands young females were unable to coordinate throwing-related joints to reach peak hand velocity before ball release. The deficits observed in timing control for young children could be explained by their lack of experience and developmental status in physical characteristics. This study also suggested that jerk is a useful kinematic variable to capture the developmental nature of motor performance.

Deterioration of Motor and Cognitive Performance in Senior Citizens

At the other end of the lifespan spectrum, one of most important and compelling findings is that advanced aging often results in slowness of response and movement (e.g., Jacewizc & Hartley, 1987; Spirduso, 1975, 1980; Stelmach & Goggin, 1989, Yan et al., 1998). A central deficit in terms of mental processing speed and motor programming capability seems to be a major cause for aging slowness (e.g., Salthouse, 1976; Salthouse & Somberg, 1982; Stelmach, Goggin, & Amrhein, 1988; Teasdale, Stelmach, Breunig, & Meeuwsen, 1991). Research has suggested several possible explanations for the increased slowness with aging. For example, Stelmach, Goggin, and Garcia-Colera (1987) found that, even though elderly subjects could use pre-cue information to prepare the motor tasks, they need a longer time than young and middle-aged adults to specify movement direction, body limbs, and extent of the arm. In addition, errors in motor programming or mental rotation were found for elderly individuals (Bashore, Osman, & Heffley, 1989; Haaland, Harrington, & Grice, 1993). Other studies have identified pathological changes in elderly's central nervous system and muscular system (e.g., McDonagh, White, & Davis, 1984; Phillips, Bruce, Newton, & Woledge, 1992), poor anticipation abilities (e.g., Jagacinski, Greenberg, Liao, & Wang, 1993), or "noise" in the sensory-motor system (Walker, Philbin, & Fisk, 1997). A number of factors may be responsible for the behavioral deterioration observed in aging populations.

Motivated by a body of studies in movement control for seniors (e.g., Larish & Stelmach, 1982; Stelmach, Goggin, & Amrhein, 1988; Stelmach, Goggin, & Garcia-Colera, 1987), Yan *et al.* (1998) specifically examined the characteristics of control in rapid and target-oriented movements for individuals who were in late adulthood and advanced aging. Their hypotheses were that aging and movement direction influence movement preparation (RT) and execution, and consequently result in an increased variability in arm movement tasks (RT, MT, pause time, and their SDs, and movement timing). Individuals from a group of young adults (20 to 30 years of age) and two groups of older adults (54 to 64, and 65 to 80 years) completed two tasks of rapid aiming arm movement that had the same movement difficulty but different movement directions (forward-backward motion, left-right motion). The results support the hypothesis that aging and movement direction affected movement planning and implementation. Seniors initiated both arm movement tasks slower (RT) and with more RT variability than the younger adults. Seniors executed the arm movements slower and less consistently than their younger counterparts. The overall results demonstrated a regression in movement quality of the seniors when performing rapid aiming arm movements. This deterioration may be related to lesser amounts of or poorer movement planning, resulting in greater use of visual feedback during movement execution.

Following this line of thinking, recently Yan (2000) completed an experiment where 20 seniors (81 years of age) and 20 young adults (25 years of age) performed two types of arm movements as fast and as accurately as they could. The first was a straight movement from the home position to the target (linear arm movement). The second was a curvilinear movement - the performer moved the hand through a circle that was located midway between the "home" and the target and 6 cm off the straight line, and then hit the target circle. Age differences were examined on the variables of MT, movement jerk, and on the profiles of movement path, velocity, and acceleration. As expected, the seniors executed both movement tasks more slowly and had higher movement jerk than the young adults. The data are consistent with the previous findings regarding the decline in movement speed and smoothness for seniors (Yan *et al.*, 1998; Yan, Thomas *et al.*, 2000). Furthermore, the assessment of movement trajectories and kinematic profiles suggests that the seniors executed the curvilinear task in two segments (moved from the "home" to the middle circle, paused, and then moved on to the target). In contrast, the young adults implemented the curvilinear task as one nonstop and smooth movement. One plausible explanation for this "segmental" or "non-unitary" fashion of execution in seniors is that they simplify the processes of movement preparation and reduce the movement demands on the task (speed and accuracy). Seniors likely utilized some type of "strategy" to reach maximum movement outcome or compensate for the deficits in motor and cognitive functions even though the form of motor execution was sub-optimal. The increased "noise" in their sensory-motor system may also have been a factor (Walker *et al.*, 1997).

Lifespan Developmental Approach

Over the last one and half decade, motor development research has extended its focus to lifespan models, particularly using senior citizens (e.g., Rabbitt, 1979; Rikli & Edwards, 1991; Spirduso & Choi, 1993; Stelmach, Goggin, & Amrhein, 1988). In addition to theoretical and methodological considerations, the major practical reason is the fast growing percentage of older American populations (Kalish, 1982). The increasing number of elderly citizens requires more attention from science and society in general. Understanding the specific difficulties, features, and needs for aging population's movement characteristics is necessary to assist in or facilitate the quality of daily life for the elderly individuals (e.g., Payne & Isaacs, 1999; Spirduso, 1989).

The lifetime changes in motor functions (the outputs of motor performance) can be perceived as an inverted "U": as children get older, they improve their motor performance; the movement skills are relatively stable during the adulthood; motor performance deteriorates as people enter late adulthood or advanced aging (Thomas, Thomas, & Gallagher, 1993; Yan, Thomas et al., 2000). To understand the developmental nature of motor skills and the impacts of environmental and biological factors on the changes of motor performance, approaching age-related differences in motor and cognitive behavior from a lifespan perspective is critical (Thomas, 1989; VanSant, 1990).

Empirically, Yan, Thomas et al. (2000) examined the developmental characteristics of "speed-accuracy trade off" across the lifespan. Participants from four age periods (pre-school children, school-age children, young adults, and seniors) preformed seven types of ballistic aiming arm movements under the paradigms of simple reaction time (SRT), choice reaction time (CRT), and pre-cuing. A diverse collection of response measures (movement "products" and "processes") was employed to characterize movement control of speed and accuracy. Generally, across the variables used (MT/velocity, jerk, timing, linearity, and pause time), either an inverted "U" or "U" shaped-pattern was identified (depending on the direction of measurement). Within this operationally defined life spectrum (preschool children to seniors), the older children and young adults typically outperformed the pre-school children and seniors in terms of movement velocity, smoothness, consistency, and movement straightness. However, the effects of movement accuracy and pre-cue information were not the same for the participants in various age groups (age by task interaction). Specifically, the older children and young adults were more sensitive to the changes of task conditions (CRT, SRT, and pre-cuing) than the young children and senior adults. A partial explanation is that the older children and young adults mainly rely on programming control (therefore, the conditions prior to movement execution are the key factors for performance) while the young children and senior adults primarily make "on-line" adjustments regardless of task requirements. However, further evidence is needed to support this reasoning.

WHAT MOVEMENT SUB-STRUCTURE CAN TELL US ABOUT SPEED-ACCURACY TRADE-OFF?

As was discussed above, a key assumption for the developmental characteristics in controlling rapid and accurate movements is the discrepancy between two major control mechanisms used by individuals in different age periods: "programming" and "on-line" corrections. Yet, an important issue remains unsolved; that is, across the lifespan, what has changed in addition to the outcome measures (e.g., speed and accuracy). In particular, for the data mentioned above, whether the kinematics of movement structures are different across the lifespan is unknown. Exploring and confirming the changes in movement structure may provide additional evidence or rationale for this line of inquiry (Stelmach & Thomas, 1997).

According to "the Optimized Sub-movement Model" (OSM, Meyer et al., 1988), motor planning is thought to produce a primary ballistic sub-movement (the beginning part of the movement) while sensory feedback guides the secondary corrective sub-movement during the latter part of movement execution (using on-line corrections). As can be seen in Figure 2, during the primary sub-movement, the speed of movement is increasing and faster (shorter MT) than that during the secondary sub-movement, where the speed is decreasing and slower. The results from Pratt, Chasteen, and Abrams (1994) indicated that young adults had a longer ballistic primary sub-movement phase (in movement displacement) and a shorter secondary on-line corrective phase (in both movement distance and duration) than senior adults. Based on OSM approach, looking into the sub-structure of movement may yield useful information regarding the issue of programming vs.feedback control in rapid aiming movement across the lifespan.

Thus, we extended these investigations by analyzing the proportion of the primary or secondary sub-movement in the overall movement dura-

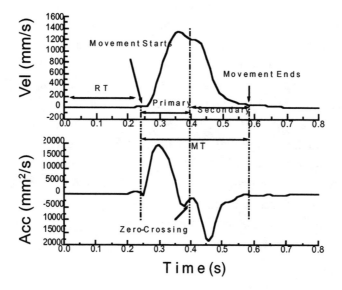

Fig. 2. Movement sub-structure and the zero-crossing of a rapid and goal-directed movement. Used by permission of the authors. Thomas, J.R., Yan, J.H., & Stelmach, G.E. (2000). Movement characteristics change as a function of practice in children and adults. *Journal of Experimental Child Psychology*, *75*, 228-244.

tion and distance (Thomas, Yan, & Stelmach, 2000; Yan, Thomas et al., 2000). The variable of number of "zero-crossings" within a complete arm movement was also examined to capture the frequency of on-line corrections during movement execution. We hypnotized that, because young children and senior adults are assumed to use more on-line control than older children and young adults, they would end their primary sub-movement earlier (likely before peak velocity), resulting in a shorter primary sub-movement than the older children and young adults, who would end the primary sub-movement after peak velocity, leading to a longer primary sub-movement. Similarly, the young children and seniors were expected to have a higher number of "zero-crossings" (on-line corrections) than the older children and young adults who primarily use programming control.

The results indicate that older children and young adults had a greater percentage of the total movement in the primary sub-movement than the young children and seniors in SRT (in both movement distance and time, Figure 3a and 3b). Yet, response uncertainty (CRT) affected the percent of primary sub-movement of older children and young adults more than on that of young children and seniors. This set of data could be considered evidence for the argument that older children and young adults use programming control whereas young children and seniors use on-line correction. In addition, when a parameter of response selection (such as movement direction used in this experiment) became unclear, older children and young adults suffered more than the young children and seniors. This significant reduction in the percentage of primary sub-movement suggested that the planning processes of older children and young adults were interrupted. However, for young children or seniors, response uncertainty appeared to have little effect. The lack of change in the percentage of primary sub-movement for the young and seniors suggested that regardless of response constraints or limitations, they used on-line corrections rather than central control of the movement. This was the reason why an "age by task" interaction was noted in this measure. The data appeared to support our contention about the developmental discrepancy in movement control mechanisms.

Moreover, the older children and young adults had a greater percentage of relative jerk in the primary sub-movement than the younger children and seniors (Figure 3c). The age differences observed in relative jerk during the primary sub-movement might be due to a larger portion of the movement being in primary sub-movement for the older children and young adults as displayed in Figures 3a and 3b. When there was an uncertainty in movement direction (CRT), the older children and young adults showed a greater change of relative jerk from the primary to the secondary sub-movements

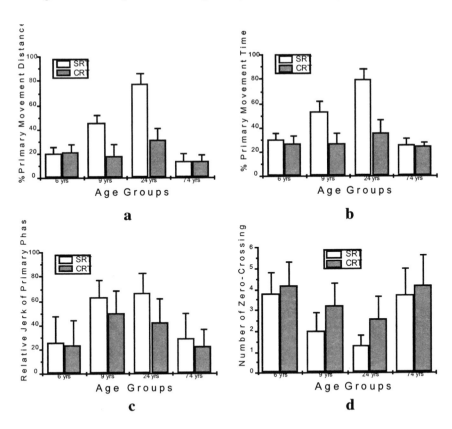

Fig 3. Percent of primary sub-movement in movement distance and time (a and b); relative jerk in primary sub-movement and frequency of zero-crossing (c and d). Used by permission of the authors. Yan, J.H., Thomas, J.R., Stelmach, G.E. & Thomas, K.T. (2000). Developmental features of rapid aiming arm movements across the lifespan. *Journal of Motor Behavior*, *32*, 121-140.

than the younger children and seniors. This suggests that response uncertainty affected the planning process for the older children and young adults. Because of the fact that the younger children and senior adults programmed a small percent of the movement (small primary sub-movement), the relative jerk did not change much. Finally, the results of "zero-crossings" further support the claim that older children and young adults rely on programming and young children and seniors are dependent on sensory feedback (Figure 3d). Under feedback control, young children and seniors seemed to make numerous adjustments to reach the target. This reduced movement speed and caused jerky performance.

Thomas et al. (2000) recently reported a study that examined whether practice could increase the percentage of primary sub-movement for young children (about six years of age), older children (about nine years of age), and college students (about 24 years of age) who perform rapid aiming arm movements. Each age group (20 participants) was equally divided into: practice and non-practice groups. All the participants had 10 baseline trials and 10 retention trials on each of five consecutive days (5 blocks, total 50 retention trials). Only the participants in the practice group received 30 practice trials prior to retention tests on these five days (total 150 practice trials). The variables of percent primary sub-movement (in both movement time and distance), overall jerk, and percent jerk in primary sub-movement were examined. The analyses indicated that practice resulted in an increment in the primary sub-movement and a reduction in movement jerk; yet, the child participants had a considerably greater improvement in the percentage of primary sub-movement (25-30%) than the adults (10%) and decreased jerk more than the young adults. The two sets of typical curves (velocity and acceleration) for each age group (from baseline trials to retention trials, Figure 4) clearly demonstrate that with practice the primary sub-movements are extended, especially for the six- and nine-year-olds. The overall results suggest that programming control in fast and accurate movements is a function of practice, leading to a smooth movement execution. The reported experiment provided additional evidence for Meyer's OSM (Meyer et al., 1988).

SUMMARY

The theories of motor programs (Keele, 1968; Schmidt, 1975) and Optimized Sub-movement Model (Meyer et al., 1988) have provided theoretical frameworks for the study of motor control in fast and goal-directed movements. A variety of movement output measures (e.g., kinematic, kinetic, and timing) and statistical techniques (e.g., correlations within and between movement segments) have been employed to examine the movement control processes (e.g., Burton, 1987; Carter & Shapiro, 1984;

Glencross, 1979; Yan, Thomas et al., 2000). One of the fundamental questions for developmental motor behavior research is that under varied movement demands and conditions (e.g., movement speed, accuracy, complexity, difficulty, or response uncertainty), how do individuals in different age periods control movements, either by programming or on-line corrections, or the integration of both. Previous studies of human motor control across the lifespan have generated a great deal of interests and new approaches for continued inquiring.

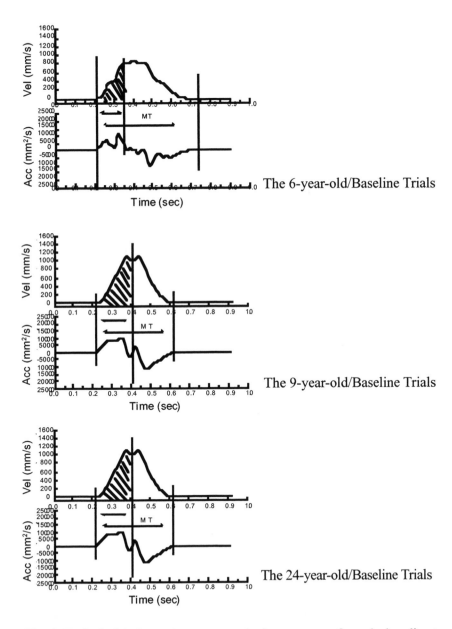

The 6-year-old/Baseline Trials

The 9-year-old/Baseline Trials

The 24-year-old/Baseline Trials

Fig 4. Typical trials for each age group: the improvement from the baseline to retention in the percent of primary sub-movement for movement distance. Used by permission of the authors. Thomas, J.R., Yan, J.H., & Stelmach, G.E. (2000). Movement characteristics change as a function of practice in children and adults. *Journal of Experimental Child Psychology, 75*, 228-244.

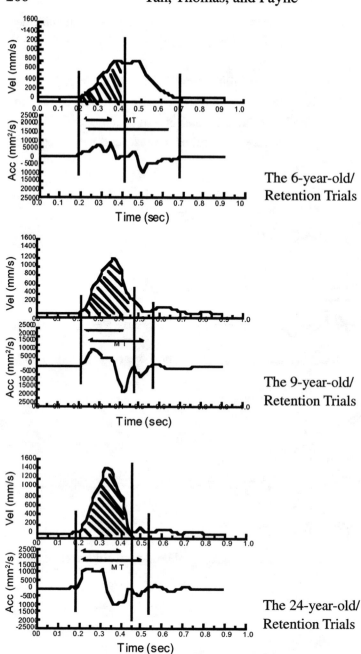

The 6-year-old/
Retention Trials

The 9-year-old/
Retention Trials

The 24-year-old/
Retention Trials

Fig 4. (cont.) Typical trials for each age group: the improvement from the baseline to retention in the percent of primary sub-movement for movement distance.

Developmental work suggests that in general, young children process information slower and with more errors than older children and adults (e.g., Chi, 1976; Kail, 1985, 1991; Thomas, 1980). Young children need greater cognitive attention to control their movements than their older counterparts (Yan, Thomas et al., 2000), which results in slower, less consistent, jerkier, and less coordinated movements than those of the older children and young adults. Experimental evidence seems to support the assumption that the developmental deficits observed in young children are due to their use of on-line control (e.g., Burton, 1987; Thomas et al., 2000; Yan, Thomas et al., 2000). However, when young children receive "cues" about the nature of the task prior to the movement or have sufficient practice, they are able to plan the movements and enhance the movement outcome. As a function of development and practice, children appear to be more likely to use programming control rather than on-line correction for the rapid and accurate movements (Thomas et al., 2000; Yan et al., in progress; Yan, Thomas et al., 2000).

When people enter the stages of late adulthood and advanced aging, their response and movement typically slow down. Central deficits seem to be the major factors for slowness with advanced aging (e.g., Jacewicz & Hartley, 1987; Larish & Stelmach, 1982; Salthouse & Somberg, 1982; Spirduso, 1980; Yan et al., 1998). The results from numerous studies reveal that the increased slowness and decreased consistency of movement with aging might be due to a variety of reasons including errors in motor programming or information processing (e.g., Bashore et al., 1989; Haaland et al., 1993), pathologies in the central nervous system and the muscular system (e.g., McDonagh et al., 1984; Phillips et al., 1992), reduced anticipation capabilities (e.g., Jagacinski et al., 1993), "noise" in the sensory-motor system (Walker et al., 1997). The results from Yan et al. (1998) and Yan, Thomas et al. (2000) are in agreement with those from Stelmach et al. (1987) that the deterioration of motor programming capabilities of seniors may be the resource for inconsistent, slow, and poor motor response and execution.

In summary, there are two major explanations for controlling movements that require speed and accuracy: programming and on-line control. Individuals across the lifespan demonstrate developmental characteristics in terms of their preferences or strategies in dealing with the movement demands of speed and accuracy. Based upon the results from an array of studies in the field of motor behavior, several areas or questions seem important for further understanding of ballistic aiming movements. First, from theoretical and methodological viewpoints, a lifelong approach offers insight into the influence of biology and environment on human motor skill development. Examining the abilities of integrating central commands and sensory feedback for fast and accurate movements may be beneficial to a better understanding of human sensory-motor system. Second, the questions of how and why young children and seniors utilize sensory feedback need further investigation. Do they rely on visual feedback or proprioceptive information for fast and accurate movements? Third, for older children and young adults, can they maintain rapid and precise movement if visual feedback is limited or removed (completely rely on programming control)? Answering these questions from a lifespan perspective may contribute to the knowledge base and application of motor behavior research.

REFERENCES

Abend, W., Bizzi, E., & Morasso, P. (1982). Human arm trajectory formation. *Brain, 105, 331-348.*

Abernethy, B. , & Sparrow, W.A. (1992). The rise and fall of dominant paradigms in motor behavior research. In J. J Summers (Ed.), *Approaches to the study of motor control and learning* (pp.3 -45). Amsterdam: North-Holland.

Adams, J.A. (1971). A closed-loop theory of motor learning. *Journal of Motor Behavior, 3,* 115-150.

Annett, M., & Annett, J. (1979). Individual differences in right and left reaction time. *British Journal of Psychology, 70,* 393-404.

Bard, C., Hay L., & Fleury, M. (1985). Role of peripheral vision in the directional control of rapid aiming movement. *Canadian Journal of Psychology, 39,* 151-161.

Bashore, T.R., Osman, A., & Heffley, E.F. (1989). Mental slowing in elderly persons: A cognitive psychophyiological analysis. *Psychology and Aging, 2,* 235-244.

Beaubaton, D,. & Hay, L. (1982). Integration of visual cues in rapid goal-directed movement. *Behavioral Brain Research, 5,* 92-93.

Buchanan, J.J., Kelso, J.A.S., & Fuchs, A. (1996). Coordination dynamics of trajectory formation. *Biological Cybernetics, 74,* 11-26.

Burton, A.W. (1986). The effect of age on relative timing variability and transfer. *Journal of Motor Behavior, 18,* 323-342.

Burton, A.W. (1987). The effect of number of movement components on response time in children. *Journal of Human Movement Studies, 13,* 231-247.

Carson, L.M., & Wiegand, R. L. (1979). Motor schema formation and retention in young children: A test of Schmidt's schema theory. *Journal of Motor Behavior, 11,* 247-251.

Chi, M.T.H. (1976). Short-term memory limitations in children: Capacity or processing deficits? *Memory and Cognitive, 4,* 559-572.

Chi, M.T.H., & Gallagher, J.D. (1982). Speed of processing: A developmental source of limitation. *Topics in Learning and Learning Disabilities, 2,* 23-32.

Christina, R.W. (1992). The 1991 C. H. McCloy research lecture: Unraveling the mystery of the response complexity effect in skilled movement. *Research Quarterly for Exercise and Sport, 63,* 218-230.

Dumham, P., & Reid, D. (1987). Information processing: Effect of stimulus speed variation on coincidence-anticipation of children. *Journal of Human Movement Studies, 13,* 151-156.

Fischman, M.G. (1984). Programming time as a function of number of movement parts and changes in movement direction. *Journal of Motor Behavior, 16,* 405-423.

Fitts, P.M. (1954). The information capacity of the human motor system in controlling the amplitude of movement. *Journal of Experimental Psychology, 47*, 381-391.

Flash, T., & Hogan, N. (1985). The coordination of arm movements: An experimentally confirmed mathematical model. *The Journal of Neuroscience, 5*, 1688-1703.

Gallagher, J.D., & Thomas, J.R. (1980). Effects of varying post-KR interval upon children's motor performance. *Journal of Motor Behavior, 12*, 41-46.

Gerson, R.F., & Thomas, J. R. (1977). Schema theory and practice variability within a neo-Piagetian framework. *Journal of Motor Behavior, 9*, 127-134.

Glencross, D.J. (1972). Latency and response complexity. *Journal of Motor Behavior, 4*, 251-256.

Haaland, K.Y., Harrington, D.L., & Grice, J.W. (1993). Effects of aging on planning and implementing arm movements. *Psychology and Aging, 4*, 617-632.

Hay, L. (1979). Spatial-Temporal analysis of movements in children: Motor programs versus feedback in the development of reaching. *Journal of Motor Behavior, 11*, 189-200.

Hay, L. (1981). The effect of amplitude and accuracy requirements on movement time in children. *Journal of Motor Behavior, 13*, 177-186.

Hay, L. (1990). Developmental changes in eye-hand coordination behaviors: Preprogramming versus feedback control. In Bard, C., Fleury, M., & Hay, L (Eds). *Development of eye-hand coordination across the life span* (pp.217-244). University of South Carolina.

Henry, F.M., & Rogers, D.E. (1960). Increased response latency for complicated movements and the "memory drum" theory of neuromotor reaction. *Research Quarterly, 31*, 448-458.

Heuer, H. (1984). On re-scaleability of force and time in aiming movements. *Psychological Research, 46*, 73-86.

Hogan, N. (1984). An organized principle for a class of voluntary movements. *The Journal of Neuroscience, 4*, 2745-2754.

Hogan, N., & Flash, T. (1987). Moving gracefully: quantitative theories of motor coordination. *Trends in Neuroscience, 10*, 170-174.

Hreljac, A., & Martin, P.E. (1993). The relationship between smoothness and economy during walking. *Biological Cybernetics, 69*, 213-218.

Jacewicz, M.M., & Hartley, A.A. (1987). Age differences in the speed of cognitive operations: Resolution of inconsistent findings. *Journal of Gerontology, 42*, 86-88.

Jagacinski, R.J., Greenberg, N., Liao, M.J., & Wang, J. (1993). Manual performance of a repeated pattern by older and younger adults with supplementary auditory cues. *Psychology and Aging, 8*, 429-439.

Kail, R. (1986). Sources of age differences in speed of processing. *Child Development, 57,* 969-987.

Kail, R. (1988). Developmental functions for speeds of cognitive processes. *Journal of Experimental Child Psychology, 45,* 339-364.

Kalish, R.A. (1982). *Late adulthood perspective on human development* (2nd ed.). Montery, CA: Brooks & Cole.

Keele, S.W. (1968). Movement control in skill motor performance. *Psychological Bulletin, 70,* 387-403.

Kelso, J.A.S., & Norman, P.E. (1978). Motor schema formation in children. *Developmental Psychology, 14,* 153-156.

Kelso, J.A.S., Putnam, C., & Goodman, D. (1983). On the space-time structure of human interlimb coordination. *Quarterly Journal of Experimental Psychology, 35A,* 347-375.

Kelso, J.A.S., & Schoner, G. (1988). Self-organization of coordinative movement patterns. *Human Movement Science, 7,* 27-46.

Kelso, J.A.S., Southard, D.L., & Goodman, D. (1979). On the coordination of two-handed aiming movements. *Journal of Experimental Psychology: Human Perception and Performance, 5,* 229-238.

Kerr, B. A. (1977). Motor control in aimed movements. In D. M. Landers & R. M. Christina (Eds.), *Psychology of motor behavior and sport* (vol 1). Champaign, IL: Human Kinetics.

Kerr, R., & Booth, B. (1978). Specific and varied practice of motor skill. *Perceptual and Motor Skills, 46,* 395-401.

Klapp, S.T. (1975). Feedback versus motor programming in the control of aimed movements. *Journal of Experimental Psychology: Human Performance and Performance, 104,* 147-153.

Klapp, S.T., & Rodriguez, G. (1982). Programming time as a function of response duration: A replication of "dit-dah" without possible guessing artifacts. *Journal of Motor Behavior, 14,* 46-56.

Langley, D.J., & Zelaznik, H.N. (1984). The acquisition of time properties associated with a sequential motor skill. *Journal of Motor Behavior, 16,* 275-301.

Larish, D.D., & Stelmach, G.E. (1982). Preprogramming, programming, and reprogramming of aimed hand movements as a function of age. *Journal of Motor Behavior, 14,* 322-340.

Light, K.E. (1990). Information processing for motor performance in aging adults. *Physical Therapy, 70,* 820-826.

Magill, R.A. (1998). *Motor learning: Concepts and application* (5th ed). Madison, WI: WCB/McGraw-Hill.

Magill, R.A. (1994). The influence of augmented feedback on skill learning depends on characteristics of the skill and the learner. *Quest, 46,* 314-327.

McCrachen, H.D. (1983). Movement control in a reciprocal tapping task: A developmental study. *Journal of Motor Behavior, 15,* 262-279.

McDonagh, M.J.N., White, M.J., & Davies, C.T.M. (1984). Different effects of ageing on the mechanical properties of human arm and leg muscles. *Gerontology, 30*, 49-54.

Meyer, D.E., Abrams, R.A., Kornblum, S., Wright, C.E., & Smith, J.E.K. (1988). Optimality in human performance: Ideal control of rapid aimed movements. *Psychological Review, 95*, 340-370.

Moxley, S.C. (1979). Schema: The variability of practice hypothesis. *Journal of Motor Behavior, 11*, 65-70.

Payne, V.G., & Isaacs, L.D. (1999). *Human motor development: A lifespan approach* (4th). Mountain View, CA: Mayfield.

Pease, D.G., & Pupnow, A.A. (1983). Effects of varying force production in practice schedule of children learning a discrete motor task. *Perceptual and Motor Skills, 57*, 275-282.

Phillips, S.K., Bruce, S.A., Newton, D., & Woledge, R.C. (1992). The weakness of old age is not due to failure of muscle activation. *Journal of Gerontology, 2*, 45-49.

Plamondon, R. (1995). A kinematic theory of rapid human movements: 1. Movement representation and generation. *Biological Cybernetics, 72*, 295-307.

Plamondon, R., & Alimi, A.M. (1997). Speed/accuracy trade-offs in target-directed movements. *Behavioral and Brain Sciences, 20*, 279-349.

Porretta, D.L. (1982). Motor schema formation by EMR boys. *American Journal of Mental Deficiency, 87*, 164-172.

Povel, D.J., & Collard, R. (1982). Structural factors in patterned finger tapping. *Acta Psychologica, 52*, 107-123.

Pratt, J., Chasteen, A.L., & Abrams, R.A. (1994). Rapid aimed limb movements: Age differences and practice effects in component submovements. *Psychology and Aging, 9*, 325-334.

Rabbitt, P. (1979). How old and young subjects monitor and control responses for accuracy and speed. *British Journal of Psychology, 70*, 305-311.

Rikli, R.E., & Edwards, D.J. (1991). Effects of a three-year exercise program on motor function and cognitive processing speed *Research Quarterly for Exercise and Sport, 62*, 61-67.

Rosenbaum, D.A. (1980). Human movement initiation: Specification of arm, direction, and extent. *Journal of Experimental Psychology: General, 109*, 444-471.

Salmoni, A.W. (1983). A descriptive analysis of children performing Fitts' reciprocal tapping task. *Journal of Human Movement Studies, 9*, 81-95.

Salmoni, A.W., & McIlwain, J.S. (1979). Fitts' reciprocal tapping task, a measure of motor capacity? *Perceptual and Motor Skills, 49*, 403-413.

Salthouse, T.A. (1976). Speed and age: Multiple rates of age decline. *Experimental Aging Research, 2*, 349-359.

Salthouse, T.A., & Somberg, B.L. (1982). Skilled performance: Effects of adult age and experience on elementary proesses. *Journal of Experimental Psychology: General, 111*, 176-207.

Schmidt, R.A. (1975). A schema theory of discrete motor skill learning. *Psychological Review, 82*, 225-260.

Schmidt, R.A. (1991). *Motor learning and performance: From principles to practice*. Champaign, IL: Human Kinetics.

Schmidt, R.A., & Lee, T. (1998). *Motor control and learning: A behavioral emphasis* (3rd ed.). Champaign, IL: Human Kinetics.

Schneider, N.M., & Schmidt, R.A. (1995). Units of action in motor control: Role of response complexity and target speed. *Human Performance, 8*, 27-49.

Schnerider, K., & Zernicke, R.F. (1989). Jerk-cost modulations during the practice of rapid arm movement. *Biological Cybernetics, 60*, 221-230.

Shapiro, D.C. (1977). Knowledge of results and motor learning in preschool children. *Research Quarterly, 48*, 154-158.

Shapiro, D.C. (1978*). The learning of generalized motor programs*. Unpublished doctoral dissertation, University of Southern California, Los Angeles.

Shapiro, D.C., Zernicke, R. F., Gregor, R. J., Diestel, J. D. (1981). Evidence for generalized motor programs using gait pattern analysis. *Journal of Motor Behavior, 13*, 33-47.

Sheridam, M.R. (1979). A reappraisal of Fitts' Law. *Journal of Motor Behavior, 11*, 179-188.

Sheridam, M.R. (1981). Response programming and reaction time. *Journal of Motor Behavior, 13*, 161-176.

Sheridan, M.R. (1984). Response programming, response production, and fractionated reaction time. *Psychological Research, 46*, 33-47.

Simon, J.R., & Slaviero, D.P. (197S). Differential effects of a foreperiod countdown procedure on simple and choice reaction time. *Journal of Motor Behavior, 7*, 9-14.

Spirduso, W.W. (1975). Reaction time and movement time as a function age and activity level. *Journal of Gerontology, 30*, 435-440.

Spirduso, W.W. (1980). Physical fitness, aging, and psychomotor speed: A review. *Journal of Gerontology, 35*, 850-865.

Spirduso, W.W. (1989). Physical activity and aging: Introduction. In W.W. Spirduso and H.M. Eckert (Eds.), *Physical activity and aging* (pp.1-5). American Academy of Physical Education.

Spirduso, W.W., & Choi, J.H. (1993). Age and practice effects on force control of the thumb and index fingers in precision pinching and bilateral coordination. In G.E. Stelmach and V. Homberg (Eds.),

Sensorimotor impairment in the elderly (pp.393-412). Kluwer Academic Publishers.

Stelmach, E.G., & Diggles, V.D. (1982). Motor equivalence and distributed control: Evidence for non-specific muscle commands. *Behavioral and Brain Sciences, 5*, 126-127.

Stelmach, E.G., & Goggin, N.L. (1989). Psychomotor decline with age. In W.W. Spirduso and H.M. Eckert (Eds), *Physical activity and aging* (pp.6-18). American Academy of Physical Education.

Stelmach, G.E., Goggin, N.L., & Amrhein, P.C. (1988). Aging and restructuring of precued movements. *Psychology and Aging, 3*, 151-157.

Stelmach, E.G., Goggin, N.L., & Garcia-Colera, A. (1987). Movement specification time with age. *Experimental Aging Research, 13*, 39-46.

Stelmach, E.G., & Thomas, J.R. (1997). What's different in the speed-accuracy trade-off in young and elderly subjects? *Behavioral and Brain Sciences, 20*, 321.

Sugden, D.A. (1980). Movement speed in children. *Journal of Motor Behavior, 12*, 125-132.

Teasdale, N., Stelmach, G. E., Breunig, A., & Meeuwsen, H. J. (1991). Age differences in visual sensory integration. *Experimental Brain Research, 85*, 691-696.

Thomas, J.R. (1980). Acquisition of motor skills: Information processing differences between children and adults. *Research Quarterly for Exercise and Sport, 51*, 158-173.

Thomas, J.R. (1989). Naturalistic research can drive motor development theory. In J.S. Skinner et al. (Eds) *Future directions in exercise and sport research* (pp.349-367). Champaign, IL: Human Kinetics.

Thomas, J.R., Gallagher, J.D., & Purvis, G. (1981). Reaction time and anticipation time: Effects of development. *Research Quarterly for Exercise and Sport, 52*, 359-367.

Thomas, J.R., Thomas, K.T., & Gallagher, J. (1993). Developmental considerations in skill acquisition. In R. N. Singer, M. Murphey, & L. K. Tennant (Eds.), *Handbook of research on sport psychology* (pp. 73-105). New York: Macmillan.

Thomas, J.R., Yan, J.H., & Stelmach, G.E. (2000). Movement characteristics change as a function of practice in children and adults. *Journal of Experimental Child Psychology, 75*, 228-244.

Turvey, M.T., Shaw, R., & Mace, W. (1978). Issues in the theory of action: Degree of freedom, coordinative structures, and coalition. In J. Requin (Ed.), *Attention and performance* VII (pp. 557-595). Hillsdale, NJ: Erlbaum.

Uno, Y., Kawato, M., & Suzuki, R. (1989). Formation and control of optimal trajectory in human multijoint arm movement: Minimum torgue-change model. *Biological Cybernetics, 61*, 89-101.

VanSant, A.F. (1990). Life-span development in fundamental tasks. *Physical Therapy, 70*, 788-798.

von Donkelaar, P.V., & Franks, I.M. (1991b). Preprogramming vs. on-line control in simple movement sequences. *Acta Psychologica, 77*, 1-19.

Wade, M.G. (1980). Coincidence anticipation of young normal and handicapped children. *Journal of Motor Behavior, 12*, 103-112.

Walker, N., Philbin, D.A., & Fisk, A.D. (1997). Age-related differences in movement control: Adjusting submovement structure to optimize performance. *Journal of Gerontology: Psychological Science, 52B*, 40-52.

Wallace, S.A., Newell, K.M., & Wade, M.G. (1978). Decision and response times as a function of movement difficulty in preschool children. *Child Development, 49*, 509-512.

Wann, J. (1987). Trends in refinement and optimization of fine-motor trajectories: Observations from an analysis of the handwriting of primary school children. *Journal of Motor Behavior, 19*, 13-37.

Warabi, T., Noda, H., & Kato, T. (1986). Effect of aging on sensorimotor functions of eye and hand movements. *Experimental Neurology, 92*, 686-697.

Welford, A.T., Norris, A.H., & Shock, N.W. (1969). Speed and accuracy of movement and their changes with age. *Acta Psychologica, 30*, 3-15.

Wickens, C.D. (1974). Temporal limits of human information processing: A developmental study. *Psychological Bulletin, 81*, 739-755.

Wing, A.M., & Miller, E. (1984). Peak Velocity timing invariance. *Psychological Research, 46*, 121-127.

Wood, C.A., & Ging, C.A. (1991). The role of interference and task similarity on the acquisition, retention, and transfer of simple motor skills. *Research Quarterly for Exercise and Sport, 62*, 18-26.

Wrisberg, C.A., & Mead, B.J. (1981). Anticipation of coincidence in children: A test of schema theory. *Perceptual and Motor Skills, 52*, 599-606.

Wulf, G., & Schmidt, R.A. (1988). Variability in practice:Facilitation in retention and transfer through Schema formation or context effects? *Journal of Motor Behavior, 20*, 133-149.

Yan, J.H. (2000). Effects of aging on linear and curvilinear aiming arm movements. *Experimental Aging Research, 26,* 393-407.

Yan, J.H., Hinrichs, R.N. Payne, V.G., & Thomas, J.R. (2000). Normalized jerk: A measure to capture developmental characteristics of young girls' overarm throwing. *Journal of Applied Biomechanics, 16*, 196-202.

Yan, J.H., V.G. Payne., & Thomas, J.R. (2000). Developmental kinematics of young females' overarm throwing. *Research Quarterly for Ex-*

ercise and Sport, 71, 92-98.

Yan, J.H., & Thomas, J.R., & Stelmach, G.E. (1998). Aging and rapid aiming arm control. *Experimental Aging Research, 24*, 55-69.

Yan, J.H., Thomas, J.R., Stelmach, G.E. & Thomas, K.T. (2000). Developmental features of rapid aiming arm movements across the lifespan. *Journal of Motor Behavior, 32*, 121-140.

Yan, J.H., Thomas, K.T., Stelmach, G.E., & Thomas, J.R.(in progress). Developmental differences in children's arm movement control.

Zelaznik, H N., Shapiro, D.C., & Carter, M.C. (1982). The specification of digit and duration during motor programming: A new method of precueing. *Journal of Motor Behavior, 14*, 57-68.